Praise for Jo An

'Easily the most exciting new book I've read in the past year is Jo Ann Beard's *Festival Days*. It is a knockout – a collection of nonfiction narratives that read like short stories, plus one short story that makes you wonder if it, too, is nonfiction. Masterly sentence by sentence, entirely original in method, the pieces are full of death and the threat of it, but their effect is the opposite of funereal. Beard's wry voice and her clear-eyed compassion make her the best sort of company' **Jonathan Franzen**, *Guardian*

'"I love how you love things," someone who loves her tells Jo Ann Beard. That love is one reason *Festival Days* is such a great book. Another is her flair for describing those things in vibrant and felicitous prose. Beard honours the beautiful, the sacred and the comic in life, and for life's inescapable cruelties and woes she offers the wisdom of a sage' **Sigrid Nunez**, author of *What Are You Going Through* and the National Book Award-winning *The Friend*

'Jo Ann Beard's work impresses me no end. Funny without being sitcomish, self-aware without being self-absorbed, scrupulous without being fussy, emotional without being sentimental, pointed without being cruel – I could go on and on with these distinctions, all in Beard's favour, but instead I'll just say that Jo Ann Beard is a fantastic writer, an Athena born fully formed out of her own painstaking head' **Jeffrey Eugenides**, author of *The Virgin Suicides*

'Beard's power comes from phrasings and insights that aren't just screaming for likes. Few writers are so wise and self-effacing and emotionally honest all in one breath ... she effects an intimacy that makes us want to sit on the rug and listen' **Sara Lippmann**, *Washington Post*

'[Beard's] books are worth the wait. A master of sensory details, she also writes with humour, melancholy and a love of animals that never borders on saccharine ... In her work, even everyday moments gleam with significance' **Michele Filgate**, *Los Angeles Times*

'A master of creative nonfiction, Beard explores life's most salient moments through facts that she sometimes fractures' **Amy Sutherland**, *Boston Globe*

'Intimate, intelligent, intense – and ultimately comforting ... Like a hot-water bottle for grief, these honest, beautiful essays and stories take on the death of a beloved animal, a friend's illness, getting dumped by a partner and other tragedies few escape' *People* (Book of the Week)

'Charged with fine detail ... Beard is so good at what she does ... In Beard's book, writing works like compound interest, each experience building on the last, which built on the one before' **Ellen Akins**, *Minneapolis Star Tribune*

'I can't think of a writer who puts words to our most difficult moments as adroitly as Beard – who so steadfastly refuses to cut away when things get tough' **Dan Kois**, *Slate*

'Beard's syntax is immortalising ... An acute quality in Beard's work makes the stories feel lived, even alive, as if they are still happening' **Rachel DeWoskin**, *Los Angeles Review of Books*

'Beard shows her dazzling skill at finding universal truths in singular situations. Beard is not just a master of the short form – she's a master of phrase and sentence, too' **Bethanne Patrick**, *Washington Post*

'Beard renders her own life and the lives of others with characteristic precision ... With each piece, she presses the essay form into new, more intimate territory' *Poets & Writers Magazine*

'An absolute marvel ... as Beard demonstrates in her writing, life as we know it is full of bizarre, sad, beautiful, unbelievable, indescribable things – events that transform our real lives into surreal experiences' **Chelsea Hodson**, *BOMB Magazine*

'[Beard's] topics range from the quotidian to the fantastic, but all are anchored by observant, beautifully written prose that's sure to rank among the year's best' *Town & Country* (Must-Read Books of Winter 2021)

'Imaginative and precise ... These sharp essays cement Beard's reputation as a master of the form ... [she] can evoke many emotions in a single stroke' *Publishers Weekly* (starred review)

'Allowing her work to exist beyond the labels of fiction or nonfiction, Beard's metaphorical patterns evince the imaginative truths that underlie her writing' **Catherine Hollis**, *BookPage* (starred review)

'Beard's keen eye for novelistic detail subtly transforms pure fact into art' **Harvey Freedenberg**, *Shelf Awareness*

'Beard is known as a nonfiction essayist, but her work often reads like suspenseful fiction' *BookPage*

THE COLLECTED WORKS of
JO ANN BEARD

First published in Great Britain in 2023 by
Serpent's Tail,
an imprint of Profile Books Ltd
29 Cloth Fair
London
EC1A 7JQ
www.serpentstail.com

Festival Days first published in USA in 2021 by Little, Brown and Company, New York
The Boys of My Youth first published in USA in 1998 by Back Bay Books/Little, Brown and Company, New York

The following essays have been previously published:

'Last Night' and 'Maybe It Happened' in *O, The Oprah Magazine*; 'Werner,' 'Cheri,' 'The Tomb of Wrestling,' and 'What You Seek Is Seeking You' in *Tin House*; 'Close' in *Big, Big Wednesday*; 'Now' in *Agni*; 'Coyotes' first appeared in *Story*; 'Out There' and 'Waiting' appeared in *Iowa Woman*; 'Bonanza' appeared in *The Iowa Review*; 'Cousins' appeared in *Prairie Schooner*; and 'The Fourth State of Matter' appeared in *The New Yorker*.

The author gratefully acknowledges permission to quote from the poems 'The Cruel Festival Time' by Nand Chaturvedi and 'Now' by Denis Johnson.

'Picnic by the Inland Sea' from *The Border Kingdom: Poems by D. Nurkse*, copyright © 2008 by D. Nurkse. Used by permission of Alfred A. Knopf, an imprint of the Knopf Doubleday Publishing Group, a division of Penguin Random House LLC. All rights reserved.

'Just Like This Train': Words and music by Joni Mitchell. Copyright © 1973 (Renewed) Crazy Crow Music. All rights administered by SONY/ATV Music Publishing, 8 Music Square West, Nashville, TN 37203. All rights reserved. Used by permission of Alfred Music.

Excerpts from 'Over My Head' by Christine McVie. Copyright © 1977 by Fleetwood Mac Music (BMI). Reprinted by permission of NEM Entertainment.

Excerpts from 'Good Hearted Woman' by Willie Nelson and Waylon Jennings. Copyright © 1971 by Full Nelson Music, Inc., and Songs of Polygram International, Inc. All rights on behalf of Full Nelson Music, Inc., administered by Windswept Pacific Entertainment Co. d/b/a Longitude Music Co. Reprinted by permission of Full Nelson Music, Inc., and songs of Polygram International, Inc.

10 9 8 7 6 5 4 3 2 1

Typeset in FreightText by MacGuru Ltd
Printed and bound in Great Britain by Clays Ltd, Elcograf S.p.A.

A CIP catalogue record for this book is available from the British Library.

ISBN 978 1 80081 788 3
eISBN 978 1 80081 789 0

Contents

FESTIVAL DAYS

For Emma Sweeney

Author's Note to the 2021 Edition

I BECAME AN ESSAYIST BY DEFAULT. My first love was poetry, my second love was fiction, and my third and lasting love was the essay. It's like a third marriage – you know that this is where you're staying, where you're going to work out your issues, for better or for worse. And yet, because we're all only human, this very book has a couple of stories in it – 'The Tomb of Wrestling' and 'What You Seek Is Seeking You' – or anyway they were first published as stories. They are also essays, in their own secret ways, and the essays are also stories.

Several of the pieces here were published first by *Tin House*, and I am grateful to Cheston Knapp and the other *Tin House* folk, for their willingness to publish my efforts without undue fretting over genre. The *Tin House* magazine will be missed by me and by others, for just this quality of openness and flexibility.

My gratitude to Cheri Tremble's loved ones, for their willingness to tell me Cheri's story, and then to allow me the privilege of imagining my way into her final moments. Werner Hoeflich, similarly, shared his story with me in great precise and painterly detail, and then stepped back and let me imagine it for myself on the page. Thank you to these collaborators and friends.

One of these days
I'll look at your face and find
The sad detailed imprints
Of the festival days

Nand Chaturvedi, 'The Cruel Festival Time,'
translated by Katherine Russell Rich
and Vidhu Shekhar Chaturvedi

Last Night

SOMETHING HAPPENED TO HER WHILE she was eating, or right afterward. She began turning in circles and couldn't stop. In my kitchen, in my car, and then in an examining room at the vet's office. I sat on the floor with her while the vet stood leaning against the wall, watching us. I was crying, but he ignored that.

'You indicated once,' he said, looking through the file, 'that we should let you know when it might be time.'

It wasn't time.

'It looks like a brain abnormality, something that's grown or shifted. We might wait a day or so to see what happens. But if this doesn't stop . . .' He paused.

'Sheba, stop,' I said, and held her. She looked like Lady from *Lady and the Tramp*, only old; she was fifteen.

It was like putting your hand on a spinning top, but as soon as I let go, she began turning again. We used to call her Top Dog because she liked to sleep stretched out on our old black Lab, her head settled on his head, both of their eyes closed. Once, many years ago, the Lab had gotten carefully to his feet, made his way to the kitchen where my husband was cooking, and accepted a treat, all without disturbing the sleeping puppy draped over his neck. The Lab lived to be fifteen too. The marriage, fourteen.

I took my hands away to button my jacket, and she turned blindly for a moment on the gleaming linoleum, then bumped into the single leg of the examining table.

'It might be time,' the vet said, putting his foot out to stop her. Except for those neon running shoes, he was completely nondescript, like an actor you aren't sure why is in the movie until the very end, when he turns out to be the killer.

At home, it didn't get any better or any worse, Sheba following herself, nose to tail, around and around in a circle while I tried to keep her steady. My neighbor came over for a few minutes and watched, her eyes round and nervous. 'This doesn't look hopeful,' the neighbor finally said.

It was dark by then, and I was kneeling on my living-room floor in the lamplight, holding her and then letting her turn, holding her and then letting her turn. It was winter, but the neighbor was wearing flip-flops.

'Aren't your feet cold?' I asked her.

'Yes,' she said, and went home.

We were used to being alone. Our house was small and dark, set into a hillside, but we had a stone fireplace and built-in bookshelves and a screened porch overlooking a blue lake, our own dock, and certain seabirds that didn't seem like they belonged there, so we chased them away each morning, or, rather, one of us did while the other stood on a giant ornate piece of driftwood and drank coffee in her sunglasses, even though nobody needed sunglasses in Ithaca.

We had brought more or less nothing from our previous life – a few pictures, some ceramic bowls, a Turkish rug that we hardly noticed in our old, big Iowa house but that became, in the new house, a focal point, the last remnant of what used to be. Sheba began urinating on it sometime around midnight, a series of dark rings overlapping and intersecting one another. By one o'clock it was my turn to pee, and I ran to the bathroom and came back to find her spun into a corner and stuck there, bumping against the baseboard.

Turning and turning in the widening gyre.

'Sheba,' I said.

The falcon cannot hear the falconer.

'Sheba,' I said, holding her face in my hands. She looked back blindly and I saw suddenly that the vet was right, something had grown or shifted, blocking her in there all alone.

I'd always known I'd have to live without her someday; I just hadn't known it would be tomorrow. *Things fall apart.* Here in the safe silence of Ithaca, I had forgotten that.

So we stayed awake all of her last night, waiting for the vet's office to open, in the living room on the Turkish rug, in the kitchen next to her food bowl, and finally on the bed pushed into the corner, my body between her and the edge. At some point I couldn't help it and let my eyes close, and when I did, it felt like I was turning, too, our lives unraveling like a skein of yarn stretched from Ithaca back to Iowa. I see my husband patting his chest and holding out his arms, Sheba jumping into them. I see the Lab wearing her like a bonnet on his head. I see her running under the seabirds as they fly along the shore. Don't leave yet, I say to my husband, who leaves. 'Don't leave yet,' I say aloud in the darkness of the bedroom.

She used to sleep at the foot of the bed, and at first light, first twitch, she would crawl sleepily up to my pillow so that when I opened my eyes she was what I saw. The aging dog-actress face – still the dark eyes, still the long glamorous ears. Don't leave yet. If I let go of her, she moves in wider and wider circles, getting close to the edge. *Come back, little Sheba.* We're both close to the edge now, peering over it into the great metaphorical beyond.

And then dawn arrives, and then it's eight, and I begin to move forward, into it, without thinking. I carry her down to the water and let her stand on the shore, the birds wheeling and making their noises. In Iowa she ran into a cornfield once and didn't come out for a long time, and when she did, she seemed thoughtful. The Lab once went on a garbage run and afterward threw up what looked like a whole birthday cake, candles and all. I carry her back up the hill and the neighbor runs out of her house, half dressed for work, and opens the car door for me.

'Is it time?' she asks me.

'Not yet,' I tell her.

All the way across town, driving and holding her in the passenger seat with one hand, I think to myself, *Don't think.* All the way from Iowa to Ithaca, eight hundred miles, she stood in the back seat on the rolled-up rug, her chin on my shoulder, and watched the landscape scroll by. I feel her humming against my hand, trying to turn, and then we're turning, we're in the parking lot, we're here.

It's time.

Werner

WERNER HOEFLICH SPENT THE EVENING at his catering job, making white-wine spritzers and mixing vodka with Tab in a spacious apartment overlooking Central Park. There were orchids, thick rugs, a dog with long blond hair. He walked home late from the subway afterward, along the gated and padlocked streets of the Upper East Side. The trees on his block were scrawny and impervious, like invalid aunts.

Once, he had seen a parakeet in one of those trees, staring down at him, shifting from foot to foot. The bird had sharpened both sides of its beak on the branch and then made a veering, panicky flight to a windowsill far above. Most of Werner's metaphorical moments were painterly – the juxtaposing of the wild bird and the tame tree, the shimmer of periwinkle, the *splurt* of titanium white that fell from it onto the pavement. He loved New York for its simple surprises, although in truth, Oregon and Iowa and Arizona and everywhere else had simple surprises as well. Cantaloupe-colored sunrises, banded cows, Dairy Queens, all kinds of things that didn't include black plastic mountains of trash and the smell of dog urine. But on that night it wasn't like that; it was cold and fresh on the dark streets. He rounded the corner and his building came into view, a turn-of-the-century tenement where, right about then – just before midnight, December 19, 1991 – another kind of New York surprise was taking shape. Deep inside the walls, three floors below Werner's apartment, a sprig of cloth-wrapped wire sizzled and then opened, like a blossom.

From the street it looked like a single building but it was actually twin tenements set next to each other and connected along the facade. Werner let himself into the entrance on the left, walked to the back, and climbed to the fifth floor, where he was greeted by his cat, Two. She trotted ahead of him into the kitchen to wait for her bounty, served on an unfurled bed of tinfoil – a pale smear of liver pâté and several translucent strands of sashimi.

Feet up, Werner dialed Eugene, Oregon, and had a nice conversation with his mother. He liked to call home late, when they were just getting to the end of their West Coast day and he was still energized, sitting in his skivvies in the over-hot apartment. The walls were bumpy and pocked, thick plaster reinforced with horsehair, but he had whitewashed them and hired someone to refinish the wood floors. They were hay-colored and gleamed in the lamplight. His paintings hung here and there, dark backgrounds with shapes emerging out of them – construction machinery, the camshaft of an ocean liner, simple tools, almost but not quite abstract.

When Werner finally slept that night, it was like sinking slowly through water, fathom by fathom, to the ocean floor. He might have been dreaming when the wiring finally ignited, carrying fire upward through the building. He thought he could feel things swirling in the darkness, but when he tried to reach for them, the weight of the water pressed him to the bed.

Sometime between four and five a.m., the tenants in 2C heard a heavy pounding noise in the ceiling, which then collapsed. Their upstairs neighbors in 3C heard the same sound and then their ceiling collapsed as well; they made it to the fire escape and began screaming. The 2C tenants left through the stairwell with their children, although the wife became paralyzed with confusion and fear and the husband had to drag her. In the panic they left their door open.

The fire engulfed 2C and billowed out into the hallway. Werner woke to the sound of screaming. He was next to an open window on a loft bed six feet off the floor. He sat up and pulled the string to the light, a bare bulb in the ceiling. Rectangular shapes jumped at him in the glare – wardrobe, doorway, rug. The screams were of a type Werner hadn't heard before.

His brain spun like a tire that wouldn't catch: the familiar terrain of his bedroom, the heavy scent of smoke drifting through the petals of the window fan, his own bent knees draped in a sheet.

He needed to get dressed and get to the street, help whoever was in trouble. He grabbed for his clothes but couldn't find the first thing he needed, underwear. He turned, and then turned back. He could see them in his memory – stacks of brightly colored boxers as well as the other kind, folded neatly on a shelf – but there was something blocking him, an invisible membrane between Werner and the next step. He stood in front of the tall, impenetrable wardrobe. He had been awake for approximately fifteen seconds. The screams were loud and prolonged, people coming unhinged.

Without his underpants he couldn't think.

It was a familiar scent, but distant – campfires in his past, in the Oregon woods. Boiled coffee, damp socks, Werner rooted to a stump, bow across his lap. Deer, someone had told him, needed at least two senses to pinpoint danger, some pairing of sight, sound, smell; otherwise they just stood there, uncertain.

Sound of screams, smell of smoke.

Werner bounded naked to the front door, flipped the locks, flung it open, and a wall of smoke hit him in the face. He slammed it shut, turned, and squinted into the apartment. More smoke was coming in through the living room. He imagined the roof and the street below. Werner had been awake now maybe twenty-five seconds and had his first coherent thought. He thought he didn't want to be naked if he had to jump off the building.

He stepped back into the bedroom, and a dry, papery gray cloud consumed him. He dropped to his hands and knees and put his cheek to the floor. With this nearsighted, close-up view, he could see smoke curling up through the floorboards, black specks inside the tendrils like a flock of birds banking and moving together. Dark geese rising into the Oregon sky. He wasn't going to find oxygen at the floor.

Time was starting to slow down.

His room was teeny and cramped; with the bare lightbulb, it looked cheap and garish, like a torture site. He pulled the cord to the bulb on his way to the window and then in darkness struggled to lift the sash. The window fan, set in the upper half of the casement, was blocking it. He thrust his fingers into the grating of the fan and tugged, but it wouldn't move. For an instant he became an animal, tearing at the immovable fan, panic surging upward, overtaking him like flames.

He let go of the fan. His arms dropped to his sides.

Once as a teenager he had gone hunting on the land of a man who was his father's patient. When his father introduced him to the man, Werner said, 'Hi.' Afterward his father lit into him, uncharacteristically, for not being more respectful – he explained that when called upon to meet someone, Werner should step forward and extend his hand. His father, a physician, was gentle and decent; that was about the only time he had ever been sharp with his son.

Now Werner made a shift. He spoke to himself firmly but kindly, like a father. *Werner*, he said, *you've got to calm down. You've dealt with this fan before.*

He remembered – it was suspended from the top by two neat hooks he had put there himself. After lifting it free, then shoving both panes of glass up and wedging them tightly into the frame, Werner stuck his whole torso out the window, sucking in air.

Everything suddenly became crystalline and calm; he could breathe. He looked around, listening, and heard sirens.

'Building's on fire! Call the fire department!' he yelled, leaning out the window.

Straight across was his building's twin, silent and dark. Off to the left, in back of the buildings, was a vacant lot surrounded by cyclone fencing. Beyond that was Ninety-Sixth Street. Sirens but no fire trucks. Below him, flames were shooting out of the third-floor windows and curling around the edge of the building.

He lost his fear. He was completely in the moment, experiencing instead of anticipating. Time stretched like rubber. Fascinated, he wandered around inside each moment as though it were a cavernous room.

Summer job at a retread factory, endless deafening days in which the hours were earned slowly through an accumulation of stiff, stinking cords of rubber to be stamped and stacked and helpless, imaginary encounters with every girl in his high-school class. Ghost girls who joined him at his locker first thing and followed him out onto the floor. He had to brush past them in order to do his work; interference – one wrong move and your finger, hand, arm is gone. The clock would hop its minutes interminably and then suddenly everyone was poised, Werner and his colleagues, men in big gloves who had been out of high school for thirty years. When the buzzer went off, they were like a herd of steers aiming for a hole in the fence.

Get out while you can, they told him.

Sound clattered back into his head and he began to hear people screaming again, this time from the fire escapes on the other side of the building. Black smoke was billowing from the windows below. The fire was working its way up, floor by floor, the wind moving the smoke to the south, where the fire escapes were. His neighbors kept screaming, many voices, desperate and trapped. Werner was sure they were dying.

Beyond the end of the building and across the vacant lot, he saw a dozen or so people at the bus stop on Ninety-Sixth standing against the cyclone fencing and staring up at the building like people at a bonfire, their faces lit by flames.

He was still experiencing perfect clarity, assessing everything he could see in a clinical manner, sweeping his gaze from the people watching to the flames below him and the strands of black smoke funneling out the windows.

He could see two options. One was taking a T-shirt, wetting it, draping it over his face, then leaving the apartment and making a run for the roof. The other was crossing the living room to the fire escape and joining his neighbors in their cauldron of despair. The stairwell to the roof wasn't navigable; he'd already glimpsed it when he opened his door. The living room was dense with smoke; if he did make it across, there was no way he'd get the window gate unlocked. It was new, put in when Werner was out of town, crisscrossed bars with a key the super had placed somewhere along the ledge above.

He was trapped, nearsighted and naked in a burning building. He reached behind, groping, and found the robe that always hung from the loft bed. He put it on without pulling his head back into the room. He leaned farther out.

Werner had said just that night to his friend James that he was sick of being a caterer and wasn't going to do it anymore. He was thinking of taking a long-ago professor's advice and becoming a fireman, a good job for an artist. Not that his fellow caterers weren't artists too – painters, opera singers, designers – but this was 1991; AIDS and Reagan had happened and Werner hadn't gotten out of the business when everyone else did. No matter how depressing it got, his coworkers growing gaunt and dying, the economy surging and plummeting, he just hung in there.

He had seen a man nearly lose a hand once, not at the retread factory but later, in college during a gymnastics meet, a friend whose leather grip had somehow caught in the apparatus when he went up and over the bar. His wrist twisted as he finished the revolution, and he hung there until they could climb up and unbuckle the glove. They laid him on the floor, and the hand looked so strange lying against the blue of the mat, the wrist bones jutting straight up, white and exposed, that someone put a Dixie cup over it.

The fire crew would have to come from behind the building, Werner realized, in order to climb up and save him; they'd have to carry their ladder through the vacant lot, over the cyclone fences, and into the dark space between the two buildings. Growing up, Werner had worked his way around his family's property on a tall stepladder each summer, moving it a few feet at a time as he trimmed the eight-foot hedge that ran along the border. From a distance, the hedge was squared off and stylized, like the neat shrubbery in a Grant Wood painting, but up close it was a dense chaotic bramble of bent twigs and thick, waxy leaves. Bay laurel. He knew its shades of green intimately. Once, far away from home, Werner dreamed of the bay-laurel hedge, of stepping inside and finding it hollow, a cool rectangular box that he could lie down in.

Firemen weren't going to save him. They didn't even save cats anymore.

His cat! He turned to shout her name into the apartment.

He couldn't believe what was behind him – the smoke was everywhere, dark and billowing. He shouted into it and then listened. After a moment, coming from somewhere far away, he heard a meow. He kept calling, and the meowing got closer and closer until finally Two was at the open bedroom door. Werner took a breath and ducked back to snatch her up. She struggled, her fur matted and sticky with soot, so he held her in front of him under the arms like you would a toddler. She yowled, raspy from swallowing smoke.

It was like trying to breathe through flannel. Werner realized he was going to die.

The dark back seat of a car in Iowa City, returning to campus from a gymnastics meet junior year. Werner and Nate, the guy who would later nearly lose his hand, folded into the back seat, Clayton the all-around guy driving, somebody else shotgun, all of them high on exhaustion and victory. Werner had a simple but impeccable high-bar mount – vertical jump, grab the bar, swing forward, arch, and then pike in to create the momentum that would shoot the legs up to a handstand. After that, the delirious, controlled fall into giant circles, the body as fully extended as it would go.

In the middle of campus, coming over a rise, they saw it just as they hit it: black ice on the downslope of a steep hill; the car in front of them skated sideways as their car hit the ice and shot forward like a bullet. Slowly revolving, the sideways car turned and headed back toward them broadside, gaining velocity, its blue flank growing larger and larger. It felt like five weeks, the time between the two cars starting to skid and the jarring impact.

That's what time felt like now, elongated and dreamlike, the outcome sliding toward him out of the cold night.

Inside the smoke, he turned with his cat, moving from the doorway back to the window, three long strides broken down into tiny, fractured increments of motion. Nude descending a staircase of absurdity – it wasn't even his fault, and this is how it ends? He almost laughed. Whatever had happened had happened on a floor below, some accident that had nothing to do with him, but he would be part of the outcome.

It wasn't so much that he'd never thought it would end this way as that he'd never thought it would end. His life was so absorbing – a series of long studio days pulling images out of the dark backgrounds. And he was moving away from that now, the backgrounds receding and the objects themselves seeming less iconic and barnacled and more . . . something else. He had wanted to see where he was going was all, had wanted to follow the work.

He was thirty-six, mid-stride metaphorically and literally. His first studio in New York had been on the property of Cohen Carpentry; the scent of sawdust and the industrious buzz of power tools had become linked with the other accoutrements of creativity – the bristling arrangements of brushes in their jars, the silver tubes of paint, the tin echo inside the turp can as he lifted it to pour. On a grant, he had gone to Europe and traveled for four months, drawn to the construction sites in each city he visited.

Enormous crawling insects with men operating their pincers, thick sinewy cables like muscled arms, pulleys with long horse-like faces, iron beams baled and lashed together like bundles of kindling, strands of rebar emerging from concrete, bent like giant curling hairs. Werner, lonely and ecstatic, made drawings of it all.

The drawings, back home, became paintings. He painted his way through the objects to what was beyond; he painted the cam-shaft of the ocean liner until it was like a word repeated so many times that it turned into something new and foreign.

Even watching all his catering colleagues growing stark, faltering with their trays, eyes getting larger as their flesh dimin-ished, Werner had never realized that something unimaginable occurred when the end slithered up. It curled around your feet and entwined you; you became part of it instead of it becoming part of you.

Once, inside the laurel hedge, Werner had found an old Crush bottle hanging suspended, completely encased by tines. The hedge had sent feelers down inside it, twisting into the bottom and then twining back up through the neck. It was marvelous and beautiful and Werner tried to pull it free, but the hedge wouldn't let go of its prize.

He suddenly saw himself letting go, just stepping through the stiff green hedge into the cool rectangular space, taking a few deep breaths, and then sleeping. He only wanted to rest. Some-times a little brown bird would poke its way in and hop among the branches. If the leaves fluttered, Werner would rest the loppers for a moment, shift his weight on the ladder, then begin again.

He had an image now of himself as they would find him, arm around the cat, and was vaguely aware that people would be upset, although right then he couldn't have said who. The best he could conjure was a blurred impression, pointillist stabs of color that stood for sisters; parents; his girlfriend, JM; friends he loved. Peter. Jeff. Chris, his old roommate, who used to sit Two on his lap, get her very relaxed and purring, then try to put her head in his mouth. She had thick whiskers, like barbed wire. Once while Werner was asleep, she had set a live mouse on his naked belly and he woke to feel it running up his torso and around his neck. They had been together for nine years now.

If he couldn't save himself, maybe he could help her. Holding the cat like a vessel in front of him, he put her through the open window and out into the air so she could breathe. It was like being on drugs, the whole world surrounding him like a tidal pool, everything taking on equal significance and richness: the color of the skin on his hand, the eddies of refracted light, the amplified sound of sirens. *Please*, he thought. *If we can just hang on, the fire department will break in and save us.*

Holding Two, both their heads out the window, he looked down and saw that the fire had reached the fourth floor; the smoke was thicker now, less porous. There would be no rescue.

The wind stopped. Holding Two, Werner suddenly couldn't see her. The wind had shifted and, like a fountain, the smoke came rushing upward, his open window acting like a funnel, sucking the black cloud inside.

Two began to struggle desperately. Werner glanced back, and the bedpost, a foot and a half away, was gone. The smoke looked like oily Jell-O, granular, particles whirling all around him.

There was no oxygen between the particles now, no way to negotiate anything out of it. The opposite, in fact; if air equaled life, then non-air equaled death, but this was a step beyond – it was non-air with poison.

In the stopped, strangled moment that followed, another thought burst loose and hung there, pale inside the black swirling column.

He would have to jump.

*

Five stories was too far to fall; he'd never survive it. He'd done it once long ago, a forty-five-foot drop, not onto concrete but into deep, still water. The bridge over Fall Creek, east of Eugene, a wood trestle built into bedrock, the surface of the water below tense and glittering, huge smooth boulders on either shore, his striped towel and white T-shirt draped over one; he would claim them after the jump, when the next guy was standing there poised to sever his spine. He had looked down at his feet, which seemed delicate at that height, wet sneakers sagging. Somebody hollered, 'Hey, Werner,' and then an obscenity, and others laughed. He thought he heard sympathy in the shouts, but that was useless, the sympathy of men. You still had to do it. He had made the mistake of pausing and was momentarily stranded under a bored blue sky, just Werner on a trestle with his delicate-looking feet and the sunburned tops of his knobby knees. He realized he loved himself, gripping the trestle as the afternoon wind thumped at him. But love or no love, he still had to step off, and so he did.

Two didn't want to be held; she was going crazy. The black funnel had engulfed them completely now, and he tried not to breathe it. Hands clamped around Two's rib cage, Werner tried to take in glimpses of the window in the neighboring building straight across, perhaps eight feet away.

Four panes of glass, two over two. Stone sill on the outside. Orange-red drapes pulled shut, a lamp behind them giving off an incandescent glow.

The window would be like his, ancient and sturdy, the glass rippled, the wood thick with a century of paint. He wouldn't have the courage to climb out on his own ledge first – too much time to think – so he'd have to do it in one motion, hop up on the sill in the form of a racing dive. He had been a competitive swimmer from ages seven to twelve, a shivering, long-limbed boy in tight goggles and regulation trunks; he had a muscle memory of the stance, the bending, the tensing of the core. His toes would have to wrap around the sill to create the proper angle forward.

He thought it all the way through and then knew enough to stop thinking about it. He was completely adrenalized now. He cinched Two under his left arm, pressing her as securely as he could to his torso, then placed his right hand, knuckles down, against the wooden sill of the open window.

He spoke to his cat: 'Looks like it's time to go.'

In one motion, up and out.

He waited an instant for his toes to wrap around the sill – they were there but they hadn't all caught yet. When they did, he pushed off.

His skull broke the wood and shattered the glass into long daggers. He went in up to his knees, which landed on the stone sill, body all the way through onto somebody's bed, right into their apartment, clanging with brightness, lights on in every room.

Startling, everything now in fast-forward, like a film whipping by; the orange-red curtains from this side were coarsely woven, the lamp knocked on the floor beaming out its white glare, the coverlet nubby, his shoulders webbed with stickiness.

He called out, his voice ringing with fright and embarrassment: 'Is anybody home?'

No answer. He tried again, louder, and then walked swiftly past their belongings and furniture to the door. He felt a twinge of confusion over leaving it unlocked; moments raced past him in a blur as he hesitated in the corridor. This building wasn't on fire but it was being evacuated; in the stairwell there were people rushing around. He yelled down at someone he recognized, a man he'd seen but never talked to.

The man looked up, startled, but then kept going, hurrying down the stairs, carrying what looked like a box of figurines. Others were lugging televisions and computers; one woman in a nightgown and ski jacket was clutching a pot of Swedish ivy, plant hanger and all, thick strands of macramé slung over her shoulder.

Outside, the street was teeming. There were fire trucks, people running, all manner of blurry chaos, and all of it flashing.

Werner, barefoot, wearing only a bathrobe soaked in blood, walked up to a fireman. 'I've hurt myself,' he said.

The fireman had seen him come out of a building that wasn't on fire. He peered at Werner in the strobe of the red light, clearly confused. A second later, the fireman disappeared.

Werner began shaking uncontrollably. He didn't know what else to do, so he tried to follow the discombobulated fireman, staring into people's faces until he found him in the cab of a vehicle.

'Are you going to help me or what?' Werner asked. His arms were covered in blood, he realized. Everything was. He'd been ruined by the glass, torn up; the guy wouldn't even look at him.

Out of the night, another apparition appeared – a skinny little homeless man, possibly crazy, wearing a filthy red sweatshirt under some kind of coat. Greasy hair, Fu Manchu mustache. He took a close look at Werner, reached out, and tried to steer him away.

Werner wouldn't move.

'There's an ambulance down the block,' Fu Manchu said. His features had receded into the grime on his face, but the voice was authoritative.

Werner resisted, backing up. In the chaos of these emergencies, he knew, people got themselves lured away from the lights and were mugged. It happened. Anything could happen.

The homeless man sighed, reached under his filthy sweatshirt, and pulled out a badge.

NYPD UNDERCOVER.

*

The doors of the ambulance had a kind of quilted aluminum paneling on them, like a lunch truck's, but inside it felt more like a camper, everything stowed in compartments, held secure with straps. Werner sat on one of the cots, and the EMTs started questioning him.

'My building caught on fire and I had to jump across into another building,' Werner explained, trying to stay calm. He was like a marionette someone was shaking.

The attendants looked at each other and then back at him.

It was predawn; the camper was warm. Somewhere, the deer were rising from their grass mats and moving into the woods, the bucks steering their antlers carefully, like women carrying kindling on their heads.

'We have to take your bathrobe off to examine you,' one of the EMTs said. Werner sat hunched as they lifted the soaking robe from his shoulders, peeling it from his back and sides. He'd seen it, every sportsman had, the frozen moment when the deer was still living, staring upward at the blackening world. Even Werner, so careful, had had to dispatch an animal at close range, the strangeness of shooting down instead of away, the surge of regret – *Why this? Why did I do this?* – before it was over and everything resumed, the bright neon of his vest, the green canopy overhead.

He looked down at his left shoulder where there were three cuts, large and startling, their pink interiors visible. His right shoulder – swooningly close – had a catastrophic wound, dark red and complicated, a fissure down into his body revealing something sinewy and glistening. He could see his own muscle, the broad deltoids that a man wears fitted over his shoulders like a cape. Werner began to cry.

He never could hold her if she didn't want to be held.

'I don't know what happened,' he said. A wave of grief rose over him, pushing him forward into something new and unfamiliar. Failure, a bottomless black lake with something moving inside it.

He began crying so hard it sounded like a fit of choking.

The EMT guys were more or less unmoved by this. They kept sneaking assessing looks at his face as they put gauze over his wounds.

'All right,' Werner said, pulling himself together, trying to sit up. The backs of his hands were like the hands of someone who has been murdered and left lying in his own blood. 'You have to tell me what happened to my face,' he said.

The men handed him a mirror so he could see what they were looking at – there were no cuts, his face was intact, but it was so white it seemed like an emergency in itself, with black rings of soot circling his nostrils and mouth. He looked like one of those spectral creatures in a Japanese horror movie, the subliminal ones shown only in flashes.

Smoke inhalation, possibility of charred lungs.

The EMTs had their walkie-talkies going, communicating with the hospital's emergency department. Amid the clatter and static, the cop returned and asked if Werner wanted him to call anyone.

'Would you call my girlfriend?' he asked. 'Tell her where they're taking me.'

The cop took down the number as Werner was strapped onto the gurney, asked if the girlfriend should bring anything.

Werner tried to think. 'Maybe she could bring me a blanket,' he said.

They conducted the ambulance through the New York streets, siren blaring. He had always wondered what this felt like. His mother didn't know where he was, none of the people he loved knew where he was right now, didn't have any idea that Werner had been forced to jump out of his life and into whatever this was.

He sobbed for a moment inside his oxygen mask. The EMT reached over and adjusted it. Calmed, Werner shut his eyes. These gondolier guys were taking care of his physical self, placing their poles in the deep canal and pulling him along. He could relax, gliding forward over black water, the things that mattered falling like coins from his pockets.

He started crying again.

The ER at 5:00 a.m. was completely deserted. A ringing, fluorescent silence, then eight people crowded around to look at Werner. Poking, prodding, asking what happened.

The EMT told them that Werner had jumped out of a burning building into another building, one that wasn't on fire, thereby saving his own life. This caused a stir.

'We gotta call the newspaper,' a doctor said.

'No,' Werner said. He looked straight ahead, not at any of them. 'I just want you to sew me up.'

A young resident began babbling. He had worked in that hospital for a while, he had seen extreme things, people in bad circumstances, people shot in the head, et cetera. You couldn't imagine the shit he'd heard, the stories people came in there with. 'But yours is the most amazing,' the resident exclaimed, his professionalism totally breaking down.

'Get him out of here,' Werner said.

They wiped his face with something cool and antiseptic but left the rest of him covered with soot, dirt, and dried blood. They wheeled in a crash cart, took X-rays, and stuck EKG leads to his chest in a careful constellation.

'Can you relax that?' the nurse asked, nodding toward his right hand. She was popping open packages of sterile tubing, preparing to put IVs in his arm, run fluids and antibiotics.

Werner's left hand was open, but his right was clenched into a fist. He opened it for her.

Resting on his palm was the brass key to the old mahogany wardrobe in his bedroom, where his underwear was kept. He had snatched the key out instead of turning it. For a second, he had a grainy flashback of himself groping dumbly at the tall dark door, whirling in panic. He stared at the key, this thing he had brought with him from his old life.

'I dropped Two,' he said.

The nurse stopped momentarily to glance down at her feet and then under the gurney. 'I'm just about done,' she reassured him. As she taped the IV in place and flicked her fingernail at the tubing, another nurse came in and without apology or ado reached under his sheet and inserted a catheter. It felt swift and brutal, like plugging a burning wand into a socket, and Werner cried out, finally, in indignation.

Everyone left. He was propped up on the gurney with things sticking out of him, unrecognizable to himself. He wiggled his toes. They were still his toes. He bent them and they bent.

The rolling table next to him was made to glide under and over a hospital bed; on its laminate surface rested the brass key with its single tarnished tooth. Werner should have been dead, but he wasn't; that part, he still didn't get. Down at the bottom of the gurney were his toes. He moved them back and forth again like levers.

The officious pink curtain that moved on little ball bearings was quiet now, a thin membrane between Werner and the world.

He waited.

*

'Mr. Hoeflich,' the doctor said.

Werner opened his eyes. It was the guy who seemed to be in charge, or anyway the one who was tallest. He was going bald in a handsome way and seemed a little bit like an athlete, one of those TV doctors who played hoops out back on a slow night in the ER.

'When can I get sewn up and leave?' Werner asked him.

'We're sending you to intensive care,' the doctor informed him. 'Smoke inhalation can lead to severe pulmonary edema.' He gave this time to sink in before he continued. 'Very dangerous if that happens. The alveoli begin to fill up with fluid and you stop breathing.'

Werner felt like swooning. Drowned by your own body. He had held Two like a vessel out the window. The whole thing seemed now like a succession of moments. In that moment, and the moment before, the smoke had been curling sideways around the building, a bolt of black cloth unwinding. Then it stopped and there was a moment of emptiness before the black current was swept upward, and he realized it wasn't like cloth at all; it was dark and viscid, like used motor oil, and they weren't breathing it, they were drinking it.

Those fucking people rescuing their TVs. He hadn't even saved his cat.

The dark lake that he thought was all around him was now seeping inside, making his lungs swell like wineskins.

'I just want to be sewn up,' Werner said.

'Yeah, I don't know why you haven't been,' the doctor replied before disappearing.

He lay there some more, congealing.

The curtain rolled open a few inches and a janitor took a look at him, left, and then returned with JM, who was unprepared for what she found, the bloody mess on the gurney. She had been

29

told only that she needed to come pick him up. Werner broke down at the sight of her. She was wearing blue jeans and a wool coat, her blond hair stuck inside her scarf, which she unwound without taking her eyes from Werner. Her face, her lovely off-kilter mouth. Like the brass key, JM had somehow made the leap with him to this new world. He put one hand over his eyes, crying.

'Two is dead, I dropped Two.'

'Werner,' JM said, touching him. 'What do you want me to do?'

'You have to find her,' he said. 'Get somebody to go around back with you, under my window.' He wanted her to find other things as well – his glasses, his wallet, five hundred dollars in a bureau drawer.

JM sat and spoke quietly to him for a while and then stood up, rewinding her scarf around her neck, this time lifting her hair free of it before leaning over him again. She would come back; she would try to bring his friend Peter with her. He felt the soft knot of cashmere against his chest and then she was gone and someone else materialized, another apparition. A Filipina woman in pink scrubs, blurry and beautiful, with coral nail polish as flaw-less as the finish on a new car.

'You haven't been sewn up,' she informed him, lifting the gauze from his wounds. 'Let's do that.'

His muscle was exposed, the ragged opening leading down to it coagulated and angry. 'And you are?' he asked her.

She was the trauma surgeon. Using a tool that looked like a cross between a pair of scissors and a needle, she gave him mul-tiple shots of lidocaine in his shoulders and torso. He looked up at the ceiling. In those paintings of Saint Sebastian, the eyes were always tipped toward the heavens. Orion in the night sky, drawing back his bow and shooting whatever was up there. All over Werner's upper body, small pains burned like stars. He didn't know if he could stand it and then a numbness started to move across him, and he felt impassive in his suffering.

Before the doctor could stitch him up, a nurse poked her head in. 'You're supposed to be down in *eleven*,' she said to the doctor, who hustled out like a student caught by the hall monitor.

Werner waited.

A half an hour later they flattened him out and trundled him along a series of tiled passageways. The hospital seemed both futuristic and worn out, like an old starship. Above him were fluorescent bulbs behind ribbed plastic panels. Wafers of light, one after the other, until he gave up and turned his head to the side. A man he couldn't see was steering the gurney expertly on its rubber treads, bumping it through doorways and, once, giving it a generous push and letting it glide alone down a quiet corridor, past a nurses' station where an African-American woman looked at Werner without curiosity.

It didn't seem utterly impossible that he had died but couldn't tell, that no one here could, that they were all dead too, guiding gurneys, giving shots, whispering along in blood-spattered clogs. His lungs felt full and frightening in his chest, like cow udders.

They got him off the gurney and situated in a bed with a stainless-steel trough around the edge. He tried to sit up and someone pushed him back down.

'I'm going to be your doctor,' someone else said, a jovial Italian man surrounded by others. They all stared down at Werner as brown liquid was poured on his shoulders. It was cold and pooled up in the trough. The doctor had a big horse needle, curved. He slung his necktie over his shoulder and began sewing Werner's deepest cuts from the inside out.

He heard someone in the group telling his story, the jump from one building to another, and a new embellishment, compliments of the lab: his carbon monoxide levels had been so high that in another ten seconds, he probably couldn't have done it, saved himself.

I didn't save myself, he thought. *It was random.*

31

You could spend your whole life swinging from rings and high bars, doing racing dives at seven a.m. into cold pools, but if the smoke happened to rise in a particular way, blocking the view of the window across from you, or if that window had a tall bureau in front of it instead of a bed, then your athletic ability was nothing more than an anecdote to be mentioned at your funeral.

This realization was new to Werner, like the sense of failure had been. It was a shameful, contaminating knowledge, jabbing him in the ribs like the finger of God. Werner felt a prodding, something being tugged upward and then released. It had been more than a half an hour since the lidocaine.

'I'm starting to feel what you're doing,' he told the doctor. 'I can feel my shoulders.' He was becoming agitated and hallucinatory; he could feel God plucking at the slippery muscle. Where were the people he knew? JM and the others. He was supposed to work that night for Glorious Foods, and it was all taking too long.

'Mr. Hoeflich, would you like a shot of morphine?' the Italian doctor asked. He stepped away from the table for a moment and then stepped back with a different needle.

Werner didn't even have to answer. They gave him a shot, but he could still feel what they were doing; they gave him another, and a moment later he felt normal.

'My lungs,' he said.

'Bronchoscopy,' the Italian doctor said. 'As soon as we're done here.'

A few minutes passed.

'Will it hurt?' Werner asked.

'It won't be pleasant,' the doctor said pleasantly.

One of the people standing around, a nurse wearing Christmas-tree earrings, left to call him in sick at Glorious Foods. Werner

32

couldn't remember the number but she said she was happy to look it up.

'Ask for Jeff,' Werner said. 'Make sure you're talking to him.' He closed his eyes for a moment; when he opened them, the nurse was back.

'He was worried you were burned,' she reported and went to work unwinding from a portable machine a flexible steel shaft the size of a drinking straw. The shaft had a camera on the end of it and the doctor began feeding it into Werner's nose, inch by inch, driving it like a spike into his brain.

He arched up on the table, and people scattered for an instant, a flock of birds rising and then settling again, this time with three men on top of Werner, trying to hold him down. He came loose, flailing, and another man materialized and piled on. Werner fought silently, the spike probing into his head, his utterly private reaches.

'Give him a sedative!' somebody said, panting, and a moment later he couldn't move.

The thing pushed its way down until it was in his lungs. He felt like he was drowning. It was worse than being trapped in the fire, being inanimate, like something already dead. He sank to the bottom of the lake, into the slippery weeds. The camera emitted a bead of light, peering at his bronchi.

'It looks okay,' he heard the Italian doctor say.

Up in the ICU he was still partially submerged as they tugged him from the gurney to a bed, a drowned man bumping against the pilings. The ICU was gleaming and technical, separated into pods, each with its own nurses' station.

'Whores,' a man said to the ceiling. 'Whoring *whores*.'

The man was covered in gauze and a sheet; nothing but a black-ened forearm and a pale horned foot were visible. It was like one of those all-night labyrinthine dreams where everywhere you turn, there is some bizarre oversize thing occurring. Werner manually tugged one leg over and then the other, helping to arrange himself between the cool railings of the bed.

'Fuck,' the man said intently through his teeth. 'Fucking *fuck*.'

'He's a homeless gentleman,' the nurse confided, 'set on fire by a group of kids.'

'I'm sorry,' Werner said.

'That's okay,' the nurse said automatically.

She prepared a morphine shot for him and as she gave it, two gowned and masked figures were ushered in to stand alongside his bed. They were wearing paper hats and booties. Werner recognized JM's eyes and then Peter's. He wept again, helplessly, like he was seeing people from his distant past.

'Werner,' they said through their masks, touching him on the legs.

They had found the wallet, the money, and the glasses and taken two bottles of good champagne from his refrigerator. Nothing else was salvageable.

They were so sorry.

He closed his eyes and paddled away on his morphine raft. He watched himself throwing a series of baseballs through a window, making a bigger and bigger hole, then saw himself throwing his cat through it, a gentle, underhand toss. He saw Two plummeting off a bridge in a cartoon landscape, and he saw himself reaching down with a long, long arm to neatly catch her, a foot above the water, on a waiter's tray.

He roused himself to talk to JM and Peter. 'I canceled my job for Glorious,' he told them. 'But I'm supposed to work for Sarah too. I think I can do it.'

Their eyebrows rose.

The nurse left her station then to escort the visitors out, and Werner reclined into the cartoon landscape, a giant resting his

back against a sand-colored butte. He reached out and grasped
the cool railing. Giants were the moves he liked best back when
he flew; they were preparation, momentum gathering for what
would happen when he let go of the bar. He did his impeccable
mount: swing forward straight-bodied, get a little tap, arch, pike,
then up into a handstand. Now he was balanced over the railing
of the bedrock bridge, high above Fall Creek.

'Fucking *Doc*,' the charred man cried out.

The fall from the trestle all those years ago had been long
enough for him to entertain regrets, although Werner had gone
in just right – perpendicular, arms at his sides in tight fists, chin
down. The impact was an explosion from below, like being hit
with a plank on the soles of his feet and socked in the jaw at the
same time. He plunged down and down, like a bullet shot into
the water, the force of it lifting his arms. In the last moment of
his descent, before he began to rise naturally and then to kick,
Werner had looked up to see a pale green pillar of light leading
to the surface.

When he woke, things were different. The female nurse had been
replaced by a male one, and the swearing man by an intubated
patient with a sighing ventilator. In the bed next to Werner's was
a small white figure, a toddler covered in gauze. Her face was
turned in his direction, but her eyes were closed.

He felt insubstantial and gossamer, like he was spun out of
glass. Still stoned but not enough. Everything hurt, even his gums.
It would take a long time for the pain to go away, longer than
the ICU and the step-down unit, longer than the ward filled with
grizzled men watching blaring televisions. Both the pain and the
residual pain, which seemed structural in nature, a kind of raw,
bludgeoning happiness that would afflict him for months, until he
managed to separate from his feelings altogether. Also long-term

tinnitus, from the blow to the top of the skull, an interior clanging that would never allow him, even for a moment, to confuse himself with the old Werner.

Two weeks later, Frank, the super, took him around back, through the rubble of the fire, into the space between the buildings. Werner knelt to examine the cat Frank had found hidden in the shadow of an unused doorway. She had pulled her body through several feet of gravel and debris to a protected spot and died there. Werner recognized the tail, ringed gray and brown.

And that took care of that.

Cheri

THEY CAME SLOWLY DOWN THE STREET, two boys on bicycles, riding side by side through the glare of a summer afternoon. She's on the curb, and the sun is so bright and hot it feels like her hair is on fire. If she glances down, she can just see the rubber toes of her sneakers and the skirt of her sundress, the color of root beer. The boys are playing tug-of-war, leaning away from each other, front wheels wobbling, each grasping one end of a long black snake. They have pale matching hair that stands up like the bristles of a brush, and their mouths are open in silent, gleeful shouts. The snake is dusty and limp, but as they sweep past she sees its eye, wide awake, and the sudden flat ribbon of tongue, scarlet against the boy's white wrist.

This is the way Cheri's life is passing in front of her eyes, in random unrelated glimpses, one or two a day. They come from nowhere, the bottom of her brain, and are suddenly projected, intense and silent as the Zapruder film, while she watches. This morning as she was eating her oatmeal what passed in front of her eyes was her first husband, shirtless against a blue sky, tying up tomato plants. And now tonight, climbing into bed, the Riley boys with a river snake, circa 1955.

The bed feels like a boat on choppy water. She pulls her foot out from under the covers and rests it on the floor for ballast. That's what they used to say to do if you were drunk and had the whirlies. The phone rings in the living room and she hears Sarah's voice against the sound of the television. In those old TV shows and movies way back when, the husband and wife had to keep one foot on the floor during the bed scenes. It meant everything was friendly instead of passionate. Well, the trick is working here tonight, the nausea is receding.

A wand of light appears and then widens; Bone's head is framed in the doorway. He pads across the room on velvet cat paws and freezes when he sees her bare foot on the floor. He stares at it in the dark with wide terrified eyes, then takes his place next to Nimbus at the foot of the bed. The girls were helping her burn leaves all afternoon and now the cats smell like marijuana smoke. In this morning's vision, her first husband was standing waist-deep in some unkempt garden of theirs, hair in a ponytail, a small frown on his face, and a joint behind his ear. Back in New York, one of her chemo doctors had discreetly mentioned marijuana for nausea, and some kind soul had given her a plate of pot brownies that she had taken like medicine, eating one each morning for breakfast. She had wandered her Brooklyn apartment in a state of muffled calm, straightening bedspreads and dish towels and staring slack-jawed out the window until the monster awoke, nudged her back into the bathroom, pushed her face in the toilet.

Cheri stretches her toes reflexively, making sure they still work. She's seen pictures of her spine, ghostly negatives resting against a light box, and the cancer looks tiny, like a baby's grasping fingers. The doctor used a pencil with bite marks on it to show her the metastases: Here, here, and a tiny bit here. Her relaxation is so complete that the bed now has the soothing, side-to-side rocking motion of a train car. Scenery floods past, mostly clumps of rocks and little hillocks scattered with dark green trees. *Here, here, and a tiny bit here.* A farm, a collie dog loping next to the tracks, and then the sudden startling face of a long-dead uncle. It seemed like he had shouted something but she couldn't catch it.

'What?' she says into the dark.

'Nothing,' Sarah whispers from the doorway. 'I was just standing here for a second.'

How had she done it, raised these two exotic wild-haired daughters? They were back in Iowa City temporarily, crowding their personalities into her little house, blearily eating bowls of cereal each morning before raking the leaves into bright piles or spading the flower beds. The rest of the time they lounged on the front porch where they kept their packs of cigarettes, smoking and having long murmured squabbles, going from flannel shirts to tank tops and back to flannel shirts again as the fall afternoons waxed and waned. Every evening one of them would ease out of the house and clunk away in motorcycle boots and vivid lipstick, down the street and into the neighborhood tavern. They mostly took turns, one of them swigging beers, shooting pool, and punching up embarrassing, elderly jukebox songs, the other at home sprawled in front of the television, pale as a widow, drinking cups of fragrant tea and eating malted milk balls by the handful.

Tonight it's Sarah standing silent against the door frame, staring intently at the floor, hands gripping elbows, listening to her mother breathe. Cheri feels the stirrings of a cough deep inside her lungs. It's the monster locked in the basement, and eventually it will storm up the stairs and burst forth, attacking her in her own home, swinging a mallet at her chest over and over. Once she can breathe again, she makes a joke out of it: I'm Buddy Hackett, I'm Gene Hackman. Nobody even pretends to laugh at this anymore; they're too tired.

'I thought you were sleeping,' Sarah says. 'The phone was for you.'

Cheri nudges a cat away from her hip, making room, and Sarah climbs in bed beside her. It's a slumber party minus the fun. She was awake; she could have taken the call.

'He said you should rest,' Sarah answers.

Who said?

Besides *terminal* and *cancer*, there are no more final-sounding words in the English language than these. Jack Kevorkian. That's who.

And then, despite themselves, they are starstruck for a moment at the idea of this spry ghoul from the evening news picking up his phone in Michigan and dialing Cheri's little house in Iowa, with its polished floors and eccentric armchairs. Backlit from the hallway, the cats' ears are almost transparent, like parchment lampshades. They watch the humans in their giddiness, faces sharp and impassive.

They'll be wide-awake alive and I'll be dead, Cheri thinks suddenly. Not just the cats, but everyone. Sarah, Katy, her best friends, Linda and Wayne. Linda and Wayne's children, the lady at the pharmacy who calls her Churry instead of Cheri, the man covered in dirt and desperation who sometimes slept on her stoop back in Brooklyn. Her first husband, her second husband, *her own mother*, all those medical professionals.

His nickname is Dr. Death, and yet when it's over, he'll still be alive.

The lump was discovered during a routine mammogram two and a half years earlier. She spent the last normal afternoon of her life on the train, Baltimore to Penn Station, taking tickets and trying not to notice that an elderly passenger had a dog in her pocketbook. Amtrak had a rule against animals riding its trains, but unless someone complained, Cheri didn't intend to notice. She planned to frown at the lady when they got to Penn, but she didn't even do that since it was quitting time and she felt cheer-ful. The Chihuahua's tiny face was poked all the way out of the bag by then, smugly gazing about.

Before her appointment, she went to the gym, ran and sweated, saunaed, showered, and tried to fluff her hair up a little. She needed a haircut more than a mammogram, but what she really needed more than either was to find her Mastercard, which had better be home on her dresser, because otherwise she had no idea where it was. She walked to the radiology place in her running shoes, going over the past three days, mentally taking her credit card out at various moments – grocery store, dinner at Ollie's, a weak moment with an L.L. Bean catalog – and putting it back in her wallet. The waiting room was disappointingly full and so she looked at fashion models in a magazine and watched the other patients until she was called.

The X-ray technician was a young woman with cat-eye glasses and an unprofessional sense of humor. She wore bright yellow clogs. Here comes the S and M part, she said as the machine closed its jaws. Click, flash; other side. She collected the trays and went off to show the films to the doctor. Be right back, she said as she left the room. And didn't return.

Cheri sat waiting, searching her mind until she thought she might have located the credit card in the back pocket of her black jeans, which were probably stuffed in the hamper. As the minutes wore on and then on, her hearing became heightened and her hands turned damp and cold. She rubbed them on her paper shirt. There was activity up and down the hall, doors opening and closing, voices leaking out. After twenty-six minutes had passed, she no longer wanted the technician to return. Every time she heard footsteps in the hall she willed them in the other direction. *Get lost, get lost*, she said under her breath, and they did get lost, until once they didn't and then the knob turned and the room was filled with the starched air of courteous detachment:

'Doctor wants more films.'

And that's how everything changed, not with the pronouncement, even, but with a woman's disengaged expression. The room was engulfed in a tinny silence as she worked, arranging Cheri like a mannequin, folding her against the stainless steel, placing an arm up here, a breast in there, sending her home. Once, a long time later, when Cheri's life was passing in front of her eyes, she caught a glimpse of it again – saw the bright yellow cartoon feet of the technician and then saw her own naked left arm, in slow, muted motion, rising obediently to embrace the machine.

The lump was a dreamy smear on the X-ray, barely there, unfeelable except in her throat when she tried to talk. She spoke to Linda late at night, each of them standing in a dark kitchen, one in Brooklyn and one in Iowa City. Lump, lumpectomy, chemo, Cheri said. Yes, Linda said, that's what they do. A silence in which both of them wished they were seven-year-old hellions again instead of what they were – a train conductor and a nurse; mothers; women who wore uniforms and looked sexy in them. Best friends since age five. It seems to be happening to both of them, although it isn't. For the duration of the phone call, they manage to remain calm.

And the illness proceeds on its trajectory, a knife, a scar, a plant-filled atrium where people sit in cubicles getting their treatments. One of the things she learns is how to vomit into a curved plastic trough while lying flat on her back. After six months another pale lump is photographed, no bigger but resolute, like a schoolyard bully who comes back even after getting a terrible pummeling. Linda waits for the phone call and when it comes she sits down. Lump, mastectomy, more chemo, Cheri says. Okay, Linda says, and she covers her face with one hand.

This time there's a tray of knives; she sees them right before the anesthesia erases her. When she awakens, her breast is gone, melted into a long weeping wound across her chest. The first time she sees it, she feels a strange numbness, a smooth blank where her shock should be. A day later the mortification is so profound and clamorous that she has to disconnect, like hanging up the receiver when someone is shouting into your ear. Her daughters fold gauze and tear tape and change her bandages without flinching. They seem larger to her in her new whittled-down state, like giantesses come to bathe and swaddle her. *I'm okay*, she says forty times a day, until she comes to believe it, and then they relax. Katy returns to school and Sarah finds a job down the street at a Starbucks instead of going back like she planned. They decided it between themselves, keeping Cheri in the dark, under the looming purple shadow of follow-up chemo.

It comes at her with talons and beak – after the first treatment, she winds up in the emergency room, tethered to an IV in a curtained cubicle, listening to the audio of what sounds like a television drama but isn't. An elderly woman calling out for help, a doctor speaking loudly and testily to an underling, a man relentlessly berating his wife in Spanish while a baby cries at regular intervals, like a chorus. At six a.m. she and Sarah crawl back into a cab and ride home with their eyes closed as the sun comes up.

And it gets progressively worse, the exhaustion and illness so wretched that she feels like a dying animal. There is something of the barnyard about all of it – the earthiness, the smells, the sheer bovine physicality of being in such a body, plodding from the bed to the bathroom on tottering legs. During a particularly bad afternoon when Sarah is at work, she hears herself as if from a great distance. The sound she's making is resonant and sustained, like the lowing of a frightened steer.

And then gradually she's well, the monster scoured clean with a wire brush, slinking off to watch her from a distance. She doesn't care. Fuck the monster. She takes up running again and sits in the sauna breathing steam into her cells, a towel discreetly knotted over the hollow spot on her chest. Eventually the stares get to her and she decides to undergo reconstructive surgery. This is routine, a process by which tissue from the groin is fashioned into a breast, like building Eve from Adam. Only it isn't God running the construction crew, it's Sloan Kettering.

Something goes wrong on the operating table. She comes out of surgery shaped like a woman again but unable to walk, one leg slack and rubbery, refusing to hold her weight. Eventually she leaves the hospital on crutches and calls Linda from a chair in the center of her living room, staring into the kitchen at her cup of tea on the counter. They're going to waive my bill, she tells her friend. Nerve damage, Linda replies. Positioned wrong on the operating table, probably. Get them to help you.

But they remain thin-lipped and silent, unwilling even to diagnose the problem, let alone treat it. She tries everything from the crutches to a walker to a leg brace, hobbling, learning to carry her tea without spilling it but never figuring out how to work on the train without standing or walking. Disability runs out and Amtrak lets her go. She loses not only her paycheck but her pension and her benefits. She drags her leg up and down the street each day like a zombie with a crutch nestled against her new breast, while pedestrians eddy around her and joggers sweat in the July heat.

It's night of the living leg, she tells Linda.

Come home, Linda says.

So her friends visit her in pairs, bearing bubble wrap and boxes and small, meaningful gifts that have to be packed along with dishes and books. Nobody can believe this is happening, although they felt the same way about the lump, the chemo, the mastectomy, the other chemo. But crippled isn't cancer, and for that they're all grateful. They've heard that Iowa is beautiful. One of her former coworkers, a man from the Bronx, asks if she will have neighbors out there. She visits the clinic one last time, stumping past the waiting room filled with women in various states of deconstruction. The medical staff seem very pleased with how the breast turned out and mildly surprised that she's leaving but they know that cancer changes people, turns them around in significant ways.

I can't walk, she says tersely. I lost my job and my pension.

And Iowa truly is beautiful in September when she arrives. She moves into Linda and Wayne's spare room and sets to work getting back on her feet, literally. She undergoes physical therapy for numbness and foot drop, and the local doctors install something called a transcutaneous nerve stimulator, which works, slowly and miraculously.

She feels bionic and hopeful in her leg brace and dungarees, restored to her former Iowa self, sitting on the dark porch at night with Linda and Wayne and one or two of their children, cats wafting around their ankles while they talk and talk. During the days, she works on her leg, walking and stretching and balancing herself, practicing with the cane until she's almost like a regular person. They rake leaves right before a windstorm and wake the next morning to find them evenly distributed over the lawn again. They have barbecues and card games. She and Linda house-hunt with fervor, horrified at what they see until one day a little house on Davenport Street goes on the market and they get wild with excitement. Wayne looks it over and they scheme; Cheri calls her mother and arranges a loan, then lands a job in an optometrist's office where she doesn't have to stand or walk and can sit all day on a stool, her cane against the wall behind her. Within three months of arriving in Iowa, she has a house, a job, and a life.

This is her town now, bathed in pale January light, populated with students and bright, vivid women, the occasional interesting man. She hangs a string of white lights around her kitchen window and buys a tall, leafy schefflera tree for the living room that she replants in an orange-glazed pot. She talks on the phone and watches television in the evenings, drunk on coziness and midwestern domesticity. At some point she begins to sweat during the nights, waking up to a damp nightgown and clammy sheets. It develops into an Iowa head cold; she can barely breathe but it's nothing to her, a sniffle with a headache. Herbal tinctures from the health-food store, fruits, vegetables, good heavy bread, lots of soup. The cold recedes eventually and she's left with chapped nostrils and a large lump on the right side of her neck.

Fear moves into the little house with her, taking up residence in the back of her closet along with the down comforter that she can no longer use. The night sweats get worse, forcing her up and into the living room, where she knits to keep from touching the lump. She can't tell if it's sore or if she's just prodding it too much. It's definitely big. Linda is worried, although she's also reasonable; it could be a residual effect from the cold.

The doctor is circumspect, steepling her hands and furrowing her brow. Aspiration is called for, a long needle into the neck like something out of a Boris Karloff movie. She's the bride of Frankenstein, she's the girl in the thin nightie cowering as the monster peers through her window. Mostly she's Katy and Sarah's mother, and they rally again, Katy on the telephone, talking of boys and clothes, her voice alive with fear, and then Sarah, who's been living in the general vicinity, on her doorstep.

She walks with Sarah in Hickory Hill Park after the procedure is done. The trees are denuded still and the sky is like milk; their faces are raked by the damp wind but there's nowhere else to go and so they walk and think, not speaking. It's two years exactly since this all began. On the way back to the house, they hold hands like schoolchildren. Before the kettle can boil, the telephone rings; the doctor wants to see Cheri in her office.

Cancer in the lymph system, metastasized from the breast.

Statistically speaking, two years at the outside, with aggressive treatment. Without it, much less.

They are sitting in upholstered armchairs in front of the doctor's desk, like applicants denied a bank loan. Sarah leans forward from the waist and sobs uncontrollably, her face on her knees, hands clutching her ankles. This is how she cried as a toddler when it was bedtime and the party was still going on. *This is my daughter*, Cheri thinks. *My other daughter is Kate.*

The doctor hands a tissue across the desk and watches Cheri intently. When finally she looks away, Cheri turns to Sarah and touches her arm. Sarah sits up, takes the tissue, and presses it into her face.

Don't cry, it's okay, Cheri hears herself saying. I had to go sometime.

The doctor doesn't disagree, which seems heartless, but also doesn't hurry them along, which seems kind. They collect referrals and then make their way through the waiting room and to the door, Sarah crying still, gently leading her mother. When they step outside into the dull afternoon light, Cheri is overcome with a feeling of weightlessness and vertigo. She's Fay Wray nestled in the monster's palm as he scales the skyscraper.

Fifth-grade skating party at Ames Pond. She can see Billy Mayfield's bare hand holding her mittened one as he pulls her along, her own feet in their pompommed ice skates scissoring beneath her as she keeps up. Crack the whip with a line of sweaty kids, and Cheri's at the end of it. Scenery whirls past – trash barrels, sparse evergreens, snow hut with faces grouped around a heater, the striped tail of her own stocking cap – and then the whip cracks and she's flung, hurtling across the ice on her back, turning once in slow motion as the clouds revolve, and then a sickening crunch. Through the ice and under, she plunges down in the dark water, skates sticking in the muddy bottom for an instant, and then rises slowly, spinning, until her head bumps on the underside of the ice. For one long surreal moment, before an arm reaches in, grasps the hood of her coat, and hauls her out, she is suspended under the warped ceiling of ice. Inside the roaring silence of the water, she looks up and sees the skates of the excited children congregating above her.

The flashbacks have begun now, coming to her when she's distracted in her kitchen, washing cups or staring into the fridge. Yesterday she was placing a flower in a vase – a lone iris, the color of grape soda – and suddenly saw a row of people yelling and shaking their fists at her. It bothers her for hours, until she finally figures out it was from back in her cheerleading days. The Ames Pond memory had been suppressed for thirty-six years until tonight. It rose unbidden, like a genie, as she eased the cork from a bottle of wine. What she had chosen to remember all these years was actually an addendum to the memory: Billy Mayfield returning her blue mitten the next day at school, the one she was wearing when she'd rocketed out of his grasp. He'd handed it to her in a brown paper lunch sack with Cheri's name written on it in blue ballpoint, a mother's spidery script.

They're drinking wine, waiting for Wayne to show up so they can get some dinner. It's cold but they put on jackets and head to the patio. Another volunteer iris, this one a strange pale yellow, grows near the garage. Cheri's garden is a tangle still but she's sorting it out; the air is fragrant with compost and lilacs.

Aggressive treatment at this stage would mean a bone-marrow transplant. One thug beating another thug, with her in the middle. She's not going to do it.

People get through this, Linda says. We'll help you.

Never again, Cheri tells her. I said so the last time.

The bridal wreath bushes along the back fence are buried under tiers of ruffles. Each blossom is a small bouquet. They were

48

married in the 1970s, Linda to Wayne and Cheri to Dave. Hippie intellectuals with garlands in their hair, intense frivolity, et cetera. Floating in and out of each other's front doors, macramé projects, and funky baby showers that included the men. Linda had two girls, then, later, a boy. Cheri had first borne Sarah, dreamy and social, then baby Kate, with her black hair and shy grin.

In her spare time, Cheri immersed herself in the tenets of the Socialist Party – which they all sort of agree with in theory, if not in practice – and moved from political idealist to political activist. She spoke her mind more and more: *I believe an injury to one is an injury to all . . . the concept of classlessness gets to the heart of the* matter – *why it's so important to try and live it, put it into action, fight for it if need be. Without that you accept less.* Should have been a warning, but they were all taken by surprise when she left them, absorbed into another life that had more meaning for her. First to Chicago and then to the South, where she worked in factories and mills putting her principles into practice, shaping her life like wet clay until it hardened, leaving her in New York City years later, punching tickets on a train and liking it. She was always the type to do her ruminating alone, in the privacy of her own head, and back then, when she'd made the decision to leave her marriage and Iowa, she'd simply announced it and then set about getting it done, ears stubbornly turned off to pleas and reason. A few weeks later she had driven away with Katy in the back seat, wide-eyed and silent, while Sarah sobbed in her father's arms, reaching out toward the disappearing car.

No chemo. She said so before and she's sticking with it. Her face is resolute in the narrowing light, unfaltering. Linda has seen this look before; right behind all that beauty and grief are the steel girders of pragmatism.

Of course, she hadn't stuck with the decision to let Dave keep Sarah. Bereft without her daughter, Cheri eventually got her back, doing penance then and for years after. This won't work that way; the penalty for refusing chemo is mostly death.

They sit quietly, watching Wayne as he approaches up the back walk. One look at their faces and he knows what the decision is.

'Smells like shit,' he remarks as he passes the freshly fertilized garden.

Now there are three of them drinking wine under the darkening sky, although one is already, imperceptibly, being erased from the tableau. They speak of restaurants and narrow it down to Indian or Chinese. Wayne can go either way, although he's up for spicy. Linda is thinking good, healthy vegetables and brown rice. She stands and collects wineglasses, tucks the bottle under her arm. As Linda starts to move toward the house, Cheri reaches out and touches her sleeve in a silent, sideways gesture of gratitude. In this withering light, they could all be twenty again, in worn jean jackets and sneakers, Wayne in his baseball cap.

An injury to one is an injury to all. She's made her decision, then, and they'll all live with it. Or, rather, two of them will.

One month later, another night sky, this time over Mexico. There are clouds adrift, and now the big yellow moon has a dent in its head. She doesn't care; it's all beautiful: the Aztec-tiled motel courtyard, palm trees in huge terra-cotta urns, their fronds rustling like corn. Katy is out walking in the night air with the daughter of another patient, and Cheri is reclining poolside, watching satellites blink overhead and sipping a concoction they gave her at the clinic. It tastes quite good, actually, if you don't think about it. Sort of like a piña colada boosted with iron shavings.

They can say what they will about alternative therapy, but it's doing as much for her as the chemo ever did and there's no throwing up involved. Mornings at the clinic are spent getting laetrile treatments, administered intravenously by smiling Mexican women who wear traditional nurse's caps and an assortment of ankle bracelets. Afternoons are given over to consultations with staff members, who take her history and offer advice on ways to coax the monster back into its cage. Lion tamers holding out spindly chairs.

She spends hours knitting in the waiting room, surrounded by the shining, hopeful faces of the truly desperate. Today a gaunt and yet somehow baggy-looking man in a slogan T-shirt – the words LOVE ME, LOVE MY HOG over a picture of a Harley-Davidson motorcycle – confided to Cheri that six months ago he weighed over three hundred pounds and was still hitting the booze.

'First my liver give out for a while,' he said, hollow-eyed and shivering, 'and then this cancer set in.' His daughter, a plain Pentecostal-looking girl in a sundress and tennis shoes, reached over and pressed the back of her hand against his forehead.

'You're dropping again,' she told him quietly and left to wander the halls of the clinic, coming back with a wheelchair and an orderly. The motorcycle man waved to Cheri ruefully as they loaded him up.

'She don't let me suffer if she can help it,' he said, staring up at the girl.

Les, a man Cheri knew from a seminar on purgatives, leaned forward after they were gone. 'He might as well drink his coffee from a cup,' he said. 'Because no enema in the world will cure *that*.' He was small and hairless, an elderly melanomic golfer in powder-blue pants. His son roams the peripheries of the waiting rooms and corridors in a suit and tie, snapping his briefcase open and shut, holding flowcharts up to the light like X-rays, one-finger typing on a laptop.

'He has to work wherever he goes,' his father told Cheri. She made a polite gesture of commiseration but he shook his head. 'He has to, he's the top over there. Nobody above him, from what

I can tell.' He ran a hand purposefully over his head and then looked at his palm. Nothing there, clean as a whistle.

'Wow,' Cheri told him, and after a respectful pause she turned back to her knitting. Stitch, drop-stitch, stitch, cast off. In the waiting room, hours recede like a glacier, leaving bottles and wrappers in their wake. She is strangely moved by all of it, the sick people and their companions, the clean antiseptic smell, the inspirational messages calligraphed and framed on every wall. The sheikh character who moves from treatment room to seminar with an entourage of mournful draped women. The elderly lady in a copper wig who sat down next to her in the body, mind, and spirit lecture, reached for Cheri's hand, and clasped it for an hour, both of them staring ahead intently, holding on to the speaker's words like the bar of a trapeze.

That seminar closed with a quotation: *Worship the Lord your God, and His blessing will be on your food and water. I will take away sickness from among you.* Not exactly *The Communist Manifesto*, but who is she to judge. Her friend listened intently and then extricated her hand, took out a small battered notebook, and wrote *Exodus 23:25* at the bottom of a to-do list.

'You don't look a bit sick,' she said to Cheri. Her eyes were wide and stark and her teeth didn't fit right. Cheri looked down at her own feet, brown in their sandals, Katy's red nail polish giving each toe its own personality.

'I am, though,' she replied.

'I have bust cancer,' the woman told her, whispering.

Today they ran into each other in the corridor and embraced spontaneously, Cheri taking care not to set the wig askew. The woman's husband stood quietly at a distance, staring over their shoulders, holding a straw purse.

This afternoon she came upon Les's son, the businessman, right here in the courtyard. Huddled on a stone ledge, half inside an overwrought bougainvillea bush, he wore a suit with the tie loosened sideways, his usually smooth hair adrift and spiky from him running his hands through it. A parody of a drunken man, only it wasn't alcohol, it was grief. Surrounded by giant blank-faced purple blossoms, he sobbed into a cell phone, eyes shut, mouth wrenched wide open in a child's grimace.

Now the courtyard is empty and dark, lit only by the muted lamps hidden amid the fronds and ferns. At the very center, the pool shimmers in its own light, like Aqua Velva. Cheri drops her robe and slides into the water, cool and bracing. She does a slow backstroke until it tires her, turns over, dives, and comes up with her hair slicked away from her face like a seal or a woman who knows she's beautiful.

Courtesy of her mother, it all is. All Cheri had to do was ask. Fifteen thousand dollars, just like that, for palm trees and exotic blooming flowers, the muggy Amazonian glade-like feel of this courtyard. All from her mother and her mother's husband, who wrote the check without flinching, buying her, if not an actual future, then the promise of a future. And the miracle is that she now feels healthy, her insides rinsed and wrung out, her exterior massaged and polished, the very blood in her veins carbonated. And it isn't better living through chemo; it's simple and organic. Fruit, coffee, oxygen, and words. *You are loved, we love you, you can live, others have lived.*

The water now feels warmer than the air, amniotic. A familiar sound drifts over the stone wall, subdued and infectious: Katy's laughter. They've returned from their walk, chatting just outside the gate, oblivious to the open shutters and the acoustic properties of the narrow street. Cheri lets herself drift backward until she's floating again, the sound of indistinct voices overcome by the water lapping against her ears. Eyes closed, she summons an image of Katy, with her wide grin and flat Brooklyn accent, hoop earrings, raucous hair; when she was in the room, you couldn't look anywhere else, nobody could. Then Sarah, she of the beautiful, deceptively serene face, hair knotted behind her head in a careless bun, choosing her words thoughtfully, then speaking them in the broad cadences of the Midwest. They're interesting, Cheri thinks. Compelling. She imagines the two of them huddled inside the rhododendron bush in her front yard, like Les's son in the arms of the bougainvillea, weeping.

The moon is high in the sky now, looking smaller and less certain. Tiny, long-legged lizards run along the sidewalks. In just a few days she'll be back home, tending her garden with its sturdy, quintessential-Iowa flowers – morning glories, zinnias, black-eyed Susans, and the tall lavender coneflowers, with their rusty hearts lifted up toward the sun, petals flung backward like arms. *You can live.* For one prolonged, irrational moment, hope circles the courtyard like a great winged heron, banking slowly over the pool and the lawn chairs, the dark foliage, and then wheeling out into the night. Gone.

Others have lived. She won't be one of them. She feels it in her bones, quite literally.

The summer that follows is long and luminous. They canoe down the Wapsipinicon River, a rowdy cavalcade of humans and their coolers, and camp along the reedy banks, faces sunburned and firelit, marshmallows melting and blackening on sticks, the green nylon glow of flashlights inside tents. They climb into the car – Linda, Wayne, Cheri and a pan of brownies – and take a road trip, fourteen hours of stupefying knee-high corn and then the mind-blowing Rockies in all their vertical splendor. An outdoor music festival in Telluride – bands they've heard of and bands they've never heard of, old tie-dyed dudes in stretched-out T-shirts and slender gray ponytails, and the new generation of hippies with radiant, stoned faces, hair dreadlocked into felt. They forgo the brownies and hike a steep mountain trail, Cheri faltering only once, when Wayne tries to haul her up onto a boulder so she can see the vista. It's her mind, not her body – the vertigo of seeing it all fall away in front of her, leaving nothing but bright air and the strange shadows of clouds far below.

The new house turns out to be hotter than expected, and the snow peas don't take off the way she thought they would, but who can complain about sun-drenched rooms and vines that produce flowers instead of food? She drives out into the Amish countryside one afternoon, returning with a black bear cub of a puppy that she names Ursa. They take long surreal walks together through the cemetery down the street, the puppy dragging her leash among the tombstones and Cheri ambling behind, reading the inscriptions and doing the math. Forty-six years is a long time if you look at it a certain way. Ursa is her seventh dog.

The glimpses from her past are benign and interesting – the sullen face of a beautiful girl framed in a Dairy Queen window; the chrome-and-tan dashboard of an old Beetle, rearview mirror draped with Mardi Gras beads; a gnarled and mossy live oak standing in the middle of a chicken-scratched, red-dirt yard; and once, amazingly, what had to be her own tiny feet, grasped and lifted into the air in the classic pose of a diaper change. Weird. And she keeps them to herself, these unportentous images, as she does the gradual onset of pain. By September the cancer has divided itself like an emigrating clan, dispersing to her liver, lungs, and spine.

She takes the news stoically, nodding. It's fall and she could make it to spring, and they might be able to shrink the spinal tumor with radiation, enough to delay paralysis, keep her mobile for a while. They show her the films, and she stares transfixed at the perfect curve of her own spine caught and held by the shadowy fingers of the monster. *Here, here, and a tiny bit here.* The doctor sets his pencil down on the desk and she stares at it, composing herself, willing away the claustrophobic images of last summer, the botched surgery, her leg dragging behind her in the swirling Brooklyn heat, numb foot scraping along the sidewalk. A zombie, a reanimated corpse. All that for this.

It might not happen, the doctor tells her. Other things might happen first.

She takes that to mean death. In the context of paralysis, it seems comforting.

We can keep you comfortable, he says reassuringly. If it comes to that.

But I can't tolerate pain medication, she says. They never found anything that didn't make me vomit.

He writes something on her chart and closes it, holds out his hand.

And this, of course, is when the world turns glamorous. Her daughters look like movie stars in their low-slung pants and pale autumn complexions. The trees on her street vibrate in the afternoon sunlight, the dying leaves so brilliant that she somehow feels she's never seen any of this before – fall, and the way the landscape can levitate with color, and even her simple cup of green tea in the afternoons, with milk and honey in a thick white mug. Warm. Her hand curled around it, or the newspaper folded beside it, or a halved orange on a blue plate sitting next to it. It's all lovely beyond words, really.

Even the pain has a sharp, glittering realness to it, like a diamond lodged in her hip. She ignores it, gardening, pruning the dead foliage, sorting out the pumpkin vines, and still she walks each day, abandoning the stone cemetery for the dazzling woods at Hickory Hill. Troops of shiny-headed Cub Scouts move through the park, picking up gum wrappers and cigarette butts, stopping to pet Ursa, jostling each other, asking if she bites. They never heard of the name Ursa, but there's so much they haven't heard of that they take it in stride.

'Our dog got put to sleep from a brain tumor,' a little boy tells Cheri. 'His name was Pete and it might have been from eating grass with pesticide on it.' He examines Ursa's head, lifting her ears and looking inside, then stands up. 'This one seems okay,' he says with an air of mild disappointment. He's smaller than the rest, compact and green-eyed, with a tumultuous stand of dark hair. An early version of all the men she's ever loved.

When he lopes away, Cheri feels strangely alone, but not unpleasantly so. Today the sky feels like company, and this winding orange-and-yellow trail. The diamond glints suddenly, causing her to gasp and squint her eyes. The pain sometimes is raucous, frightening; other times, it's a dull glow in her chest, like she's inhaling embers. It's her spine she can't stop thinking about, the recurring, disquieting image of being alive inside a dead body. Ursa turns toward home and Cheri follows at a distance, noticing how her knees bend and straighten with each step.

The girls are burning leaves next to the curb, great crackling piles of them. She sits on the front steps with her afternoon tea and watches, not speaking even when spoken to. She just wants to rest everything, her body, her mind. Unbidden, as she brings the white cup to her lips, a memory appears: Her refrigerator in an apartment down south, from the time when she worked in an airplane factory cleaning parts, up to her elbows in toxic gunk all day, despising it. A Suzuki quote, sent to her by a sympathetic friend, pinned to the scarred door of the fridge where she could see it each evening.

When you do something, you should burn yourself up completely, like a good bonfire, leaving no trace of yourself.

The girls pause to lean on their rakes, Sarah talking, Katy shaking out her hair, retying it. The fire has reduced itself to a thin meandering plume, like cigarette smoke, while leaves continue drifting down from the sky. *Burn yourself up completely.* That's it, then. She stands and looks at her daughters, raking coals in the waning light.

'I'm done,' she tells them.

*

She doesn't think of it as killing herself; she thinks of it as killing the monster. That's why a gun would be so satisfying. But impossible, of course, given her circumstances. With window-leaping, you have a crowd, and in Iowa City that could mean one or two acquaintances. Drowning isn't possible; she tried it. In the bathtub, just as an experiment, to see if she'd have the nerve.

No one tells her not to do it. She isn't the kind of person you say that sort of thing to. Instead, everyone grows silent and wary, both daughters vacating the house for long hours, coming home for meals, steamed vegetables and instant rice or carryout from a downtown restaurant. Burritos dumped on a platter, refried beans shoveled into a bowl. Katy serving it up, Sarah pushing it around her plate. Cheri sipping ice water, lost in the pros and cons of her afternoon's research.

'Did you know a person of my weight would have to fall fifteen feet to break her neck?' she asks suddenly. That's why people like to hang themselves in barns, where they can step off a rafter. Works better that way, otherwise you've got the problem of dangling there until suffocation occurs. No barns in the vicinity, unfortunately, but there is a garage. She's still going back and forth on asphyxiation.

Katy and Sarah stare at her, unblinking, forks suspended.

'No, I didn't,' Sarah says finally.

So much for dinner. The girls clear the table without a word and adjourn to the living room and the evening news. Cheri stays in her spot, chewing ice cubes and waiting for Linda, who has taken to stopping by each evening. Pills would probably be the best, but whenever you hear *suicide attempt*, it's pills, and whenever you hear *suicide*, it's something more decisive – a bullet, a rope, a long sparkling plunge from a bridge.

The cough begins its slow ascent, giving her time to brace for it. Rattling and chaotic, it sounds like a paint can filled with gravel and rolled across the floor. By the time it's over – the gravel slowly diminishing to sand, shifting, allowing her to breathe again – Linda is beside her and the girls are in the doorway. Ursa moves from one to the next, offering a rawhide bone.

'You eat?' Linda asks, eyeing the dishes in the sink.

'I'm eating water,' Cheri tells her, holding up the glass of ice.

In the living room, Vanna White prowls the row of letters in a dress as gauzy and form-fitting as a shroud. The television is always on now, one show melding into another, nobody really watching and nobody able to turn it off. As the evening progresses, they stare into the muted flickering light, first Sarah and Katy, then Sarah and Cheri, then just Sarah. At eleven o'clock the phone rings, a man asking for Cheri Tremble.

'She's in bed,' Sarah tells him, 'but she might still be awake.'

'No, no,' he says. 'Let her rest if she can.'

Cheri had written the letter outlining her situation, her intention, and asking for his help only a few days before. He plucked it out of his stack of appeals and responded immediately – the impending paralysis and her inability to tolerate painkillers were the deciding factors. If the medical records support her account of what's going on, Kevorkian is willing to help.

It's all true, Sarah whispers.

The living room is dim, lit only by the moonglow of the television. It all looks unfamiliar suddenly, and temporary, like a movie set. Kevorkian sounds just like a regular doctor, only sympathetic. He asks Sarah several questions – about Cheri's support system, how much care she needs, what her pain levels are like right now. Before hanging up, he explains that his patients have to come to him; he can't go to them.

He laughs at this, ruefully, and Sarah laughs too. She has no idea why.

In the dark bedroom at the end of the hall, Cheri is floating, unaware. The sleep train is just leaving the station, tracks

FESTIVAL DAYS

unspooling like a grosgrain ribbon. The familiar Amtrak scenery rocks past: sparse woods, long brilliant flashes of water, the ass-end of a Delaware town, row houses with garbage bags taped over the windows. A neighbor from her childhood hangs sheets on a line wearing a housedress and men's shoes; as the sleeping car passes, the neighbor turns, watching its progress, shielding her eyes from the sun. A farm dog, running too close to the tracks, and then the face of someone she may have known once, an uncle, perhaps, gaunt and shadowed, telling her something she can't quite hear.

'What?' she says into the dark.

It's left up to her to set the date; Kevorkian is flexible. It's October now, and Cheri explains that she wants to make it through Christmas.

'Oh, I hope much longer,' he says.

This touches her deeply for some reason, his empathetic response, his hope that she can remain alive as long as possible. He doesn't even know her! His voice is soothing over the telephone, and kind. More like a pastor than a doctor, really, but the medical questions he asks are sharply intelligent. For the first time Cheri is able to describe the pain in unminimizing terms. The relief of this causes tears to course down her cheeks, although her voice remains steady and businesslike.

She's to contact Neal, his assistant, when she has a date. Neal will give her directions on what to do then. For now, just try to be comfortable, get what she can out of her days, settle her affairs. And tell only the people who must know.

Kate, Sarah, Linda, Wayne.

She dresses as herself for Halloween – starkly thin, the extraneous flesh chiseled from her face, neck, wrists – and doles out chocolate bars to a sporadic procession of Disney characters and unraveling mummies. One boy with fangs and a plunging

60

widow's peak hauls his sister up onto the porch, a tiny blonde in a Pocahontas outfit. She holds her bag open distractedly, mask atop her head, peering past Cheri into the living room.

'The lady who lived here before died,' she says. 'And we've got her parakeet.'

Her brother glances up at Cheri and then quickly away. 'She's lying,' he says apologetically, dragging the little girl off the porch and into the darkness. The dog follows them for a moment and then materializes again in the porch light, wagging her tail at the bowl of candy.

Ursa will go with Sarah, and the cats probably with Linda, unless Katy speaks up. This house to her mother, who paid for it. She spends the next week sorting through her belongings, musing, then composes a will and places it in the top drawer of her dresser. To the Petersons she writes:

> Linda, please take my gardening hat, the one I wore at Telluride. Wayne, you could use a good corkscrew. I'm fond of my brass one, made in Italy (at least I think it's brass). I've had it about seventeen years. Brandice, help yourself to your favorite sweater, and Kailee, to your favorite piece of jewelry. Schuyler, take my fishing pole and catch some big ones for me, okay? TJ can have my assistant conductor hat pin from when I worked on the trains in New York City. It should be where this will is.

Her daughters, of course, are more difficult. The lists have to be weighed, items shifted back and forth until a precarious balance is achieved:

> Sarah, I'd like for you to have my jade necklace, silver tea set, darkroom equipment, camping stuff, crystal vase, my books, and my exercise bike. Also the family heirloom silver and brass curios and the picture of McGregor and the blanket from Mexico.

Kate, I'd like for you to have my silver chain necklace, ruby ring (which Gramma has), camera and accessories, rocking chair, bike, round mirror, word processor, stereo and political books and pottery from Mexico.

By early November her yard is done. If there were going to be a next year, she would have moved some of the plantings – the peonies closer to the house, the little yew farther away. But it's set for now, everything mulched, her tools cleaned and stored in the basement. By the time she has her household in order, the exhaustion has become so acute it feels like sandbags are hanging from her limbs; sometimes just pushing the hair back from her face takes more energy than she can summon.

The lady who lived here before died. The body devolves into compost, but we live on in our parakeets. She dreams of them, fluorescent feathers glimpsed through dark foliage. Her naps have become restless, sweaty affairs, the pain now unceasing, surrounding her and fading, like the Doppler wail of an air-raid siren. She half imagines it will get better, like a fractured bone or the stomach flu, but of course it can only get worse. Worse than this!

She has Thanksgiving with Linda, Wayne, their family, and her daughters. They linger at the table for a long time, telling stories and drinking coffee, Cheri so exhausted by the effort of sitting upright that she mostly listens, watching their familiar faces in the warm light, attuned to the murmur of daughters in the kitchen, the comforting sound of water running. By the time she leaves – supported on either side by her girls, Linda following behind with leftovers to stow in the trunk – Cheri is so depleted that she can't keep the perilous thoughts at bay. She's nauseated with envy and rage, the unfairness of it all.

And of course, nobody truly understands, but she can't see how it would matter if they did. The sandbags, the diminished lung capacity, the clangorous pain. It's all so intensely personal and claustrophobic, the heightening present mixed up with the banal past – this morning she nearly swooned from the vertiginous sight of her old maple dresser rising and falling, a pistoning bedpost, and the striped-shirted body of her brother Sean flinging himself up and down as they jumped on her bed. And last night she only catnapped, moving from bed to armchair and back to bed, dreaming random images of turkey farms, of rickrack on the neckline of a blouse, of the Beatles walking single file across a road. Once, right before dawn, she looked down in her dream and saw phosphorescent insects alight on her hands and arms.

I can't make it to Christmas, she tells them. I thought I could but I can't.

The news is devastating; she supposes it's possible none of them really believed it before now. The girls collapse against her and then grow strangely calm, wandering shell-shocked through the house, speaking to each other in thin echoing voices. Linda flinches when she's told, then breaks into tears, hands over her face.

They have three weeks to get used to it. After some consideration, Cheri chooses a Tuesday, the most nondescript day of the week. She calls Kevorkian's assistant, Neal, then books a flight to Detroit for December 16 and a night's lodging in a Bloomfield motel. According to the plan, that's where the suicide will occur. Her body will be taken from the motel to the hospital and then to the morgue, where somebody – the coroner? – will perform an autopsy.

She wants cremation, a small service, no flowers. Katy goes with her to make the arrangements and they try not to be too surreal about it but have to keep consulting their list.

The funeral director is a young man with intensely sincere eyes and pure, palpable compassion. Cheri grows sleepy in his presence, forgetting some of the things she meant to bring up.

'What about transporting my body if I should die elsewhere?' she asks.

'If you're choosing cremation,' he says carefully, 'then that can be done at a facility near where the death occurs.' He pauses, thinks. 'And we'll work directly with them to receive the, uh, from there.' He stares at the backs of his hands for a moment, turning his wedding ring one way and then the other, an absentminded gesture that gives her time to fill in the blank. Her body, reduced to a mound of kitty litter in a biscuit tin.

'Okay, then,' she says, and they all stand, formally, and stare at one another. Katy is wearing the miserable look of someone waiting for a tetanus shot, determined to be brave for the nurse's sake. The funeral director touches Cheri's arm and looks into her eyes; his own are red-rimmed, which takes her by surprise.

People are so kind! She reels from it sometimes, the mute commiseration, the gestures of support and assistance so subtle she barely recognizes them as such. Katy, the first time she helped her mother take a bath, had seemed merely to be idling, recounting an anecdote, sitting on the closed toilet seat with her legs crossed, eyes roaming around the edges of the room. When Cheri had finished bathing, Katy lifted her out of the water – casually, still talking – and wrapped her in a towel. Never in the whole process (holding out the underwear to be stepped into, retrieving sweatpants warm from the dryer, tugging a pair of thick cotton socks onto the feet) did either of them let on that they'd performed a transposed version of this twenty years before.

Linda telephones people in their circle, urging them to visit now if they want the chance. A few friends stop by during the afternoons and evenings, bearing casserole dishes or loaves of bread. Putting the food away in the kitchen gives them time to compose themselves – they were warned, of course, but nevertheless it takes a moment. The deterioration has accelerated in the last days, ravaging her body but leaving her face as translucent

64

and still as frosted glass. They kneel next to her rocking chair as they leave, keeping it together, promising to call in a few days, see how it's going.

Her breathing is labored after these visits, either from the exertion of talking and smiling or from suppressing the panic that rises up when she tells them goodbye, unable to confess her plan, to take proper leave of her friends. She retreats to her bedroom and lies on top of the covers, arms folded around a pillow to keep from coughing, tethered to an oxygen tank by a length of clear tubing. The cancer has taken over completely now, crowding her out of her own body. When she touches her chest, it's the monster she feels.

In eleven days it will be over. Eleven! Alone in her room, she whimpers with the terrible grief of it, of being forced to abandon herself like a smoldering ship. It's impossible to imagine not existing, she discovers, because in order to imagine, you must exist. The best she can do is picture the world as it is now, without her in it. But even then, she's the one picturing.

On the morning of day nine, she rests on the sofa and watches, absorbed, as a man climbs a telephone pole, his belt weighted with tools and an oversize red telephone receiver. He stabilizes himself with a safety harness and then gets busy untangling a skein of multicolored wires, holding the red handset to his ear, possibly even speaking into it, although she can't imagine to whom. Once, he takes pliers off his belt, gives something a good twist, and a sprig of snipped wire falls through the air to the grass below. Something about the scene, framed behind the glass of her living-room window, embodies what she's been struggling to understand. It's momentary, a flash of insight so brief it can't be seen but must be remembered, like the glimpse of a shooting star. The man with his cleats thrust into the pole, his weight tangible in the leather harness, the dark red of the telephone against the bright yellow of his hard hat, and then the tendril of wire falling away from his pliers – this is the world without her in it.

On the eighth day, she imagines dying with her eyes open, the naked vulnerability of it. She's got to remember to close her eyes and keep them closed, no matter what. And if Kevorkian approaches her and she panics or starts bawling, will he give her a chance to calm down or will he take it as a sign that she is conflicted, not ready, and refuse to go through with it? She forces herself to visualize the final scene over and over until it loses its meaning and becomes as ritualized as taking communion. No last-minute change of mind, no hysteria; she will simply greet him, explain herself in measured tones, express her gratitude, offer her arm for the needle, close her eyes.

By day seven, she understands air travel will be impossible, unendurable, because of her weakened state. A new plan is made for Wayne to rent a van and drive all of them to Detroit – Cheri, Linda, Sarah, and Kate. None of the others can be present at her actual death, of course, since it's illegal, but still, they'll be taking her there, nine hours away. Cheri feels momentarily frantic at the idea of this, her loved ones having to participate in her fate, but she can't hold on to it. Too sick, too busy grasping her own thin hand, pulling herself along. Almost overnight, she feels herself beginning to detach from them, not because she wants to, but because she needs her own full attention. This is simply part of what happens.

Linda comes over in the evening to wait with them, a little blast of refreshing cold entering the house with her. She brings food as well and leans against the kitchen counter as they eat, chatting, then busies herself as best she can by sweeping up the fallen leaves from the schefflera tree, folding clean towels, petting Ursa. When she goes home, they resume the vigil, tiptoeing around the house in their sock feet, staring for long moments at the television or at their own spectral faces reflected in the dark windows.

Wayne shows up a few days before they are to leave and sits with Cheri awhile, making quiet small talk until she tires and then saying goodbye, squeezing her hand momentarily before he stands. Sarah and Katy call to him from the backyard, where Ursa has chased one of the cats up a tree. They are near tears, both of them walking in circles, trying to coax the cat down in high urgent voices. Wayne climbs a few feet up the tree and lifts the cat off a branch, manually detaching each claw, hands it down to Sarah. When he glances back, Cheri is standing at the kitchen window, waving thank you.

On the last night, Linda makes sandwiches for the trip, egg salad with lettuce, while Wayne plots the route using a road map and his computer; Sarah and Katy, after a dinner of yogurt and leftover soup, place the cats in bed with their mother and watch as she pets them and they purr, as Ursa puts her nose up on the covers and gets her ears combed and her face kissed; they listen as she reminds them: I love you, my *chicas*, never forget.

And Cheri, on her last night, weeps with relief when she's finally alone, suffers about five minutes of teeth-chattering fear, calms herself by imagining the faces and whispering the names of all her past dogs, then lies quietly with the pillow pressed to her chest, watching the interior images that click on and off like slides.

Near dawn, she sleeps for a while and dreams of gathering Easter eggs: a violet one nestled between the white pickets of a porch railing, a pink-and-green one camouflaged in the grass next to a wire fence, an azure one balanced perfectly and precariously on a water spigot.

They leave under cover of darkness, like duck hunters or criminals, barely whispering. They settle Cheri on the bench seat in the middle of the van, oxygen canister next to her, daughters behind her. The van door glides closed with a soft thud, and while Wayne climbs in and situates his coffee, Linda stares out the windows at the neighborhood emerging in the grainy light. Straight-edged prairie bungalows surrounded by sugar maples and oaks, Cheri's little corner house painted a curious shade of dark vanilla with bright white trim; a thatch of low evergreens pressed against the porch. It all seems so calm and unadorned, as full of hidden promise as the bulbs planted beneath the kitchen window.

Cheri refuses herself even one last look. That was then; this is now.

She needs more oxygen already, just from the effort of getting this far. Linda turns on the dome light and adjusts the dial; Cheri breathes deeply, head down to combat the nausea. Sarah begins crying silently in the back, and Katy leans forward to touch her mother's shoulder. The town flattens into countryside and they drive due east, straight into the sunrise, pillowy December clouds edged in apricot. Linda passes the thermos to Katy, and Cheri lifts her head briefly, asks to have the oxygen turned up again.

Halfway through Illinois, she begins to panic over possibly having to go to the hospital if the tank runs out and can't be refilled. She had made all the plans for the trip, including how much oxygen to bring, but her needs have increased sharply over just the last few days. If she has to go to the hospital, they'll call her doctor, and her doctor will put two and two together. Inside the tight black place behind her eyelids, she watches herself clench her fists and hold them up against the sky.

Wayne tracks down a pharmacy in Joliet, and Linda somehow gets the tank refilled. All they know is she walked in with it empty and walked out with it full. Determination and twenty-five bucks, she tells them. Cheri keeps her head in her hands through the next two states, trying not to vomit. Sarah and Kate take turns comforting her and resting their foreheads on the back of her seat, dazed and leaden. Car crazy, longing for a cigarette.

68

Cheri lifts her head briefly and seeks out Wayne in the rearview mirror. 'I need to stop at a bathroom,' she tells him.

He finds a funky, old-fashioned Clark station where he can pull right up to the washroom door. Two of them help her use the facilities while the other two lean against the van and smoke. Cheri has never been this freaked out in her life, and that's saying something. One thing she's learning is that it's important to stay in the moment, not to leap ahead even fifteen minutes. Right now, she's staring at herself in a shadowed washroom mirror; now she's in the cold wind next to the car trying to get her gloves on. Now they slide the door open and she steps back, looks at her daughter's face. Now she's getting settled, taking the oxygen tube, returning the stare of the guy pumping gas. Frozen cornfields, a deflated barn, a looming underpass, and then the interstate. She drops her head down into the cool damp shell of her hands. Now the buffet and roar of semis, now a quavering sigh from somebody inside the van. The tires begin making a rhythmic clicking noise, passing over seams in the concrete.

Cheri opens her eyes intermittently and stares at her knees, just to stabilize and remember where she is. Lying down isn't possible, although that's why they got the van. Her lungs are full, and the nausea is overwhelming. Breathless and gasping, she runs down a twisting white corridor inside her head, the blat of a siren bouncing off the walls; suddenly the narrow hallway opens out onto a suburban backyard, the floor becomes grass, and she's on a swing, knobby knees pumping, reaching toward the sky with her Keds. The chains go slack for a long instant each time the swing reaches its apex. She's panting with reckless exhilaration.

'Do you need it turned up?' Linda's voice, disembodied, and the monster inches away; Cheri's breathing calms.

'Thank you,' she whispers into her hands.

The swing now has stopped, and, still seated, she walks herself around in a circle, twisting the chains, then lifts her feet and spins, body canted so far back that her hair brushes the dirt. She's breathless and dizzy under the limp August sky until someone reaches out, turns up a radio, and cold invigorating oxygen flows into her nose. Another someone gently stabilizes her as the van banks onto an exit, takes a left turn, glides over a bump, ascends, descends, and stops. When she looks up from her cupped hands, they are idling under the canopy of a Quality Inn.

Thank God. She retreats into her hands again.

Behind the registration desk is a holiday wreath and a mirror; in the mirror is the face of a crazy person who looks only marginally like Sarah. She pulls it together as best she can – tucking in the migrating strands of hair, straightening her jacket, clearing her throat – before meeting the eyes of the clerk. He's a man in his fifties, white-haired, wearing glasses.

'My mother reserved a room,' she tells him. 'Cheri Tremble?'

He stares at her, assessing. 'Where is she?' he asks.

'I'm getting the room,' Sarah answers slowly. 'She's in the car, with a headache.'

He continues staring at her for a moment, then steps into an office and calls someone, speaking low but keeping an eye on the desk and the young woman shifting from foot to foot, zipping and unzipping her coat.

Sarah deliberately turns her back on him. The lobby is awash in a franchised gloom – couches here and there, glass coffee table with an extravagant arrangement of silk flowers, and a breakfast station with a do-it-yourself waffle iron and plastic bins that dispense cornflakes. The clerk steps up once again to the desk; the wreath behind his head is decorated with spray-on snow and sparkling plastic fruit made to look like marzipan. He knows what's going on.

'I'm sorry, I can't give you a room,' he tells her.

'Why not?' she asks, incredulous.

'We've had some problems with Dr. Kevorkian,' he says. He looks pleased, which frightens Sarah. She thought he was calling

70

his boss, but it could have been the police. He has the excited and pious expression of a man capable of making a citizen's arrest.

'This is crazy,' she answers, backing away. 'We have a reservation.'

'Huh-uh,' he says loudly. 'Nope.'

And then Sarah's back in the van, telling Wayne to drive, get out of there; Cheri's struggling to breathe, unable to make a decision, all of them thrown into a panic that propels them out of the parking lot and back into the early-evening traffic. They drive around in circles for a few minutes until they find a pay phone and Linda leaves a message for Kevorkian's assistant, Neal Nicol. They wait as long as they can, motor idling in the cold, rainy twilight, oxygen tank dwindling, Cheri suffering wave after wave of anxiety. The fear of dying tonight is nothing, she realizes, compared to the fear of still being alive tomorrow morning. She leans forward and then back, rocking herself slowly, trying to calm down. No one returns the call, and after a while they pull away reluctantly and drive a few blocks more to an Office Depot.

Linda, Katy, and Sarah go inside and compose a fax to Kevorkian, explaining their predicament in all caps:

TO: DOCTOR
FROM: CHERI'S FRIEND

CHERI TREMBLE IS IN THE DETROIT AREA. SHE WAS NOT PERMITTED TO REGISTER AT THE QUALITY INN . . . WE HAVE TRIED TO REACH NEAL A NUMBER OF TIMES WITHOUT SUCCESS AND WE ONLY HAVE ONE SMALL TANK OF O2 LEFT . . . WE ARE FAXING THIS FROM OFFICE DEPOT IN BLOOMFIELD.

The store is warm and well lit; a man stands in line near them holding a wastebasket and a package of Bic pens. The boy at the copy counter takes their fax and sends it without comment, then lingers nearby, casting sidelong glances at Katy. A few feet away, down the office-equipment aisle, a young couple in matching ski jackets feed a piece of paper into a shredder and watch as it emerges in long, graceful strands.

The phone rings and a fax begins chugging through.

Thank God, Linda whispers.

Sarah and Kate stand next to the car in twilight, smoking and waiting for Neal, who is on his way. The drizzle stops momentarily and one by one, the parking-lot floodlights buzz to life, turning everything green. Inside the van, just visible through the smoky glass, Cheri is sitting once again with head in hands.

'This is fun,' Katy says.

'Yeah,' Sarah answers.

They can hardly look at each other, faces bathed in the alien light. Each knows what the other is feeling, being so urgently compelled toward something they are profoundly and instinctively opposed to. Not Kevorkian, exactly, but the simple fact of Cheri's death. Neither of them has fully absorbed the fact that if all goes as planned, she will cease to exist *this evening*. This evening! They scan the faces in the cars that glide past, easing into and out of parking spaces, people on their way to buy envelopes. Before anyone has a chance to get worried, a car pulls up, and a large man jumps out and hugs them. Neal. They're to follow him to Kevorkian's house.

They wind through an affluent neighborhood, past suburban castles with iron gates and leafless, glowering trees; inside the van the only sound in the long interval between the windshield wipers is the wheeze of oxygen moving through the tubing. It's trash day

in this neighborhood, garbage cans materializing and demateri-
alizing in the thin steam that rises from the streets. They follow
Neal up the driveway of an unassuming ranch house tucked
among the sprawling mansions. Suddenly, a man is framed in
their headlights, peeking out from the attached garage. Gaunt and
sunken-eyed, with a military crew cut and an animated expression, he gestures for them to pull inside and then hops nimbly
out of their way.

Jack Kevorkian, as seen on TV.

Relieved and terrified, everyone bursts out laughing, even
Cheri.

The burden is shifted, somehow, with that momentary release
of hysteria. In his cardigan sweater and open-collared shirt,
Kevorkian has the amiable and authoritarian air of a retired
general. He is clearly the center of the group, in control, his
voice resonant and welcoming as he introduces himself and Dr.
Georges Reding – a psychiatrist who, along with Neal, will remain
in the background as witness and assistant.

Wayne half carries Cheri into the living room, where plastic
chairs have been arranged in a semicircle, one of them draped
with a blanket to make it more comfortable. Katy sits next to her
mother; Sarah sits at their feet. Whatever numbness had gotten
them all through the long ride from Iowa is wearing off. The
house feels temporary, like an office set up in a trailer, and the
men seem both hearty and furtive, like Bible salesmen.

Cheri is awake now, unintimidated. These men are familiar to
her; she understands the dynamics of idealism, the personality
traits of a certain kind of fanaticism. She rallies, gives a coherent
account of her medical condition. They want to ascertain that
this is her decision.

'Yes, mine,' she says clearly. She holds her oxygen tube out like
the stem of a wineglass and gathers herself before speaking again.
'I have only forty-five minutes of oxygen left.'

'We have time,' Dr. Kevorkian says kindly. 'Don't worry.'

Katy and Sarah stare at each other, wide-eyed and trembling. Forty-five minutes is fifteen times three. Everything is welling up, faster than they can absorb it.

Dr. Kevorkian speaks to all of them, describing what he calls a patholytic procedure, the intravenous injection of a combination of drugs that will make her go to sleep, relax her respirations, and stop her heart. Cheri listens carefully, nodding, and then signs her name over and over, *Cheri Tremble*, until she's hearing it inside her head like a chant.

Linda and Wayne must sign papers as well, and they are told to leave the state via the most direct route possible. It's all printed out for them: the coroner, the funeral home, what to do and when.

Cheri hands her driver's license to Kevorkian for identification of the body, then gives her billfold, address book, and glasses to Sarah.

It's time.

And now the girls are dissolving, wailing, saying their goodbyes in a chaos of hands, mouths, faces, hair, tears. At one point or another, both are in Cheri's lap, holding on to her, crying so violently and so desperately that everyone is trying to shush them. They're inconsolable; every time they pull themselves away and start toward the door, they turn back to their mother. Cheri is trying to soothe them, kissing foreheads, whispering. Her tank now says thirty-two minutes.

She says a hurried goodbye to Linda and Wayne, reaching up to embrace them weakly, then watching as they gather her daughters and try to lead them from the house, each one breaking away briefly, running back to kneel at Cheri's feet, sobbing.

Cheri calls out to Linda, 'Take care of them!'

'I will,' Linda promises, her face haggard and despairing. It's all a jagged blur of grief: the careening house, Katy's heaving shoulders and Sarah's stricken face, Wayne's jacket-clad arm as he tries to usher them from the room, Linda's own unspoken words of farewell fluttering inside her chest like snared birds.

At the door, Sarah turns and starts back toward her mother again. *You can't just leave a person like this*, she thinks. *You can't.*

'Sarah!' Cheri says sharply.

Sarah stops. Her mother is sitting in the draped chair, the three men standing in the shadows behind her. *You can't leave a person like this.* But she sees from her mother's expression that it's too late.

Cheri is leaving them.

When they're gone, the house is filled with a beautiful, queer silence. It's like the airy, suspended moment that follows the last reverberating note on a pipe organ. *I'm alone*, she thinks, her heart suddenly clopping inside her chest like hooves, her head too heavy for the fragile stem of her neck. No family, no friends, no way out except through. She slumps forward in a swoon and then immediately rights herself, overcompensating like a drunk. *Please*, she thinks, picturing herself erect and composed. *I'm sorry.*

When the men first touch her, she flinches and cries out but then grows calm as they minister to her. Two of them help her down the hall to a small bedroom, prop her up with pillows to ease her breathing, tuck a rolled-up blanket under her knees, cover her with a thin blue chenille bedspread.

Dr. Kevorkian takes a seat next to her. He explains that the tank is at eighteen minutes, and when it's at ten, if she's ready, he will start the procedure. Cheri half closes her eyes and reaches out, entwines her fingers with this stranger's. She's beyond words now, transfixed by the images flickering inside her head, left hand gripping the folds of chenille.

At first it's meaningless, frantic electrical impulses taking the form of memories – a Mexican lizard on an adobe wall, panting like a dog; a pair of dusty ankles; her father in a sports coat, nuzzling a kitten; her brother Sean with a sparkler framed against a night sky, spelling out her name with big cursive flourishes, the letters disappearing even as they are written. And then the pain is gone, leached out of her so completely that she feels hollow and weightless, borne aloft, the back of her head tucked into the crook of someone's elbow, legs bent as they were in the womb, flannel feet cupped in the palm of a hand. Spellbound, she uses her last minutes to gaze up at her mother's young face.

Cheri?

She nods, still watching her mother, and someone takes her arm.

The needle is cold, and in a moment she's numb, separated from the men by a thick layer of ice. She breathes slowly in the narrow pocket of air, and the children in their bright skates congregate above her head. She lingers there for a moment, her cheek pressed against the underside of the ice, until a hand reaches down and pushes her under.

Maybe It Happened

MAYBE SHE WAS A KID. Maybe she wasn't quite house-broken. Maybe she was playing outside one summer afternoon with a couple of older cousins who were. Maybe they got deeply absorbed in a game where she was the baby and they were taking care of her. Maybe this involved cooing and her being pushed in a wagon and having bows tied into her slippery, nonexistent hair. Maybe when the moment came that the baby should have gotten up out of the wagon and excused herself to go indoors and use the facilities, the baby decided instead to really get into her role. Maybe she wet her pants.

It's possible the older of the cousins was nine and possible that the younger of the cousins was seven. It's possible that the nine-year-old wore a fashion-conscious sherbet-orange skirt and a ruffled midriff top, making her seem even more sophisticated than her actual years, and possible that the other one wore a sleeve-less white blouse, gray pleated shorts, and glasses with light blue frames, making her seem like a seven-year-old teacher. It's possi-ble that they were bored, stuck at somebody else's house for the afternoon with nothing to play with except a little kid who had just sat there and peed while they were petting her, like a puppy. It's possible that they abandoned playing mothers then to go sit on the stoop and squint into the summer sunlight, waiting to have their pictures taken so they could be seen many years later as they looked that day, hugging their knees, silently sharing their pop-bead wardrobe, one wearing the bracelet, the other wearing the necklace.

Perhaps the baby who wasn't a baby climbed up on a metal milk crate like they used to have back then and peered through the window at her mother and her aunt. Perhaps her mother was sitting at the kitchen table with her head stuck through a plastic tablecloth, drinking coffee from one of the pink Melmac cups that would outlast all the people in this story and all the people reading this story. Perhaps the mother was smoking a cigarette and was holding it out every so often so that the aunt, who was wearing plastic gloves and mixing up a vat of hair dye, could take drags off it. Perhaps the flat bottle of liquor that the mother and this particular aunt favored was sitting on the table. Perhaps they had dosed their coffee with it in order not to 'kill the children.' Perhaps just beyond them was the small, neat living room with its chunky green furniture and its cabbage-rose draperies closed against the sun. Perhaps all the way through the house, nearly to the front door, was their telephone table on which sat the heavy black telephone with a dial that the kid in soggy shorts stand-ing on the metal milk box could barely even move. Perhaps the mother herself sometimes resorted to using a stubby pencil to dial this phone, which suddenly rang out in the tiny house, a loud, old-fashioned sound, startling everyone and causing the milk box to wobble and the mother, who was getting her head painted dark brown, to say 'Shit' in a loud voice.

*

It's likely that then the tipped milk box pitched its rider onto the dirt by the back door, embedding a piece of gravel in her right knee, leaving a pale blue O-shaped scar that, along with two accommodating moles, would form what she would ever after think of as that knee's stricken face. It's likely as well that the mother, wearing her plastic-tablecloth poncho, walked through the living room with its one dramatic dark green wall to the telephone. Just as likely is that the aunt stayed where she was, setting down the bowl of dye and whatever she was applying it with, which was why while the mother was picking up the phone and saying hello and then listening to what the caller had to say, the aunt was peeling off the gloves and stepping out onto the back stoop to pick up the kid who had fallen onto a sharp rock and was wailing. It's likely the aunt was confused for a long moment that afternoon about why, after she got the soggy child with the bloody knee calmed down, she still heard crying.

Or did she? Maybe on those hot summer afternoons, when coffee made women languid, when the scent of trellis roses mixed with the scent of ammonia, when girls pretended they were mothers while mothers pretended something else entirely, perhaps anything could happen.

But then again, it's maybe possible, perhaps likely, that it never did.

The Tomb of Wrestling

SHE STRUCK HER ATTACKER in the head with a shovel, a small one that she normally kept in the trunk of her car for moving things off the highway. There was a certain time of year in upstate New York when the turtles left their reedy ponds to crawl ponderously through the countryside and wound up strewn like pottery shards across the road. The box turtles Joan could pick up with her hands; this was the shovel she had purchased to move the snappers to the ditches. Luckily, she had taken it from her trunk in order to straighten out her compost situation. The barrel stank so terribly that her neighbor had mentioned it, an aerobic smell of digestion, of tomatoes and corn cobs and coffee grounds combining to form such a bright sharp stink that the neighbor, who lived down the road and was loaning her a gutter-cleaning attachment for her hose, suggested Joan start alternating small shovelfuls of soil with each bucket of food scraps. So the shovel was leaned up against the side of the house, right next to the kitchen door, a few inches of its business end buried in a torn-open fifty-pound bag of peat slumped on its side. She hadn't torn the bag open like that; it wasn't her style – she was a person who stowed a shovel in her trunk for rescuing amphibians. The bag had been torn open by her husband, a man who sometimes was so impatient he would rip right into the side of a package of bread if the twist tie was snarled. It was not the most appealing trait, and yet in this moment, glimpsing the gaping hole in the plastic, Joan felt a surge of protective instinct where her husband was concerned. She had to save his wife! So she'd reached down, lifted the ergonomic-handled, titanium-headed shovel, and stepped into her kitchen with it.

The stranger was standing with his back to her, staring into the refrigerator. In the split second when he knew she was standing behind him but hadn't begun to turn yet, Joan heard the mechanical whir of a hummingbird sipping angrily at the feeder. The hummingbirds had bad personalities, always trying to spear each other away from the trumpet vines and the feeders, their thumb-size shimmering bodies aglow with bad intentions. She couldn't think how hard to hit him – it seemed first of all terrible to hit him but also wonderful. Inevitable. She had to do it or he would realize she hadn't died when he strangled her and would come after her again. Or one of the dogs. He seemed to hate the dogs, and the big one, Pilgrim, had attacked him and been kicked a number of times for it. It was brutal and routine, as though he were dispatching a duty that he neither agreed nor disagreed with. The dog had retired with a prolonged yelp to some dark area inside the honeysuckle. The little one, Spock, right now was whining and raking his toenails on the side door, making long feverish gouges in the wood. Joan could see the gouges in her mind's eye, some tiny part of her brain still attuned to home maintenance.

She decided in that split second between the man's hackles rising almost visibly and his beginning the turn away from the refrigerator and toward her that she was going to hit him in the head with the shovel using every bit of force she could summon. She was a slight woman ... or, no, she wasn't; she had been a slight woman, but now, depending on how you defined it, she was middle-aged. Her arms and legs were still decently coltish, but her torso had all the nuance of a toilet-paper tube. She had lost her beauty before she even knew she had it; looking at old photographs, Joan saw that she had been willowy, soulful, glossy-haired the entire time that she was thinking of herself as stark, bug-faced, lank.

She couldn't imagine using all her force; it went against who she was – a female, for starters – but there was no choice. Having never before hit someone with a shovel, or even with her fist, she didn't know what to expect with less than a full effort or, for that matter, *with* a full effort, so it stood to reason that she had to let fly completely and utterly, otherwise she might only stun him or piss him off. She took a step forward, grabbing the very end of the shaft, the physics of it returning to her from something she had learned working at an art gallery many years ago.

'Let the hammer work for you,' Roy had said, showing Joan how to hold the hammer near the end, allowing the weight of the head to add momentum to the swing. Roy had been pretty far out there for an Iowan – he had kinky hair that rose straight up from his scalp like blond flames, wore sharkskin shirts and baggy cuffed pants, and made sculptures out of found materials, big, compli-cated, beautifully crafted assemblages with baseball themes. He was the director of the gallery, and when he was excited he would take off and run straight up the wall, leaving sneaker tracks that she had to paint over. When they were finished hanging the shows, he would climb up onto the tallest stepladder they had and jump it like a big pogo stick down the rows of track lighting, stopping and adjusting each lamp in turn so that the paintings were perfectly illuminated. After she had worked with him for five years, Joan was forced to make a rule that he couldn't ride his bike inside her house.

So instead of choking up on the shovel handle the way she might have automatically done, considering all the times her first husband had shown her how to choke up in order to really smack the Wiffle ball down the back sidewalk into the pitcher's face (their friend Kurt, stoned and graceful), she remembered Roy's advice and the destructive, comforting weight of that old art-gallery hammer as she swung it toward a nail. Joan lifted the shovel end as high as her ear and put all her weight behind the swing.

Unbelievable, the small details you notice. He had a piece of individually wrapped cheese in his hand when he whirled around. She was actually embarrassed about that cheese, had put it in her shopping cart with the idle thought that she'd better not run into anyone she knew or it would be revealed that she sometimes broke down and bought cheese food instead of cheese, just for the sheer laziness of peeling the cellophane away and slapping the orange tile directly onto the bread. Her husband couldn't believe she ate that crap – just yesterday, when she was making a sand-wich with it, he had looked over her shoulder and said, 'We can do better than that, can't we?'

So the man was holding her secret cheese and swiftly turning around, and the refrigerator door bounced against the wall and the shovel made a clanging sound, that's how hard she hit him.

It rang, titanium on bone, like a clapper on a bell. She might have thought that the worst sound a shovel hitting a head could make was a melon-like sound, but it wasn't. This was the worst sound a shovel hitting a person's head could make – a muffled bell-like gonging, like a gravedigger hitting rock.

And the melon sound might have been preferable, though gorier, because what if the gonging meant that the man's head was preternaturally hard, that the shovel had met its match? Once when she had flipped a turtle and scooped it up, instead of retracting into its shell, it lolled its head out toward her, upside down, opening and closing its beak fitfully. When she set it in the tall grass and flipped it right-side up, its feet came out lightning fast and it turned on the shovel. For an instant, she had felt the mighty turtle's strength and rage right through the titanium and the wood handle. It had shaken the shovel like a terrier would shake a knotted sock before continuing on its prehistoric way, the tall grass shivering in its wake.

The man, the stranger who had her blood on his hands, who was still holding the square of cheese between his thumb and forefinger, didn't fly sideways to accommodate the spade thudding into his temple; that was what she'd half expected, him flying sideways into the cereal and wineglass cupboard, but her experience with this sort of thing heretofore was from cartoons. None of these specific thoughts were going through her mind, of course; they were more like synaptic realizations, pulses of understanding, except that understanding implies process. There was no process, no hesitation, because she was operating like a simple organism in that moment, one that was programmed to survive, like a sperm or a hammerhead shark.

She had lived on a lake when she first came to New York, after Iowa and her divorce, before she met her new husband and moved into his sprawling farmhouse. Her rented place, the upper half of a duplex, had been set into the side of a hill and surrounded by tall reaching trees, elms and oaks and the like, creating a fringed green awning that cast everything into a perpetual dense shade. Every morning she woke to the sound of Round Lake slapping the legs of the dock down below; it was like cold astringent in the face, the loneliness of that sound after her busy chattering life in Iowa. Nothing to keep her company but her own self and the soothing, flapping-moth feeling inside her skull that she registered not as depression or anxiety but as a balance of both states – a kind of stasis that led to endless hours of sitting at a desk or standing on the varnished porch, staring down at the mossy path and the wavering blue lake.

She had never stood around like that before, just looking. In Iowa everything had been visible, exposed to the elements; there was no subtext, nothing to break the furrowed monotony but subtle geographical undulations, all the rows of corn suddenly banking in unison like a flock of birds, a Dekalb sign at distant intervals, the occasional yellow cat furtively walking along a ditch. Here in upstate New York, there were the endless shadows, the low ceilings, the gloomy stone fences full of snake holes, trees bending over roadways, everything grown into everything else, warren-like and confining.

One day the landlord's henchman had shown up to take out a tree and some brush. He spent half the morning sitting on a stump sharpening a scythe blade and then oiling, link by link, the chain in his chain saw, all the while listening to something playing through his earphones and drinking out of a huge, dirty cup with a snap-on lid. Maybe it wasn't coffee in the cup, or maybe it was coffee and something else, because he managed to make an error in his tree-cutting calculations. The tree, instead of falling directly down the hill along a narrow, unforested trough between the cabin and the water, fell on a slant, hitting the trunk of a neighboring oak with a resounding thunderous smack. That second tree had fallen against the trunk of a third tree, which landed with a crack against the trunk of another tree, until four trees in all had crashed to the ground with an enormous rustling noise, like big girls in petticoats tripping each other.

So when she hit the stranger in her kitchen, that's how she brought him down, like felling a tree. The ringing blow to the side of the head, the flat of the shovel against the temple, and he landed on his side, between the refrigerator and the counter, which was covered with the makings of that day's pathetic lunch, a leftover dish made with pale slabs of tofu. It had wobbled unattractively on the way to the table, but Joan had eaten it without paying much attention, absorbed in the newspaper. It had almost turned out to be her last meal; they would have found it in her stomach at the autopsy: tofu helper. A vegetarian from beginning to end.

As a midwestern child, she had gotten to know food in its sentient state right in her grandparents' chicken-scratched yard. Joan had loved the white hens with their meditative clucking, red combs and yellow legs, rhythmic, bobbing way of walking. Twenty feet beyond the chickens began the dirt field where the hogs were kept, the pink rubbery noses poked through the fence, the tiny wicked eyes, the little lean-tos they called home. The pigs had babies that Joan's grandfather would hold for her to pet, which she did, panicked and sorry, as they squealed in abject terror, the same syllable over and over, while their mothers snuffled and bit each other. In the next enclosure were the cows, standing on low mountains of manure, staring between the chewed planks of the fence, bright metal tags stapled into their ears. The color of the tags indicated at what future date the cow would be evicted from its body.

Joan's grandfather was a part-time butcher who drove a panel truck to people's farms and killed their animals for pay. It wasn't told to Joan, who had a hard enough time petting a baby pig that didn't want to be petted, but once she had glimpsed something strange: a group of blood-smeared shaved sheep in a dejected clump; a lost calf, tall with rickety legs and twine around its neck; and a lamb on its side in the dirt, woolly legs bound together. The lamb had lifted its head and stared at Joan as she walked toward it, but right at that moment her grandmother began calling her, urgently, in a false lilting voice, the way you might call a puppy away from a busy road.

'Dearie, come here!' she cried gaily. 'Come to Grandma!'

There had to be a rope around somewhere. Where? Joan was starting to feel the adrenaline leave her body. *He had tried to kill her.* For a second she almost swooned – her grandmother had called her dearie, she had been a little girl in a ruffled midriff top, somewhere she had a picture of herself in it squinting at the ground while someone in baggy trousers held a long fish up next to her. The fish was being held by the gills, and its tail was flexed just enough to show it was still alive; it was the same height as Joan. On the back of the photo, her mother had written *Keepers.*

She needed to immobilize him before he came around, if he came around. Rope, rope, rope. She was too afraid to leave the kitchen and go to the toolshed to look for rope; what if he woke up, what if she came back and he wasn't here. She'd seen it, everyone had – the blank span of linoleum, the moment of sick realization, the grab from behind, hands around the neck, the woman lifted from the floor, gasping like a fish. Joan raised the shovel and hit him again, this time a soggy, glancing blow to the shoulder.

He stirred and collapsed deeper onto the linoleum, like he was filled with sand. It reminded her of the old Friday-night fights, dramas in which men in satin shorts alternated between pummeling each other in the stomach and hugging. Her father had been a fan, watching from a green armchair with the family's white terrier on his lap, eating ice cream from a mixing bowl, using the toes of one foot to scratch the top of the other one. If Joan or her siblings wandered into the room and stood staring at the television, he would describe what was happening as the guy fell backward onto a milking stool or stood swaying, swollen head hanging down on his chest, or when the guy's spaghetti arm was lifted in its heavy glove by the referee. 'He clocked him,' her father would explain.

Joan had loved her father, a tender, hopeless drunk who stayed off the booze for long periods, confusing everyone and causing her mother to switch back and forth between cheerfulness and relentless bitching tirades. It was a tumultuous household, as many were in those days, but it had the white terrier and a blue parakeet, and Joan's mother made matching flannel nightgowns not only for her daughters but also for their dolls, baked pies every Sunday morning, and put a plywood Santa in the front yard each December. Joan's father, when he was sober, was a classic backyard putterer; he knocked together bird feeders, staked tomatoes, hung buckets neatly from spigots, and sang to the children and anyone else who would listen, songs about paper dolls and drinking. Once, he got annoyed at Joan for bugging him while he was shaving and he took the towel from around his neck, gave it a twirl, and flicked it at her. It was so out of character he might as well have donned a hockey mask and gone after her with a carving knife; she sobbed until she was ill and had to stay home from school that day, huddled on the couch in the darkened living room, watching reruns.

It seemed entirely possible she might have clocked this man to death; there was something too settled about the way he was arranged on the floor. He had cornered her upstairs in her study, just walked in and said something offhand and expectant: 'Here I am,' or 'Hey, I'm here,' or 'Okay, I'm here.' For a good number of seconds she had been utterly confused, embarrassed that she couldn't remember who he was or what business he was there on.

'I'm sorry,' she had said haltingly. 'I can't remember what we said.' As though there had been an arrangement made earlier for a man to come stand over her and grin as she sat in her soft chair with manuscript pages on her lap. When she started to stand, he stepped forward and gave her a gentle push backward, the tips of his fingers on her breastbone, and she sank down, confused. Who was he again?

And then, with a sudden zooming clarity, she realized he was a stranger who had come into her house and up her stairs and was now addressing her, pushing her down when she went to stand up. With the clarity came a tight, compressing panic. She made a noise and tried to scramble out of the chair, kicking at his legs. He took her by the back of the head and ran her into the wall; she lifted her hand to shield her nose, which nevertheless broke on impact. It was a totally visual experience; she didn't feel a thing – the sight of the forty-year-old wallpaper coming toward her, rows of parasols and roses, followed by a bright yellow explosion, her own innocent knees for a second, then she was crouched before him, one hand holding her nose, the other raised in front of her, like a student asking a question in class.

Second grade, unable to raise her hand to ask Mrs. Darnell if she could go to the bathroom. Endless lessons, the opening of desks, lifting of books, rustling pages, chalk and eraser. The replacing of math book with language book, the stark impossibility of making it to the lunch bell. Unable to hold it and unable to ask, a drowning person in a warm, insistent river, eventually Joan just let go. As she stared fixedly at the blackboard, a hideous amber current moved steadily up the aisle past her desk, past the desk in front of hers, and then into the territory of the desk beyond that one.

That afternoon, after lunch at home, the ruined Brownie uniform stuffed into a laundry basket, the silent diplomatic companionship of her little girlfriends on the playground, she returned to find the floor around her desk miraculously cleaned up. Later, during art class, when everyone was milling about, tearing paper and mishandling paste, Mrs. Darnell crouched next to her and whispered, 'Don't ever be afraid to raise your hand.'

He took her outstretched arm, twisted it behind her, lifted it upward until she cried out, and then held it there, stepping on her right foot with his thick boot, holding her in place. She tried to resist the impulse to wrestle her way out of it – his arms and hands were iron; it was like straining against the bars of a cell. But he was tearing the muscles in her upper arm and cracking the delicate bones of her instep – if he would just let her arm go, if he would just pick up his boot! She writhed frantically, panting, and then she went still.

When Joan was with her first husband, they liked to get high, eat candy, and challenge each other to competitive games – say, jumping over the sofa from a standstill, pitching dirt clods onto a tin roof, or holding afternoon-long wrestling bouts in the table-less dining room of their farmhouse. This was during a time when her husband wore patched overalls and no shirt, and Joan wore cutoffs and a famous halter top made from two bandannas tied together; they had a willow tree that looked like a big hula skirt, a collie dog, and a blue bong. Life was fresh and new, and they were learning everything: that dill pickles were actually small cucumbers, that oregano started out as a leaf, that going back to the land meant you should remove your top if somebody needed a hanky.

She and that husband were so perfectly matched in spirit and sensibility that they were like littermates, tripping each other, rolling around, hopping on each other's backs, getting rug burns. Sometimes, depending on the quality and quantity of the dope, they forgot themselves during their wrestling matches – Joan yanking on vulnerable areas and scratching, him clamping her head under his arm, poking a finger up her nostril. Then they struggled in earnest, tugging and swearing, worrying the dog, until finally Joan's husband got fed up and pinned her. Just like that. Pressed to the floor and straddled, her wrists manacled in one of his hands.

It was always shocking, that utter helplessness, as though she were one of her own childhood dolls being laid to rest after a session of playing. When that happened, just for a moment, fear would bloom inside Joan, dark and frantic, uncontainable, at the sight of her husband rising above her, foreshortened and monumental, like a tree growing out of her chest.

Years later in that marriage, they had grown so bored they went back to school instead of back to the land – he studied horticulture and Joan studied art history. Him in a greenhouse, pruning shears in his pocket, folding the petals of a flower. Her in a darkened auditorium, chin in hand, making thumbnail sketches of paintings in a notebook: clocks draped over trees, crutches holding up broken noses, a woman with bureau drawers set into her chest, knobs shaped like nipples. A single knotty carrot, a pipe hovering over the words *Ceci n'est pas une pipe*. She drew her husband's face with their little brass pot pipe. *Ceci n'est pas un mariage*. In the black auditorium, a new slide clicked into place and Joan stared, pen suspended over her notes. Another Magritte metaphor: a room filled up with a huge garish rose, its petals bent back against the ceiling, walls, and floor. *Le Tombeau des Lutteurs*.

The stranger kicked her legs out from under her, flipped her onto her back, and sat on her chest, pressing her arms to the floor with his knees. He looked around.

The bookshelf, the table next to her armchair, the lamp, the cord to the lamp.

From that angle, her first husband had looked like Tom Petty, droopy-haired and stoned, restored to affection for the pink-faced girl pinned beneath him – but this was a stranger, his hair dark and lusterless, flopped down over his forehead. He was hurting her, compressing her lungs, swinging his head back and forth, scanning the room in an exaggerated manner. For what? What was he looking for?

He leaned back to grope for something, shinbones pressing like rebar into her upper arms, and she realized she could shout.

Crazy. To make her last word be a dog's name.

PILGRIM!

The stranger took the yardstick leaning against the wall and laid it across her windpipe.

Ceci n'est pas une pipe.

Outside, Pilgrim pulled his head, shoulders, forepaws, and torso from a groundhog hole out by the back fence. He stood listening intently to the summer evening, nose lifted, and then turned his dirty face like a radar dish toward the house.

It was the same yardstick she had used earlier in the day to measure her stocking feet, each one in turn, to see if they were exactly the same size. She was more of a scholar than a mathematician – every time she measured, she got something different – and managed to occupy herself for a pretty long time. The dogs were with her and she had measured their tails, the big black dog with a long nose and the intelligent brown eyes of a chimpanzee and little Spock, thickset and amiable, with a triangular head that he could force like a wedge into all kinds of spots.

He had just that morning captured a chipmunk in the daylilies and carried it, squeaking, around the front yard. Joan had thrown open the window, leaned out, and called to the dog in a high, insistent, flattering voice. He looked around in alarm and then up to where she was. He began wagging his hindquarters, lifting his ears high off his scalp, trying to figure out what she wanted.

'Come here, Spock!' she cried coaxingly. 'Come here, boy!'

That long-ago lamb lifting its head from the ground had bleated at her, a drawn-out pleading, lonely sound. She'd only just remembered it. 'Spock-eeee!' she cried in a singsong and then made as though she were running away from the window.

Spock dropped his prize and ran to meet her at the front door, panting.

*

Joan thrashed, arching like a fish tossed on the bank, and then quieted, focusing on getting air past the obstruction on her throat. She concentrated, gasping, staring past the stranger, who seemed impatient, almost bored. He bounced a little, pressing on the yardstick, when he thought she wasn't suffocating fast enough.

Pilgrim trotted around the house, nose to the ground, past the limestone wall, the lilac bush, a mound of disturbed dirt, the faint heady cologne of a cat, the bed of smooth river pebbles, a clump of hyacinths, and suddenly he ran into it, like a thick pane of glass – *Stranger* – and followed it around to the front door, snorting frantically against the frame of the flimsy screen. *Stranger*.

He sounded the alarm.

While Pilgrim was excavating the groundhog tunnel, Spock had been napping in the fern bed behind the outhouse, an unused shed with tattered flower-sprigged wallpaper and a worn plank with two sad holes in it. A garter snake lived in there, and some tiny large-eyed mice. Earlier, unbelievably, a possum had gotten up on the roof of the shed via a little tree that could barely support its weight. Spock had been so invigorated by this he had taken down all the trumpet vines. The possum was still up there, inert and pink, and Spock was sprawled on his back asleep, large paws retracted against his chest, delicate fronds smashed flat beneath him.

The stranger exerted the required pressure without even glancing down at her, as though he could more or less do it by feel, like gliding underneath a chassis, tightening a bolt, gliding out again.

If the yardstick had been wood it might have broken, but it was metal with a cork backing. Flexible and inefficient, suffocating her, but slowly. It was as though her windpipe were a thin blue tube being wound tightly in gauze, layer after layer.

Let the yardstick work for you.

Roy and Joan in that long-ago art gallery, after hours, moonlight washing across a grove of pedestals on which they placed metal sculptures. Roy made up names for the amorphous polished blobs: *Underpants I, II,* and *III* and *I've Fallen and I Can't Get Up.* He and Joan wore cotton museum gloves and listened to new-wave music on the radio. They were lingering in the gloom, putting off going home to their respective spouses. A song by Elvis Costello came on, a ballad, irresistible. They danced in the dark gallery, white hands on each other's backs, singing along: *I see you've got a husband now.*

The metal yardstick pinched her neck and she saw glistening particles around the stranger's face, which had darkened, the room flattening up against his head like a cutout. Joan didn't exactly fake her own death; she simply left the scene of the crime – stopped resisting and faded backward into herself like a fish swimming to the bottom of a pond.

Roy wasn't even around anymore. He had died of cancer. Joan looked for him in the murk. At the lake near where she'd first lived when she came to New York, whenever it rained, fat, tattered goldfish rose from the depths to nibble at the drops, as though a big child were shaking food into their bowl. She used to watch them from her porch, slender glimpses of orange beneath the blue, varnished surface of the lake.

She should have been a painter; she'd always known that.

Joan had seen a physics demonstration once where a bullet was fired into a slab of gel, its trajectory made visible by a jagged tunnel in the pale amber block. Just in that moment, gazing up at the matte brown of the stranger's hair, she heard it again, the sound of the report like a cap gun right next to the ear.

Joan had known someone who was shot, but he wasn't anywhere in sight; none of the people she might have expected to see were at the bottom of her pond. Mother? Father? Her eyes were wide, searching, but the only thing visible was her own hair, drifting in front of her like seaweed.

The stranger was startled away from the task at hand; he clambered to his feet, tripping over Joan's body, and lurched against the wall. Pilgrim had hooked one of his muddy toenails through the screen and prized the flimsy door open a foot or so against its latch. When he let go, the bottom of the door snapped shut against the wood frame, creating a sharp report that reverberated through the house. He did it again, then gave up, threw all his energy into a baying, hysterical howl.

Stranger . . . stranger . . . stranger.

Spock found himself in front of the house before he even knew he was awake. He ran around the yard, barking into the evening air.

On the roof of the shed, the possum opened one eye.

Too much commotion at once: the cacophony of dog yelps, the sharp noise like two blocks of wood clapped together, the blurred sound of toenails being raked across a screen. The stranger glanced down at the body, boneless and vacated, mouth slack, eyes fixed and staring. More in common now with the carpet or the chair than with him. He looked out the window to the yard below. The black dog was trembling and baying, staring at the door.

In the woods behind the house, a silver coyote glanced up from what used to be a deer. The nearest neighbor, just getting home from work, stood next to his car for a moment listening to Pilgrim and Spock and then went on inside, where his wife was cooking dinner and his sons were watching *The Three Stooges*. Good old-fashioned black-and-white mayhem and the after-work sound of meat frying.

The stranger stepped on Joan's outflung hand as he strode from the room.

Way back in the Iowa farmhouse days, Joan and her first husband had woken one morning to find they had survived a tornado. There was a wide swath cut across the cornfield next to their shed. The tornado had gone through a fence neatly, lifting it like a row of stitching from a hem, and then turned and run along-side the house, uprooting the soft-faced pansies and leaving in its wake a farmer's feed bucket, a muddy wind sock, and what looked like a waterlogged stuffed toy that turned out to be a kitten. Joan hadn't wanted to go to the cellar during the night because she had seen an obese toad down there, a horrible depressing creature who seemed to have eaten himself into a corner – he had grown so fat that his arms and legs didn't reach the ground; he was like a soft gray stone about the size of her foot, resting in a puddle of ancient exploded preserves. So they had remained upstairs on their mattress on the floor with the collie between them, getting up on their elbows every once in a while to peer out at the wild, whipping storm. At some point they had watched a ball of blue lightning travel back and forth between the house and the barn on an electrical wire and thought they might be going to die, but still they had lain in bed, unwilling to face the giant toad.

Joan hadn't let her husband bury the kitten that was flung onto their sidewalk in the tornado. At the last minute, while placing it in the hole, she decided maybe it wasn't really dead and carried it out to the tall grass and left it there, just in case.

She came slowly back to herself there on the floor of her study, lungs inflating and deflating until she could feel everything at once: crushed nose, thread of blood running across her cheek, the blue stem of windpipe.

The kitten had been gone the next morning, carried off in the jaws of whatever carries things off in the night. The sounds they would hear sometimes in that farmhouse, in the darkness, insane snarling fights, agonized cries deep inside the corn. From outside came the sound of Pilgrim's growling attack, a sickening thump. Joan pulled herself up to the window and looked out. The stranger was kicking her dog. Once, twice, off the flagstone stoop and into the shrubbery, yelping.

Then only Spock was visible in the early-evening light, a white dog with a stick in his mouth, keeping just out of reach.

The stranger swept his boot sideways, knocking her geraniums off the stoop, homely Martha Washingtons with neat scalloped leaves and lavender fringed petals. It was like kicking someone's grandmother.

Her neck, her dog, her flowers.

When she was a little girl, her grandma Bess had hung bed linens on the line down at Joan's height, letting them rest wetly on the clean grass as she set the pins, then lifting the line high with a notched pole until the sheets were off the ground, snapping feebly around in the breeze. Joan would walk in a kid trance through the damp white rows, a clothespin pinching each of her fingers, feeling the thin cloth against her face.

In the gloomy confines of that grandmother's living room was a mirrored coffee table made of cobalt glass that reflected Joan's face in a mesmerizing way, blue and desolate. She had loved that grandma, a silent, opinionless woman from the unpopular side of the family. At Grandma Bess's house, there were no frightened farm animals, no knife-wielding butchers; she had her own gentle version of hens and chicks: cunning little succulent plants that spread in a low green flock across the cracked dirt by her back door, kept alive with periodic drenchings of dishwater. She used a rusted enamel dishpan with a rock in the center for a birdbath, and she did her business out back in a shed. Once, eating dinner at someone's house with her parents and sister, Joan had piped up to remark that her grandma Bess had the same kind of soup pot underneath her bed. That was one of Joan's famous childhood jokes, although she herself didn't get it at the time.

She peered down at her spilled geraniums, the curtain like a shroud against her face. The clay pots were broken into large pieces. She had spectral visions of herself on the front lawn – there was young Joan at her grandma's house, whirling through the laundered sheets as the sparrows landed on the rock and sipped at their bathwater; there was Joan crouching to look at the hens and chicks; there was Joan kneeling, gazing down through the blue-coffee-table atmosphere at her image floating below, dis-embodied and deprived. She had to touch her own mashed nose just to see if she was still alive.

The pain was dazzling, invigorating, like poking her brain with an ice-cold wire; she did it again, this time imagining a pair of shining tongs pushing alcohol-soaked cotton balls into her head. She'd read that in a story somewhere, a woman staring helplessly at a doctor as he packed her mangled nose with what felt like burning snow. Joan closed her eyes and pressed firmly against the shattered bridge, until she was rewarded with a surge of endorphins.

She opened her eyes.

He had been looking for something to lure the white dog, that's why he'd gone in the refrigerator in the first place; he had decided to make a clean sweep of it, because he hated dogs anyway and the fact that the thick white one thought this was all a game – well.

The stranger liked to play games himself, and this was one. Have a slice of cheese, dog, if you call this cheese.

In another Magritte metaphor, a man stares into a mirror and, instead of seeing his face, sees the back of his own head. The dead woman behind him was noiseless, but he felt a shift, the still air giving way as the shovel was cocked back, and then he somehow was behind himself, seeing what she saw right up to the moment that the black bowl of the shovel hit the side of his head, at which point he heard not the sound of a gravedigger hitting rock but a sudden loud silence.

Joan had already killed something once, with her car, on a bitter night when snow was blowing into her headlights. A flash of antler, a shoulder thudding into the front bumper on the passenger side, and suddenly the animal was up on the hood of her car, sliding across it, into the windshield, and then off onto the ground, taking the side-view mirror and leaving a trail of fur. It was late on a black night, and Joan had been so startled that she screamed as she pulled the car over and looked behind her. There was nothing. Then something, a glimpse of turmoil, over on the gravel, the deer struggling to right itself, chin on the ground, trying to gather its legs beneath it. She began to tremble and cry when suddenly the cracked windshield sagged inward and fell all around her, into her lap, down the front of her coat, like chunks of ice, and she drove on, into the windy stinging darkness, her face frozen.

Driving away from the dying deer was the worst thing she had ever done; it was how she had come to know herself as a coward, and for a long time afterward she had tried to atone by helping things off the road, either before they were killed or after, which was how she ended up with the little titanium shovel in her trunk. She used it now to reach across the man and push the refrigerator door closed.

*

His grandmother had been worn out from being married to a drunken gravedigger and raising six children and various grand-children next to a sprawling cemetery. Just a backyard, a runoff ditch, and then acres of tombstones – some old, mossy ones with rounded shoulders and stricken, ornate messages and some modern, ranch-style ones in bright, rectangular granite inscribed with more circumspect messages. The old gravedigger himself ended up cremated, reduced to a pile of grit that seemed more like him than the previous version.

So the gravedigger's grandson knew his way around a shovel, because they all did, or the boys anyway. They had to sit in the equipment shed during the services, each an agonizingly slow and silent play that couldn't be hurried no matter what – there was always somebody who needed two people to help them walk, there was always a kid who lay down on the ground in his good clothes, there was always a pair of startling legs tottering in high heels; there were always old people who had to walk around saying hello to other tombstones before hobbling back to their car, getting in, starting it, and then fucking sitting there while it warmed up or cooled off. Only when the last car had finally crunched along the gravel road to the gate could they pick up their shovels and head across to cut up and throw dirt on each other while the old man cussed at them.

It was actually a nice thing to think about, the mysterious stately behavior of the black-clad people, the smell of rich dirt, the worms that didn't know they were cut in half. He let it keep him company now, wherever this was.

Joan had seen a number of dead things in her life, and although the man on her kitchen floor looked strangely flat and ruined, he didn't look dead. On his side, one arm lodged behind him, the palm facing up, the other arm slumped forward at the shoulder, elbow bent, the hand resting somewhere under the edge of the cereal and wineglass cupboard. She needed to get that hand, somehow put it with the other hand, and tie them together behind his back.

Rope, rope, rope.

All around her, things had come loose from their meanings and were washing in and out with her breath like tidewater: the planks of late-afternoon sunlight laid across the kitchen floor, the plaid dog leash looped over a chair, the garish jewels shimmering next to her lunch, cast by the prism hanging in the window over the sink. A giant rose, a single knotty carrot, a man in a bowler hat, his face obliterated by an apple.

Ceci n'est pas toi.

In fact, she had been a good-natured child, cartwheeling around the lawn, throwing the ball for the family's terrier, grinning gap-toothed into cameras, whistling, constantly with her arm hooked around the neck of one skinny cousin or another.

Her neck, her dog, her flowers.

Out the kitchen window, a heron stalked the edge of the pond, searching for grubs, jabbing its long beak into the mud and then tipping it up toward the sky, like a frail child playing with a sword. Beyond the pond, inside the woods, the coyote lay stretched out on the ground with a bone between his paws, like a dog. The bone had strings of flesh attached to it and fur, some of which he peeled off and some of which he went ahead and ate. He hadn't killed the deer; a truck had hit it, and it had crawled off into the woods and tried to bury itself.

There were crows trying to bother him but unless they came down, he refused to be bothered. They were above him, squawking.

*

It sounded like the comedian he used to watch on TV, the big man who wore an overcoat and a pirate's scarf and who traipsed up and down the stage, bent over his microphone, squawking in helpless rage at the stupidity of women.

Oh! Oh! Oh!

You cuuuuunt!

Now his cemetery was dark, the tombstones like bones poking up out of the ground. The ones he had liked were the ones who died before their time – men in their thirties, women in their twenties, three-year-olds. Hurried along by farm accidents, childbirth, whooping cough. You could feel the unfairness hanging over the markers.

Once, he helped bury a coffin two feet long, ivory-colored with chrome handles, that housed a waterhead baby who'd died at birth. That's what people called it then, and that's how he had pictured it, a baby with a head made out of rainwater. The features, the ears, everything; a baby's head that looked like a clear glass jar, only it was water.

He felt like finding that baby's grave and stretching out on it, resting his head, which it seemed like he was carrying in his hands; he couldn't tell. It might be where it was supposed to be but it felt like a balloon, only solid, and with a bad spot, like a melon that had sat in the melon patch too long. This bad spot didn't feel like mush, though; it felt like rain. Or not like rain, like pain.

She had visited a morgue once and seen a body with a bullet wound. In a hospice room, she had seen her mother die and, later, in a room down the hall, her father; in a hospital chapel, she had seen a stillborn baby in its mother's arms. The bullet created a precise, catastrophic hole that was deeply startling, even though she was prepared for it; her mother had been awake until the end, struggling and translucent, like a baby bird forced out of the nest; her father, picked clean by the vulture of cancer, had grown quieter and quieter until even his heart devolved into silence. The baby had been lavender, and perfect.

Spock circled the house, checking all his posts, stopping to fan his leg at the corner of the shed, the stand of daylilies, both Adirondack chairs. Usually when the crows sounded like that, it meant something was out there to eat, and he and Pilgrim would pace along their invisible border and try to see what it was and who was eating it.

He had mostly run out of urine but he still had his stick, one with a twig coming off it that if he turned his head would poke him in the neck. When he found the right spot, Spock was going to settle down and chew the twig off. For now, he just kept turning his head, letting the twig dig its own grave.

The kitchen was strangely beautiful. Joan looked down and saw flowers foaming at her feet last week as she took a shortcut through the Queen Anne's lace. Something weird was happening to time – it was swirling instead of linear, like pouring strands of purple and green paint into a bucket of white and giving it one stir. Now was also then was also another then. She saw Spock nosing through summer brambles with a stick in his mouth and her husband in the snow cutting a Christmas tree, making the Jack Nicholson face he always made when he had occasion to use the ax. *Honey, I'm home!*

The hand that was under the edge of the cupboard, she needed to get that out of there so she could see it.

*

The stranger was somewhere else now. The tombstones were gone and he was in his chair, in the dark. It was late at night and the comedian was on TV, ranting and sweating through his overcoat. *Oh! Oh! Oh!*

He pointed the remote but he couldn't turn it up. His fingers weren't working.

You biiiiitch!

The comedian had been hurried along by a drunk driver, T-boned on his way from a gig. Gigged on his way to a T-bone. They used to catch frogs, he and his cousin Kyle, and do the most inventive things to them. Sometimes, though, they just fished, and that was almost as fun, simply because of Kyle. Nobody didn't have fun when they were with Kyle, who ended up hurried along by mysterious circumstances involving diving off a bridge drunk.

Once, in physics class, Joan had seen footage of a bridge with a fatal design error; when it was stressed, the bridge began bouncing, then rippling, and then undulating, flinging off tiny horses and wagons and canvas-topped Model Ts, until it literally came loose from one shore and began flapping like a sheet on a line. She had never forgotten that film, the darkened classroom awash in boredom, the teacher's voice intoning, the jumpy scarred footage, and then the sudden electric shock of seeing something so interesting and bizarre. In school, of all places.

In retrospect, it may not have come loose from the shore; she isn't sure. But the undulation, the rippling forces hurling the carriages and cars, that part she didn't dream and she didn't embellish for herself. When Joan was growing up back in Waverly, Iowa, she once had the opportunity to attend the Miss Waverly pageant, when her mother's friend's son's girlfriend was a contestant. It was the most sophisticated thing Joan had done up to that point – the pageant was held in the high-school auditorium, a velvet-curtained venue that nobody from Joan's elementary school had ever had occasion to visit. The girlfriend contestant, Connie something, was freckled and dazzling with an ineffable quality Joan had never seen before, and it was fitting that she be up for Miss Waverly. She wore her hair ratted high and folded into a French twist for the gown competition, and teased bangs and a shining false braid that draped across her shoulder for the swimsuit one. There wasn't a lot of talent coming out of Waverly – one girl in fact mixed a cake onstage, wearing a gingham apron and reading the recipe in a loud, theatrical voice – but Connie's mother had rigged Connie up in a black leotard and given her a long white chiffon scarf – like, really long – and in the dark auditorium, under a black light, Connie had run out from the wings flinging the scarf before her. You could see glimpses of her eyes occasionally as she ran back and forth, and sometimes a purple grimace from her teeth as she exerted herself, but mostly all that was visible was the rippling scarf as she flung it and ran after it and flung it again. The place was speechless afterward, and then erupted into wild clapping.

For weeks after that Joan and her sister would put on swimsuits and race around the backyard with long scarves made from a ruined bedsheet until they ended up sweaty and defeated, the strips of stained sheets growing lighter and lighter while their arms grew heavier and heavier.

Other things could be used to tie someone up, but what? Meaning had begun to swirl along with time. Looped over one of the kitchen chairs was a plaid copperhead, its face a silver clasp. It was like a scene in a book she had once read, where a dog was bitten and ran home over a terrible distance with the snake, huge and black, dragging like a leash. In the same book, the rising river overcame a cage full of lion cubs, a man tried to asphyxiate himself, another man was trapped under a log and drowned as the tide rose, another man listened to criminally hip jazz, and another man lashed his severed forearm to a boat. Men, men, men.

That's what she'd been reading about when he'd barged into her study: the strange notions of the surrealists, with their unmoored minds and their brutal depictions of women. Limbs severed into doll parts and rearranged; high heels turned upside down and presented on a platter like a roasted bird, paper frills on their stilettos. Little girls with hair like kudzu staggering down a dark corridor, a reclining woman with food heaped on her and men with utensils eating her abdomen and breasts. A tangle of women arranged by the artist – his mustache sharpened into the kind of antennae catfish use to feel their way through the muck at the bottom of the pond – so their naked bodies created the impression of a skull. *In Voluptate Mors.* Through pleasure into death.

Joan's family had fished for sport, sitting on banks, pulling worms apart like licorice and pushing them onto hooks, hauling out catfish and bass, discarding the junk fish by tossing them into the weeds to suffocate. Joan was forbidden to put them back into the water and would just crouch there, willing them to die. Sometimes, a long time later, one that she had told herself was dead would flop, just once.

In the distance, crows were screaming about something. They were trying to tell her to get out of there. Forget the rope. *Go! Go! Go!*

The women artists of that long-ago era were ferociously steel-eyed, their limber bodies occasionally bent in the service of one photographer or another, but rarely did they smile, even at picnics.

No, no, no.

Time swirled in its paint bucket, and she saw her own family at play, her father in an undershirt and her mother in a billed cap, both of them grinning. In the background were bluegills hanging from a stringer, each the size of a baby's hand.

*

Next to the front porch, under the arborvitae, Pilgrim pulled himself forward through the bramble to the flagstone. There were knives in him that stabbed each time he moved, and he growled at them.

The birds and the squirrels and the chipmunks had a certain feel to them, and so did the toads, but sometimes other things would move through – a fox, a skunk, the black snake, un-shy and curious, probing its nose along the stone foundation of the house and then coiling into the depression next to the willow stump, inanimate, like something that might have fallen off the wheelbarrow. Spock was made nervous by the black snake and would whine under his breath until it moved on. To Pilgrim, the snake was nobody's business but its own, though he didn't feel that way about everything. For instance, the groundhog or the man in the kitchen.

He had left his chair now and was moving through the darkened house, looking for something. The TV flickered in the corner like an aquarium. Whatever he was looking for, a tool or a weapon he could use as a tool, was eluding him. Gliding under the chassis, tighten, tighten, gliding back out. Something Kyle said once, now that he's remembering Kyle: If he ever had a daughter he would name her Chassis, because it was pretty. They were talking cars, all of them, and everyone had turned around and stared at Kyle.

Once you understood basic physics, you could use things as tools that weren't necessarily tools. A screw turned just so into a block of wood would lift the cap off a beer bottle more efficiently than a church key; a strand of dental floss would slice a cheese-cake more cleanly than the sharpest knife. Et cetera. He would never use the right tool if he could use a better wrong one. Unlike the old man, who would demand his Polish problem solver (aka the hammer) and then whale on whatever it was until it broke free or just broke. Which is how one of the boys got three of his fingers cut off at age eleven during an episode with a tree branch caught in the mower blade.

Gimme muh problem solver, the old man had said. And then: *Lift the gawdam thing.* And then *whack, whack, whack,* until the blade sprang free and finished its revolution.

It wudden spose to do that was what the old man said to the sheriff, who drove out to look around after the hospital reported that a boy was brought in minus several fingers. Afterward, the old man cut up about what had happened to regain his authority. *I thought he was a bawling like that cuz he dropped his posies,* he said in a mincing voice. They were meant to laugh and they probably did.

Not much was asked of those kinds of men back then; all day surrounded by manure and recalcitrant machinery, they just simmered in their meanness. The women too – every egg his grandmother cracked had shit and feathers stuck to it, every shirt she scrubbed with her own knuckles and ran through the wringer came out of the wash still smelling like the old man. She knew how to improvise a tool too; maybe that's where he learned it. Everything from a wooden spatula grabbed off the back of the stove to an extension cord to the old wire rug beater, which the boys called the Doug beater after a particular incident that got it retired permanently.

His head sloshed, making him feel seasick. He was looking for – what again? A tool? Something he could use to pry something else open. They used to tell the younger boys they were going to dig the coffins back up and make them look, but it never really scared them. They knew better; it was just flat-out too much work.

Doug had almost gotten retired along with the wire rug beater. He looked like he'd gone through a threshing machine, and all for bringing a tree toad into her kitchen, which the older boys had told him to do. They tiptoed around for days, staying out of her way as she tended to the wet rags and what all else that she had to keep putting on him. Age seven.

The TV people were swimming behind their glass but he couldn't make out who they were. Or where this was exactly; it had the feeling of home but he couldn't really see that well, so it might be someplace else. He was used to being wrong in the head, but not wrong like this, where he was just wandering around in the dark. He moved closer to the TV and in its flickering light he saw scattered across the rug those long-ago posies, pink and red, with their grime-rimmed nails and their gaggous stub ends, as real and unreal as anything in a Halloween haunted house.

Suddenly, he remembered stepping on her hand as he strode from the room and how it moved under his boot like a snake.

When Joan was a little girl, her sister used to torment her by pretending to be dead, slumped in a corner of the living-room sofa, mouth slack, eyes fixed and staring, Wally Gator on TV, their mother banging around in the kitchen.

'I know you're not,' Joan would say at first, sitting down in an armchair with her snack; she'd watch television, peripherally keeping tabs on the eerily still body across the room, getting more and more certain that her sister was alive but at the same time more and more uncertain. 'I'm telling,' she would try.

Nothing but a clanging stillness from the corner of the couch until eventually Joan couldn't take it anymore, the utter lack of sister where there used to be a sister, panic rising like a tide, lifting her out of her chair, and floating her across the room, where her sister would inevitably frighten her so badly that a long piercing shriek would leap out of Joan, unfurling into the domestic air of the household.

'If I hear it again, I don't care who did what. You'll both get the yardstick,' her mother would say, standing in the doorway with a spatula in her hand. She liked a yardstick because it had an efficient and democratic feel to it – both offenders could be attended to with a single whistling swat. It didn't hurt, although Joan nevertheless became frantic and had to be chased down and dragged back, pleading for mercy like she was being taken to the gallows. Her sister would bend stoically over the sofa and just before the moment of impact move forward so that the yardstick hit the other person first. She told this tidbit to Joan when they were in their thirties.

Let the yardstick work for you.

She touched him again with the shovel. Nothing.

A credit card as a door key, a hollow pen as a tracheostomy tube, a self-locking trash tie as a handcuff. Or using an already employed tool in an off-label way – a fence post as a sundial, a flag as a weather vane, a drinking fountain as a urinal. Or even better, turning a regular tool into a meta-tool – a crowbar to kill a crow, for instance.

Oh! Oh! Oh!

He'd never hurried along a bird, but he could see how somebody might. His head felt different now, huge and hollow, like a fragile eggshell that all the yolk has been blown out of, forced through a tiny pinhole, turning his head into a big white dome with an echo. In school once a teacher had used a pencil to lift a human skull, inserting it into the eye socket and then turning it while pointing out its various features. The front, the side, the back, and all the while the skull nodding slightly, balanced on the pink-eraser end of a no. 2. He had felt an illicit jolt right at the moment the pencil disappeared into the eyehole; the deep, almost shuddering pleasure of it. *In Voluptate Mors.* Maybe three or four times it had happened over the years, his disreputable life appearing unexpectedly in the middle of his reputable one, like a harlot coming forward to slip her arm through the parson's.

He was wedged somewhere, one shoulder wrenched up under him, the big hollow dome of his head resting against something hard. Wherever this was, it felt like he was filling the space completely, as oversize and momentous as Paul Bunyan. All he needed was his ax.

Joan and her best friend, age fifteen, standing alongside a hot blacktop road in bikinis and sandals, hitchhiking home from Linden Lake; a GTO pulling over and picking them up, the two guys leaning forward obligingly to let them into the back seat.

Joan was shy, but her friend had folded her knees into the space between the bucket seats and thanked the driver and his friend. 'It was a heat wave out there,' her friend said fervently. She had large green eyes, expressive high-arched bony feet, and hair the color and texture of straw. The passenger-side guy was shirtless, his arm resting on the open window. Joan, directly behind him, was getting a faceful of BO. She gathered up her long tangled hair and pressed it against her nose.

They turned off the main highway and went down a labyrinth of country roads, winding slowly and talking between themselves as though the two girls weren't present.

'Should we rape them?'

'I don't know, what do you think?'

'It's up to you.'

'How about if I rape one and you can rape the other one.'

'Okay.'

'Which one do you want?'

'Both.'

'Me too.'

Even though Joan thought there was a good chance they were

kidding, she was overcome with regret, there in the back seat listening. At her own stupidity, at how she hadn't understood what not supposed to hitchhike meant but now understood it completely. Her mother in a blue pantsuit with a pocketbook hanging from her arm, saying, 'Boy, I better never hear of that.'

As her friend shrank backward, shy Joan moved forward, leaning between their seats and grinning.

'Let's get some beer,' she said.

They didn't even glance at her. The car slowed and turned onto a dirt lane that widened into a dirt road and then went over a stream.

'We need beer, you guys! Is there a place around here?'

Nothing. And then the driver glanced back at her. 'It'll be more fun,' she said, 'and we've got money.'

The other guy turned around in his seat and pointedly looked them up and down. They were wearing nothing but bikinis the size of eye patches and damp T-shirts.

He snorted.

Just at that moment, her friend braced herself and started kicking the driver in the head over and over, using her leather-soled sandals like paddles against his ears and the back of his skull. When he hollered and swerved, she began on the other guy, her legs churning between the seats, attacking his shoulders and head. He swung at her; she placed her feet against the back of the driver's seat and pushed with all her might, screaming and yanking at the guy's hair until he ran the car into the gravel and opened his door. He was pinned against the steering wheel, struggling, as Joan's friend clawed at his head.

'We were kidding,' the driver bawled. 'Kidding!'

The other guy stumbled onto the ground and let Joan out. The friend pushed her way past the driver, grabbing his ear and screaming, 'You fucker, I'll kill you!' as she clambered out.

They peeled away in a swirl of dirt, honking and extending

their middle fingers. Total country silence as the dust settled and the heat resumed. Joan and her friend realigned their eye patches, walked a mile or so back to the hard road, and, because there was nothing else to do, stuck their thumbs out.

The dogs could work in tandem when the situation called for it. From the flagstones, Pilgrim lifted his nose and sniffed Spock sniffing him. High in the oak tree the feral cat watched them. Tandem required teamwork and stealth, one of which Spock was good at and the other of which he was definitely not. He circled Pilgrim now, a white blob in the dusk, his stick dropped somewhere and forgotten.

He'd always thought about it later, what he wanted to tell Kyle that time everyone was talking about cars – that he himself liked Chamois as a girl's name.

The thing he never could get over was that Kyle ended up keeping cats. Two of them that he always made like he was torturing in his free time, Sinker and Pet Sematary, but they hadn't gotten the memo and continued to climb up onto his lap and onto the back of his chair, meow in his face for food, et cetera.

Cats can swim. They don't necessarily want to, but they can. Kyle could swim too, but when push came to shove, he didn't.

People will surprise you. Like this dead woman, who didn't seem all that dead in that she was poking him in the shoulder with something.

Joan knew for a fact that human beings were sturdier than they looked. She had watched her mother struggling, sinking and waxy, the aperture of her world growing smaller and smaller until she was staring at her family through a pinhole. Then the pinhole closed and there was nothing but the grip of her long graceful hands. Inhalations and exhalations, long sighing moans that seemed to be words, or parts of words.

This was back in the art-gallery days, and Roy's mother had been sick too, dying of cancer at the same time that Joan's mother was dying of cancer. Different kinds, different hospitals, and Roy and Joan sprawled morosely in their chairs at work all day, comparing notes. Sometimes they closed the gallery and went to the movies, where they would sit in the darkness and hold hands. One day Joan started crying and couldn't stop; another day it was Roy. Once, they blew everything off to go down the street and drink until they were beside themselves. They staggered to a local hotel and tried to get a room but were refused. Neither could figure out why – they shouted at the desk clerk, a young black woman who shook her head and walked away, then came around from behind the desk and escorted them by the elbows out the revolving door. They climbed into Joan's little car and drove up and down the empty pedestrian mall, honking and veering around the benches and stone planters. That's all that happened, though it became one of Joan's most vivid memories: the dark, beery neighborhood bar, the beautiful old restored hotel, the kindness of the desk clerk, the late-night interior of the Volkswagen. A few weeks later, Joan came home from the hospital after her mother's death, sat down on the sofa, and stared straight ahead for a long time, waiting for something.

Whatever she was waiting for never came, but Roy did. They sat in silence, eating the doughnuts Roy had brought with him and drinking the coffee that Joan made. At some point Roy said, 'I guess my mom won.'

The first time had been a game – Pilgrim digging at the base of the stump with Spock positioned behind him, jumping up and biting at the loose dirt as it was flung into the air. Suddenly, the dirt took shape and the shape was a mole and Spock caught it, and dropped it. A flat lozenge of fur with no face and little flesh paddles for feet. Pilgrim turned it over with his nose, stepped on it, and bit it.

Done.

His mother had been fed up with him before he was even born, according to the legend, pounding on her own stomach wherever he kicked, Whac-A-Mole-style. He remembered exactly nothing of her except a looming sense of dread and an expanse of cool gray. Apparently he crawled overtop of one of her magazines and tore the pages and she rolled it up and whipped him with it until he ended up living elsewhere.

I moved out when I was one, he used to tell people.

The cool gray was probably from when they took him up to her casket. Not because anyone gave a shit but because they wanted to see what he would do. Which was nothing, just like now. Do nothing while they're expecting it and soon enough they won't be expecting it.

Out at the edge of the pond, the heron was poised on one stick leg, neck extended and head tilted, as still as a lawn ornament. In the heron's mind, time didn't swirl or move; the past and the future were thoroughly blended into the present and the present was focused, like a gooseneck lamp, on the dappled bank. In the shallows were the flickerings of tiny fish, and right at the edge of the water a small delectable frog sat motionless, indistinguishable from the mud and grass as long as he didn't blink.

The bird's success was based on movement so slow as to be indiscernible. The frog's was based on blending and powerful back legs that could propel him with a plop two feet out into the pond. Should the need arise.

The second time they worked in tandem had been a squirrel. Spock didn't want to let go when Pilgrim grabbed it too, and for a moment it became a tug toy, but then it made a sound like a kitten and Spock did let go.

The third time they worked in tandem, the groundhog had been coming perilously close to the invisible fence. Pilgrim and Spock were at their stations, waiting, as he dragged his blubber back and forth between one mound of dirt and a neighboring mound of dirt.

When the groundhog finally made his mistake, they were on him, and just for an instant, before they dragged him in, the fence got involved too, vibrating through their collars in its own excitement.

The heron slept in an enormous laundry basket at the top of a tall tree. There was a certain point when it would be summoned up there by an invisible force that was both external and internal. The force was exerted at a specific moment, right before darkness settled its skirts over the pond.

He no longer looked like a sandbag. He was flat and still, but the air around him seemed animated. Joan stepped back, reached out, put the blade of the shovel on his shoulder, and pushed. Nothing, but it felt different somehow.

Light was penetrating his dark living room; it was grainy and swirling, amniotic. He felt rinsed clean and pure, like the baby with its head full of rainwater getting ready to be born.

He moved his finger and it moved.

Joan felt it more than saw it. Some subtle movement. The hand under the edge of the wineglass cupboard was awake.

The frog blinked an instant before the invisible force caused the heron to open its wings and lift off. The frog was either in the pond or in the heron as it flew slowly past the kitchen window, long legs dangling, and Joan felt the gray shadow just as the dogs arrived at the kitchen door and threw themselves at the screen.

Somehow, lightning fast, the stranger had her by the ankle. Joan lifted the shovel like a sword as the dogs bayed at the screen.

Back when the mighty turtle grabbed the shovel, Joan had had to drag him across the grass for a few feet before he let go, and that's what she did now, tugging her foot until the stranger's arm was fully outstretched, his head lolled back, the hand like a constrictor around her ankle.

Turtles are not amphibians, as Joan always forgot. They are reptiles.

She leaned back as far as she could until she could just reach the screen door with the shovel.

Let the dogs work for you.

His grandmother had come out in the yard, picked up those long-ago posies from the ground, dropped them in a coffee can, and carried it back inside. He heard himself grunting now the way she had when she bent over, and he was being hurried along, tugged back and forth as the dogs worked in tandem until he heard himself making a sound like a kitten. When the delicate blue stem of his windpipe was finally unwrapped, the stranger felt a great happiness overtake him. *In morte voluptas.* Through death into pleasure.

Chances were he'd end up where Kyle had ended up, and nobody didn't have fun when they were with Kyle.

Close

I HAVE TO PREFACE THIS by saying that I spent my winter break trying to finish writing a book that I've been working on forever. By *forever* I mean two years past its deadline and at least one year past the point when I realized I had done thousands of hours' worth of mind-breaking labor on something probably only my sister and a couple of other people would ever read. Of course, writing for my sister – actually writing my sister, because she's in the book – seems to me like a worthwhile enough endeavor, since I have no choice. Once I start something, I always finish, for better or worse, because it's my personality. And once you begin an essay or a story or even a lecture, as many know, it takes on a life of its own. It's like getting on a sled at the top of a hill; you're steering – perhaps – but you're mostly a passenger. Writing a book, as it turns out, is the same, only very, very different – in my case, at least – because over the course of five years 'or so,' the snow has melted and there's just grass and gravel. It takes a lot to get the sled moving, and then it goes only a few inches.

So that was my winter break: sitting on my sled every morning for hours and then trying to capture my ducks in the afternoon.

I have eight ducks.

These are technically domesticated ducks, but *domesticated* doesn't mean they like you – in fact, just the opposite. They are called domestic ducks because people eat them, and they know it. All summer they were their own ducks, swimming on the pond and eating grubs from the bank. They can't fly, having been engineered as meat factories, so when winter comes, they need to be moved to a safe enclosure. But I couldn't catch them, even after the pond began to freeze, getting smaller and smaller until all that remained was a bathtub-size hole we were keeping open with a heavy pipe and our own arms. The predators began to arrive like suitors. Every night – coyotes, bobcats, foxes, raccoons. Tracks circling the pond, getting closer and closer, until one afternoon, as I stood there, a weasel came running across the ice and attacked them right in their bathtub.

The interesting thing is that to a duck, the human with the garden rake fighting the weasel is scarier than the weasel itself – this is the shame of meat-eating, that these amazing creatures with shimmering heads and bodies that look like stained glass are most afraid of the predator fighting off the predator. We did all survive – weasel, woman, flock – though I had to sit outside with a rake on my lap that night. I felt rightly responsible for the ducks after all the wrongs that have been done to them, from their obscenely heavy breasts to the little wooden boxes they get stuffed into at the farm auction. The boxes are duck-size – as in, exactly the size of the duck. All we could see were their terrified trapped faces, and getting them out was like pulling something through a knothole. Their poor wings.

I should say, I didn't even mind sitting next to the pond most of the night, possibly being crept up on by a bobcat, because it was new to me, and so much of what I do isn't. It felt like material for an essay: sitting on a log with a rake across my lap in the black country night, surrounded by snow and stars, wearing an old floor-to-ceiling down coat I bought in Ann Arbor in 1992 when I was having a midwestern-style nervous breakdown.

Actually it wasn't a breakdown, it was a breakup, but that's another story.

So I spent my winter vacation sitting on the writing sled in the mornings and trying to capture the ducks (for their own safety) in the afternoons, and at some point I got a call from Vijay asking me to give a craft talk in our school's writing lounge, which we for some reason call the Pillow Room, right after the new semester started.

I had two thoughts right away. First, I know more about art than craft, and second, what if the Pillow Room truly were a pillow room? All one giant pillow, where you had to wallow instead of sit in straight chairs and where all the walls were padded and lava lights were on low coffee tables. I had these thoughts on my sled, by the way. If I could give a craft talk in a true pillow room, I might have a better chance of making sense, simply because half the people in the room would either be high or feel high.

But to go back to the idea of art over craft – what I really mean to say is that the art comes from the craft. The first thing I tell students, and tell myself, is that there's nothing new under the sun (second thing is not to use clichés). We as a culture become jaded and bored by nearly everything we see; spend an evening in thrall to your devices, and you'll witness the gamut of human experiences and emotions. So in order to make art (literature) out of just that – human experiences and emotions – we have to find new and surprising ways to convey our insights. That means we have to have insights, which means we have to think, and that means we have to work to create art out of life, to bring something new to each sentence, a surprise for the reader. Not in a pyrotechnic way, but through intelligence, through our powers of imagination, and through the rigorous refusal to waste a reader's time.

But that said, an interesting thing happened when Vijay called me on break and asked me to please write a craft talk. With a real job to do, I suddenly became newly absorbed in my book.

In 1973, when I graduated from high school, I could type 112 words a minute – yes, with a lot of errors, but it got me a job at the local army installation, where errors didn't matter. That job was hard and boring, like sitting on the writing sled with seven men who wanted me to make their coffee. Which I did. And I didn't even drink coffee back then – in 1973, I was an eighteen-year-old bowling-alley girl who drank Pepsi at eight a.m. and smoked Winston Longs in the office. In my top desk drawer at that army installation, I always had a book open. Anything from *The Love Machine* to *Ulysses*; it didn't matter to me. It only had to have words.

I didn't know from writing, as they say, but I knew from reading. And in the end – if we're talking here about teaching the craft of nonfiction – then I will confess that I don't believe writers learn a great deal from having their work critiqued by an editor or a teacher or colleagues. Learning to write comes from reading, both the work of published writers and of our peers, and from using one's powers of insight and creativity to analyze what one reads and figure out why it works when it does and what is missing when it doesn't. This is where knowledge is gained, and it's slow and frustrating, nebulous, diffuse, much less direct and directed than having someone write *Great!* in the margins of a story or – in the case of many personal-essay workshops – *I need to know more about your mother. Why did she hit you so hard?*

Nebulous, diffuse. Lodged in that last sentence, a tiny hanging footbridge back to what I was telling you before. The definition of *nebula*: 'any diffuse mass of interstellar dust, gas, visible as luminous patches or areas of darkness.' Remember me sitting under the starry sky in the country blackness, waiting and listening for predators, feet frozen?

Every essay, every academic talk, every writing effort can be deepened through observation and detail, can be made evocative, can contain interstellar dust, luminous patches, and areas of darkness. There's transcendence to be found in these connections – in the nebulous and nebulae, ducks and darkness – if we have the patience to wait for them.

So, now: the part of the talk that is about the ducks and Dennis Nurkse. I had dinner in December with Dennis – ducks, dinner, December, Dennis – and told him about my dilemma: that Annie Dillard's weasel was going to kill my ducks because the ducks wouldn't let me catch them and put them in the duck house.

'I could catch ducks,' he said.

I explained to him that no, they couldn't be caught. The meat, the breasts, the fear of everything, the way they could scatter and run. Being Dennis, he listened thoughtfully, considering all the angles.

'Yeah, I could catch them,' he said.

If a poet could catch them, I said to myself, why can't a prose writer? I may not do it as succinctly, but I don't need to. I have all of break, the part, anyway, in which I wasn't sitting on the sled.

So I did what a writer does – I imagined my way into the mind of a sitting duck. Because misery so often comes down on them from above, ducks are sensitive to looming shadows, the falling ax, the diving hawk, and though these ducks can't fly away from ground predators, they know to flap their big wings as they run, removing much of what there is to grab and flustering me in the confusion. I had to become invisible to them in order to get close enough to the duck-house door to jump up and slam it when one of them slowly and warily picked its way inside to the bowl of cracked corn. It took a whole day of sitting motionless in a lawn chair in the snow and the big down coat to trap seven of them and push them through the tiny back door into an enclosure. The last one – a small female with a green-black body and a delicate, dotted-Swiss head – simply wouldn't be tricked. She was bonded to the first one caught and instead of venturing in and out of the duck house had spent the day standing or lying on the grass next to the enclosure as close to her friend as possible. All that separated them was the wire and the fact that one would eat and the other would be eaten.

Night was coming, and so were the coyotes. I knew that Dennis would have been able to catch that duck. He had written in a poem in the very *New Yorker* that I was reading on my lawn chair: 'The light under the poplar was mottled / but the shade of the pines was feathered.'

I disrupted the duck; she flapped away, realized she was hungry, moved toward the duck house, but was too wary of me to go in. So I went into my own house to watch out the window. Across the pond, unbelievably – but this is nonfiction, right? – the weasel appeared, scrounging around in the snow-covered weeds, making work for itself as the afternoon darkened.

I let myself out silently and stalked her, inch by patient, motionless, un-breathing inch, as she made her way over the course of two hours to the door of the house. More of Dennis's poem: 'We were bundles of self-canceling voices – / flight and response, punishment and reward, / hostile adoration, panic and certainty.'

At some point she stopped seeing me. I stood exactly behind her as she made her wavering way down the path to the dark doorway. When she moved, I moved. When she stopped, I stopped. It was like a cartoon. She never turned around, just cocked her head to the side – a duck's eyes are on the sides, like a horse's. The other ducks, funnily enough, were standing inside the wire watching. As she moved and I moved – a giant, silent step or two – they would go wild, flapping and quacking.

Look behind you! There she comes! That's not what you think it is – a lump of dirty snow – it's the Ann Arbor coat that reminds her of her nervous breakup!

But the duck would cock her head a split second after the lump of dirty snow stopped moving. The duck dallied, the weasel worked . . . and Dennis's words again: 'But still it was not evening, / still the world was ending, / always we resented the breeze / for choosing and marking us, / still a song too short to sing' . . . and then . . . 'moved two famished sparrows / like pawns from branch to branch' . . . she crossed the threshold and I rushed forward, closed the door.

I have eight ducks.

It's a lofty goal, to imagine translating one's own personal experiences in a way that instructs and illuminates, moves and inspires, another human being. Even attempting to do such a thing is heroic; that's why I think workshops ought to begin with praise – for what the author has attempted to do, if not succeeded in doing – and then, since good writing is about thinking, a segue into an exchange of ideas inspired by the essay at hand. The most important question to be asked is 'What is this piece about below the surface?' The writer doesn't necessarily need to have an answer to that question – the route to creating art is meandering and brambly, and most artists can't tell you exactly how it's done – but in any case, the reader has to be able to answer the question.

Because a good essay – for that matter, a good short story, memoir, novel – is about ideas, that's how it elevates itself beyond and above its nominal subject to illuminate something universal. Literature instructs, which means the writer has to be wiser and more knowledgeable than the reader. So half of my teaching efforts are spent teasing forth these ideas and issues embedded in the work I see in nonfiction workshops. The other half of my efforts are spent trying to convince students that making art is in fact difficult, is supposed to be difficult. Writing school isn't any easier than med school; it's just shorter.

There's a great essay by Annie Dillard called 'The Death of a Moth' that I return to again and again, both as teacher and as writer.

It is, on the surface, the story of a lonely woman who lives with her cats and goes to the woods to read about Rimbaud in the light of a campfire. Under the surface, that important deeper layer, it is about what it is to be an artist, to burn yourself up so completely in service to your work that you are transfigured, like the moth in the candle flame, or sacrificed on its altar, like Virginia Woolf. It's almost embarrassing, as much of Dillard's work can be, in its egotism and nakedness. It's a shocking essay for a lot of reasons, not the least of which is its unerring description of the natural world. Her images are neon – a flare of light that illuminates a blue sweater sleeve, a sudden flash of jewelweed, a burning moth cloaked to the candle like a monk in saffron robes.

E. B. White in 'The Ring of Time' says, 'Under the bright lights of the finished show, a performer need only reflect the electric candle power that is directed upon him; but in the dark and dirty old training rings and in the makeshift cages, whatever light is generated, whatever excitement, whatever beauty, must come from original sources – from internal fires of professional hunger and delight, from the exuberance and gravity of youth. It is the difference between planetary light and the combustion of stars.'

All we can hope to teach, I think, is what to aspire to and, perhaps, what standard to hold ourselves to. E. B. White taking on a task that he acknowledges will be too great for him, the poet who believes he can capture a frightened bird because he will accept no less of himself, the writer sitting patiently on her sled waiting for snow, Annie Dillard staring through her papered-over windows into the forest of imagination, Virginia Woolf in her sodden wool coat with its roomy pockets.

But for now, the ducks are tucked close in their shed, with its mounds of clean scattered straw and its red bulb sending out a beacon of warmth to the weasel, who believes as strongly as a poet.

What You Seek Is Seeking You

YOU GOTTA TAKE THE DOG,' Nathan insisted over the phone. 'Don't you remember how much you love the dog?'

'I admired the dog,' Stephen said. 'Totally different thing.'

Aiko had once caught a squirrel and then let it go in a mind-blowing act of canine chivalry. Stephen, visiting, had seen the whole thing from his brother's deck: The Lab ambling through the garden, her stomach swinging from side to side, sniffing thoughtfully at clumps of flowers and freshening up her scent trail. Across the yard a squirrel paused upside down at the base of a tree, its tail pulsing. Suddenly, the dog made her move; the squirrel twisted feverishly back and forth and then gave up, hanging limply from Aiko's mouth, eyes bright, waiting for what would come next.

'I never told you this before,' Stephen said, 'but Melissa told her to kill it. She throws open the bedroom window and goes, *Fucking kill it, you mutt.*' Melissa was Nathan's wife, tall and erratic, an elementary-school teacher who was constantly saying and doing things you didn't want associated with children.

'Oh my God!' Nathan murmured, appalled. 'Isn't that exactly what I've been saying?'

Stephen knew where this was heading. If he didn't agree to take their dog, he was going to have to listen once again to Nathan's circuitous explanation of why he had been having sex with the woman who did their taxes.

'See, Melissa could even make a dog go against its own nature! I'm telling you, there's something about her that makes you just want to do the opposite of what she tells you.' Nathan listened for a moment to the noncommittal sound of his brother paying no attention, the intermittent crumple of a newspaper. 'You just have to disagree with somebody like that, right? Don't you?' Nothing. '"Fucking kill it, you mutt," and the dog drops the squirrel. I mean, you basically have to drop the squirrel; it's the only reasonable response. Let me ask you,' he said as though what he was about to say was a new thought, one that had just come to him, 'can you believe I stayed married to her for almost four years?'

'Who, the dog?'

'What?'

'You were talking about the dog, and then you said, "Can you believe I stayed married to her for almost four years?"'

'What the fuck are you talking about?' Nathan said, peering into the fridge. He was going to make himself some eggs. Fuck the way he'd been living, Pop-Tarts thirty times a day. Fuck Melissa and fuck Renée too, for that matter, signing up for an online dating service, him having to run across her self-satisfied face on his computer screen at three o'clock in the morning.

'You were talking about the dog, and then you said, "Can you believe"—'

'Could you shut up? You got any awareness of how backward you are? I mean, you're my brother, but you can't even follow a simple conversation.' The last egg in the carton had something dark green smeared across the shell. 'This is just great,' Nathan cried. The pan clattered in Stephen's ear. Stephen turned the page of his newspaper. War, war, and more war. He heard the sound of Pop-Tarts being fed into the toaster.

'How many of those do you eat a day?' he asked.

'Why don't you come out here and cook for me, you ignorant fucking nerd?' Nathan shouted into the phone, so loudly that Stephen shrieked in response. It felt like someone had stuck a tuning fork directly into his ear canal.

'Nice high-pitched scream,' Nathan said, laughing meanly.

When the dog had set the squirrel down on the grass, the squirrel flipped over and then vanished; a microsecond later it stared down, panting, from a high branch. It would be temporary, a few months, until they were sorted out.

'All right,' Stephen said. 'Send her.'

So Nathan put Aiko on a plane in San Francisco, and she arrived in Ithaca eight hours later (six hours after the tranquilizer wore off), foam-flecked and trembling. Stephen, who was running about a half an hour late, found her in the baggage-claim area, the crate haphazardly dumped into a corner so that in the echoing swirl of airport bustle, she could see only a scuffed wall. He turned the crate around with his foot and bent down to take a look. There was a heavyset yellow dog peering out with a look of desperate, studied blankness on her broad face.

She spent her days in Stephen's backyard standing on top of the picnic table barking ceaselessly at the gray Ithaca sky or doing demolition work on his lawn, digging not holes but salad-bowl-size depressions every few feet and pulling down the trumpet vines that clung to the tall wooden fence. She would tug on them until they were stretched across the grass in long strands, their narrow purple flowers collapsing like wet crepe paper. Sometimes she napped in the poppy bed for an hour or so, sprawled on her back with her pale belly exposed, large dirty paws retracted against her chest, stout body framed by the delicate fronds smashed flat beneath her.

'We do *not* do that,' Stephen would tell her firmly, pointing to the ankle-turning holes, the trampled flower beds, the quarter-inch-deep toenail grooves in his back door. '*Ever.* Not.'

She whimpered in agreement and bolted in a fevered, dirt-churning circle, barking hoarsely into the evening air. As Stephen crouched to pet her, she raked her front paw across his face.

Since Nathan had stopped taking his calls, he complained instead to his mother. 'My yard is now toast,' he said into her answering machine.

She picked up while he was still speaking.

'So what? You're helping someone out for once,' she replied briskly. 'What's a yard? Is there anything more meaningless?'

This to her plant-biologist son, the one who worshipped moss. Next to his bed, right now, was a catalog listing nothing but varieties of fern. Every luminous green imaginable, every kind of intricate fringe.

'Thanks for understanding,' he said.

'Thank *you*, Stephen, for assisting your brother,' she replied pleasantly. 'If Nathan can mend his situation, then he must do so; if not, he'll move ahead.' She paused, pointedly, then went on. 'Perhaps you'll learn something by being involved with this about how to conduct a successful relationship.'

'Say *what*?' Stephen asked.

'You heard me,' she said. 'And we're not going to belabor it.'

His mother, Eleanor Klein, was an elderly and formidable pediatrician who still saw patients three days a week. She also managed Stephen's father, an Alzheimer'd scientist who spent those same three days in his office at UC Berkeley, worrying the pens in his penholder and asking the secretaries staticky questions over speakerphone.

On these days, Eleanor packed him a lunch, spoke forthrightly to one of his colleagues about accompanying him to the washroom – if he went by himself, he tended to get stuck inside the repeating pattern of identical stalls – then drove to the clinic, where for seven or so hours mothers (and sometimes fathers) would place their babies on the examining table and tell her stories of their infants' charm and precociousness.

'Yes, well,' she would reply. 'We expect that at this age.'

The information Stephen's father requested of the secretaries was highly specific but nonsensical, like the quasi-scientific talk in science fiction movies. His voice toggled in and out as he fiddled with the phone, making him seem more and more like an astronaut lost forever in outer space.

'I'm not sure, Morrie, but shall I check for you?' one of the secretaries would call out from her side of the transmission.

'Yes, please do, and bring me the answer, don't page me,' he would order her.

'And where will you be?' Said a little meanly, perhaps, because although he'd had Alzheimer's for the past three years, he'd been demanding for at least thirty.

He would look around, swiveling in his chair. Wall, window, picture, papers.

'I don't know,' he would say.

The Kleins had always been high achievers. The parents had both studied to become doctors and both were subjected to the quota system, allowed to succeed only if others of their brethren didn't. In Morris's case, it was an accepted practice – in Canada, Jews had to get better scores than everyone else in order to qualify for higher education, so Morris shrugged and did what they asked, ranking just above his peers, WASPs and Jews and whatever else they threw at him. He went on to college and then on again to become a doctor of science, a botanist who made a name for himself in the delicate, knife-petaled world of lilies.

Eleanor, educated in the States, was subjected to equal and

alternating doses of contempt and admiration. She ignored both, for years methodically chiseling her way through the granite ceiling until she found herself in the bracing, ammonia-scented air of pediatric medicine. She did a rotation in Africa, and met her husband, Morris, there, he of the pith helmet and wild eyebrows. It was like a waking dream – the blue cinder-block clinic, her fingers pressing a silver disk against narrow brown backs, the glaring sunlight, the feverish, ecstatic nights.

When Stephen was a child, the family moved from Canada to the United States so that Morris could take a job as a professor and researcher at the University of Illinois at Urbana-Champaign. In every direction, deserted roads and long green corridors of corn. Riding in the back seat in the summertime, dazed by hot wind, Stephen and Nathan would stare out their respective windows, taking in dizzying insubstantial glimpses down each row until they were carsick.

Stephen was the smartest kid in his class, always, and the strangest. He was a nerd with a high nasal voice, and fine black hair floating above his scalp, long gibbon-y arms that were always in the air, the left one resting on its elbow, propping up the right one, during the lengthy period that the teacher stared around at the other students, waiting.

'I don't want another answer from Stephen,' she would say to them ten times a day, and he'd reluctantly put the arm down. After another ten times, though, she'd have to give up, because even with the bar lowered, her students would stare at her, waiting for her to call on the Jew and get it over with.

In a precise and scathing voice she'd address Stephen without looking at him. 'I guess you're going to have to help us out.'

With that, he'd deliver the answer in an offhand staccato style.

Walking home at the end of the day, he was routinely attacked and pummeled by all manner of schoolchildren. His own class-mates, weighty midwestern kids, thuggy older boys, giant girls with red fists. He had two semi-friends, wispy kids nobody else liked, who would whale on him as well, just for the sake of it, twisting his arms, kicking him in the shinbones, pulling on his thin foamy hair until he was flailing and grunting. But even as this was occurring – as they stormed him, as he helplessly tried to push and pinch his way out of it – the real Stephen was curled like a fetus inside the sheath of his body, waiting to be delivered.

'I don't know how to help you,' his mother responded. 'I suspect there's nothing to be done.'

'But your own kid is being attacked!'

'You're better than they are, Stephen,' she said firmly. 'And that should be of some comfort to you.'

'How would you like somebody making fun of something about you?' he said under his breath.

'What do they make fun of?' she asked.

He remained silent for a moment, then spilled it. 'My proboscis,' he said. She tilted her head back and looked at him steadily, the way she stared down at the toddlers while palpating their abdomens.

'Ignore them,' she said finally.

They had a Dutch au pair when they first moved to Champaign, an unhappy ruddy-cheeked dental student who once fell down the stairs with the vacuum cleaner, arriving at the bottom with the wind knocked completely out of her. Stephen saw it all, the struggle to get the heavy machine down the stairs, the uncooperative hose smacking her in the face as she lugged the canister along, the simultaneous tangling of the cord and barking of the ankle, the missed tread, the cartwheeling of girl and machine, the two distinct thuds – her and then the vacuum on top of her.

For a long, imprinting moment, she stared at Stephen from the gleaming mahogany floor, crimson-faced except for the white rage spot forming under each eye, mouth opening and closing in the lull before her lungs filled with air. Years later, when he saw depictions in the movies of women in labor bearing down for the final push, he would flash back to the sprawled Dutch girl regaining her breath and then bellowing at him in pain and frustration, yanking her hair and pounding her heels against the carpeted steps.

Since this ended up being his most vivid memory from childhood, it probably paved the way for his later entanglements with a series of short-fused foreign women. All doctoral students, all specializing in some sort of criticism, mostly of him. By the time he got to the last one, he had more or less worked through his fear of being yelled at in an accent. That one, Mette, didn't even come close to breaking his heart; in fact, he was glad to be rid of her, a sharp-featured Norwegian beauty with food issues and a predilection for bickering, even about things he agreed with her on.

She was hollow-boned and elegant, very blond (everywhere), with a delicate, feline face. She dressed carelessly in clothing meant to be slid into and out of like a pair of clogs – soft shirts that gaped open alarmingly, revealing the bas-relief of her clavicle, knee-length skirts that swirled when she moved, and, sometimes, a pair of sagging argyle socks. For a while he couldn't stop looking at her while she slept, read, rode in his truck, or reached behind her head and flipped her hair around in practiced moves that produced either two milkmaid-style braids or a smooth chignon. She cooked gourmet meals, swishing around his kitchen in her thick socks and thin skirt, the profile of one small red-tipped breast winking into view each time she moved.

'You are much less intelligent than most people believe,' she would say, crushing walnut meats with the side of her knife and tossing them into a skillet.

She threw up dinner with a businesslike flexing of the chin and a few short ratchety coughs. Out it would come in a long efficient strand, like a cat dislodging a hairball. She had no shame over it either, but that didn't mean anything; she had once sat down to defecate while he was standing at the bathroom sink shaving.

After a decent interval, he broke up with her. She raised her eyes from the magazine she was reading and stared at him.

'You are breaking with me?' she asked. It was rhetorical; he knew better than to answer. 'But Stephen. You are such a stinking piece of shit.' She lifted her long arms over her head and gently twisted to the right, a yoga stretch, and then to the left. 'A useless turd, and it's certain you will die alone, awake, and filthy in circumstances.'

He still saw her at the co-op from time to time, carrying a thin bunch of organic carrots to the checkout or trailing a pale hand along the granola bins. Once as he moved past her she whispered something so obscene and ungrammatical it stayed in his head for days.

It was right around then that he ended up with Aiko, who for all her difficulties had thrown up in front of him just one time, the front third of a bucktoothed underground creature that wasn't part of the catch-and-release program. And not that it was anyone's business, but he and the dog slept together easily, on their backs, with a foot of gritty sheet between them.

In the early evening Stephen would trade one lab for another; leaving his experiments percolating, he would race home to get Aiko out of the yard and then drive back up the hill, where they took long contemplative walks alongside the creeks and through the gorges of the Cornell campus. Following her on the leash was no more possible than holding on to the bumper of a departing car; he went from that to a sixteen-foot rope wrapped around his right hand and pulled taut as a guy wire. With Nathan's one-word texted blessing (*Whatever*), he decided to let her run free.

That first time, they sat in the cab of his truck for three minutes, Stephen laying down the law while Aiko stared straight ahead through the windshield. 'And I mean it, you *come* when you're called, Aiko. Aiko, *come*,' he practiced. She refused to look in his direction even when he tugged her head around to face him.

He opened the driver's door and she was overtop of him and gone before he could do anything but clutch his gonads. While he sat in the truck trying to think what to do, she came barreling back into view, stopped short, ears lifted up off her head, and crouched with her rump in the air. When he got out, she tore off again, returning as he rounded the first bend.

He liked to walk along, those evenings, thinking idly about science or sex, the joy of the bounding dog infecting his own life. It all seemed good, the experiments sputtering and dying in the petri dishes, the other experiments that yielded results his graduate students would carefully pen into notebooks, the muted pint-size grandeur of the Ithaca landscape with its plummeting overlooks, hanging bridges, and moody, hopeless skies.

It was a long way from California, the place he considered home, where they had moved him in the summer between fifth and sixth grade and where he was miraculously reborn as just another kid with a banana-seat bike. He went to a big California high school where everyone had a gimmick; his was that he was exceptionally smart. People called him Steve, without italics.

During college he discovered the Grateful Dead and that horizontal gene transfer occurred in plant cells from mitochondria to chloroplasts. One led to dope-driven guitar lessons and the other to much, much acclaim in the field of plant genetics. Eventually, he was able to combine the two and wore tie-dye in his own lab.

Toward the end of their walk, while he was musing along, Aiko would occasionally bolt right up the wall of the gorge, leaping from nothing to nothing like a mountain goat until she disappeared into the brush at the top. A moment later he'd see her dime-size yellow face staring down at him before she took off for Frat Row, where groups of Greeks held barbecues on the lawns. She would trot into their midst and steal bratwursts off the fire or out of their hands, gulping them as she ran.

Stephen would have to drive from mansion to mansion on his way home, peering into the throngs of backward-capped boys and lean-hipped girls, all of them holding plastic cups of beer. If Aiko hung around and Stephen didn't show up, they would take out their phones and call him.

'Dude, your dog,' they would say.

When Stephen was home from college one summer, eating breakfast in his parents' kitchen, there was a knock on the door. His father got up, went down the hall, and opened it. Without a word, he closed the door, walked back to the table, sat down, and picked up his newspaper. There was a pause, and then another knock. Eleanor got up and went down the hall. She returned with a guy who looked exactly like Stephen's dad.

This was Morris's son from his first marriage, abandoned with the wife at the three-year mark, named Stephen. Eleanor was calm and relatively unsurprised; she'd been writing support checks on this young man's behalf for more than twenty years. She sat him down with a stack of pancakes.

'Your name is Stephen Klein?' Stephen Klein asked him, appalled. This was the first he was hearing of it, and the guy had bristling eyebrows and exactly, exactly the same face as his dad.

'It is,' the other Stephen said quietly. He looked at Eleanor with a kind of reverence, picked up his fork, and began eating.

'Stephen C.?' Stephen's middle name was Charles.

'M.' The first Stephen's middle name was Morris. Morris, by this point, was gone, out of the room, out of the house, somewhere else. Stephen C. couldn't remember. What he did remember was that he spent the day with the older brother, getting high and showing him San Diego, and then at the end the brother went home on a bus, back to some little town in Ottawa, and nobody ever mentioned him again.

Over the course of the summer, Stephen gave up on a lawn, and by fall on the concept of grass in general. By early winter, the backyard was frozen into stark midwestern-looking furrows. Aiko enjoyed the cold as much as Stephen and rode with him to the hockey rink every morning at five thirty. Once there, she fell back asleep across the seat while he tried to cover the net for an hour or so – the joyous wintertime sounds of ice being carved by skates, the scrape of the sticks, the muffled shouts. Afterward, the intramural handshakes, the steamed windows of the truck cab and the yellow dog's greeting, his goalie gear dumped in the mudroom, where it would gently exhale its stench all day.

It never stopped snowing, stinging evaporating needles of lake effect, and the white sky seemed to begin right above the roofline, creating the coldly claustrophobic pre-suicide atmosphere that Ithaca was known for. By mid-November, the campus gorges were iced over like luge runs and the parks opened to the hunters – the paramilitary-crossbow season was followed by the more standard Jack-in-the-thermos shotgun season, which was followed by the season of starved and staggering deer.

Once when he and Aiko were taking a turn around a pond in early winter, she skidded out onto the ice and broke through, yelping and drowning. Heart thudding against his breastbone, Stephen had to stretch out like a starfish on the groaning surface and heave her up onto the ice. She rolled over, hauled herself to her feet, then took off running, tail tucked. Hours after nightfall he was still searching, driving around with his frozen head out the window, shouting. Finally he saw her, curled up on a sprung

WHAT YOU SEEK IS SEEKING YOU

sofa on the veranda of a frat house. She listened while he called her quite a few times, slapping the side of the truck for emphasis, before she stood up slowly, stretched fore and aft, and ambled out to see what he wanted.

The next day Nathan called. He was ready for his dog back.

He missed her semi-desperately once she was gone, but the worst of it passed in a few days. It was like having a girlfriend leave, the agony of the clanging silence juxtaposed with the ecstasy of eating takeout burritos over the sink. With Aiko gone, weekends were the hardest, staying in bed too long, staring through the sky-light at the milky clouds.

On Saturdays he always showered with his orchids, stand-ing carefully amid the clay pots, steaming himself awake, and then rode his bicycle up the steep icy hill to campus. At the lab, thankfully, weekends were the same as weekdays – lank people in unfashionable clothes hunched over the bench, the morning smell of burned coffee gradually segueing into the afternoon smell of microwave popcorn. They all had interior lives, he could tell by the things they taped to their office doors, but it hardly ever leaked out in their dealings with him.

For a while he would just wander around, looking over their shoulders, asking questions, making his own set of notes. Then, when they were totally freaked out and nervous – he didn't mean for them to be, of course – he settled himself on a high stool to begin staring into a microscope, dividing cells with a delicate, threadlike tool. This was precision work that not many people knew how to do. He'd been trained by a French researcher, Yvonne, in a dark Paris laboratory. He had lived there for a year on a Guggenheim, rollerblading across town to the wrought-iron gates of the Institut de Biologie Physico-Chimique, the elderly Yvonne waiting for him in her sensible shoes and low-cut smock.

He placed one slide after another in the frame of the scope and created a series of strands on each.

By the time he looked up, the place would be empty, the equipment robed, the fluorescents buzzing. His was always the only bike on the snowy hill, a long rocketing plummet in the dark. Once home, he got stoned and fooled around the house, stirring up the compost worms, tinkering with the downstairs toilet, hanging idly from the chin-up bar. After the second weekend by himself, he decided to invite people over. There were two graduate students who could carry on conversations that weren't based on Star Wars, and there was also Thor, his best friend from hockey; Thor's girlfriend, Chris, a lesbian-seeming redhead; Deirdre, a technical writer who lived down the street and watered his plants when he traveled; and the tuneless hummer, an Israeli visitor who was collaborating with him on a paper. He would try to keep it from being one of his famous desultory dinner parties, forced marches through vegetarian terrain with concert tapes of the Dead playing in the background. He would correct the most obvious errors from last time – he'd turn the heat up and put the worms in the basement. He'd get ketchup.

No one minded that he was preparing a seitan dish; the clouds had been hanging so low over Ithaca for so long that people were willing to entertain any notion. Everyone said yes, and Deirdre wanted to bring a friend, which caused him a little twinge of regret, since he had considered going out with her if things didn't pick up. It seemed possible she thought he was gay because of the orchids, and he had imagined revealing otherwise, scattering a little surprise across her smooth white face. Although it was true she had seen him with Mette and, now that he thought about it, maybe with Sigrid too. Sigrid had been hard to miss, a keyed-up flame-haired girl who wore an eye patch for a while due to a racquetball injury. So actually he could probably scratch the idea that people thought he was gay.

Anyway, Deirdre left a message saying she would bring a friend unless he called and told her not to, and Thor left a message saying he wanted to bring a different date, not Chris, but that Chris wanted to come too; they had stayed friends, et cetera. All this voice-mail enthusiasm made Stephen feel as though he had already entertained, causing him to forget about the party completely until the very last minute – past the last minute, in fact.

He tried to do too many things in one day was the problem, and none of them pertained to a dinner party. So he didn't make it to the co-op before it closed; he didn't refrigerate the cheesecake for the suggested six hours; and he didn't allot any time for showering. In the final moments before his guests' arrival, the slab of seitan was thawing on a radiator, the dishwasher had chugged to a stop, and decorator cheeses were settling into a warm slump on a brightly colored Portuguese plate. There was a spectral dusting of flour in his hair and on his shirt, but a successful batch of homemade noodles hung everywhere in the kitchen, like soft damp worms.

Oops. He grabbed the compost box and ran it to the basement, and while he was down there the front door banged open and what sounded like the entire party pushed their way into his foyer like a herd of steers, milling around and stamping the snow off their feet. He crept up the basement stairs, listening to his guests greet one another, then tiptoed back down again, peeling off his dirty shirt. He sorted quickly through the hockey-tainted pile of clothes at the mouth of the laundry chute – this morning's jersey had opened like a rank parachute over the entire stack – then hurriedly put the original shirt back on. At the top of the stairs he realized it was on backward, Bob Marley's face between his shoulder blades. As he pulled his arms out of the sleeves and shrugged it around, the basement door opened.

*

She had moved to Ithaca from Iowa City with her dog. They lived picturesquely at the edge of a wood in a shingled cottage surrounded by pine trees and deer paths. It was like living in a snow globe, a silent scene that you shake up only to watch the snow swirl and settle again on the trees, the roof, the rural mailbox. On the rare days that the sun shone, she would emerge from the silent house and climb the hill to the shed, load wood onto a child's sled, a yellow plastic saucer, and then give it a push. The saucer would slide down the snow-packed slope, revolving, coming to rest against the foundation of the house. She wore a wool hat that made her forehead itch and a long coat that was like an arctic sleeping bag with sleeves. The small brown dog, picking her way along the top of drifts, cast a lavender shadow. The dog was elderly and cheerful; the firewood was heavy.

Night arrived in late afternoon; the wood-burning stove creating a circle of oppressive heat in the living room, leaving the other rooms dark and chilled, like the interior of a closed refrigerator. She didn't hate it, but she didn't like it much either. There was nobody bothering her, true, but eventually, she was discovering, people need to be bothered. Her job wasn't even full-time, didn't pay well, and was nearly as isolating as her house – she worked alone in a tiny office at Cornell, managing a social psychology journal whose editor was across campus in another building, conducting his research and performing his teaching duties.

Nobody in her building knew her or what she was doing there, and the only people who spoke to her were those who stood in the courtyard by the mailroom a few times a day to smoke cigarettes. Her own smoking had increased to madwoman, to inpatient levels, ever since she'd come to Ithaca in the late summer. Slowly, over many weeks, she formed a bond with another smoker, a pretty young woman named Alana with mall bangs and fiercely pressed blue jeans whose twin sister was dying of lymphoma in Florida. She asked after the sister every few days and Alana would report the latest, shaking her head in disbelief and resignation, sometimes crying, sometimes turning her cigarette around to stare into its fiery end.

'It ain't good,' she would say, stubbing her smoke against the side of the building and running a finger under each eye. Alana worked in the mailroom with two men, cutups who worried about her behind her back but were only able to joke. They were no help to Alana during the long afternoons of sorting and thinking, picturing her own face rising up in front of her jaundiced and suffering, her own head, grimly bald.

Nobody ever asked Joan anything about herself, because nobody cared. People back home somewhat cared, but not here in New York. Her own relatives didn't get her situation – they all understood her to be living in New York City. The ones who did seem to follow that she was in Ithaca thought it was a suburb of Manhattan.

'It's five hours from the city,' she told her uncle at her goodbye party.

'Let me ask you,' he said, narrowing his eyes. He considered himself worldlier than the others, a short-haul truck driver who frequently drove into the Loop in Chicago. 'How far are you from Central Park?'

'Five hours,' she said. 'Five hours away. It's Ithaca, Uncle George, which is across the entire state from New York City.'

'Do me a favor, listen to your old uncle,' he told her. 'Stay out of Central Park at night. There's nothing in there you need.'

Her park was called Treman, its upper entrance less than a mile from her house, and she and the dog hiked there every day, descending through damp granite that led to a series of narrow passages and jumbled steps past a foaming waterfall. From the shadows, the falls looked like an endless supply of milk being poured down a drain. At the bottom was a small footbridge with the word SMILE gouged into its railing, the *S* made with three straight lines like a lightning bolt, or a Nazi symbol. She took these walks partly to get away from smiling and would frown her way through the boggy acre of skunk cabbage, through the damp field of ferns where they had once seen a garter snake with its mouth unhinged swallowing a frog, and then onto the steep switchback trail that led through the forest. Every day they did the four-mile loop, the dog double time, running ahead and then back to check on her progress, both of them panting along. They rarely passed anyone unless you counted the trees, tall and good-natured, their gnarled roots man-spread over the path.

She liked to think of nothing except what she was doing, following the plumy tail of the dog. This foot, that foot, this foot, that foot, this foot, that foot, this foot, that foot, this one, that one, this one, that one, this one, that one, this one, that one, this, that, this, that, this, that, this, that, this, that, until eventually there was nothing but the path and the occasional thought scudding across the blue sky of her mind. It was everything she had wanted when she came to Ithaca, and less.

She had enjoyed her life back in Iowa City up to a point, working for a space physics journal at the university, living with her husband and their dogs in an old house surrounded by oak trees. She liked the scientists, their amiability and their focus, the way they understood complicated, invisible things but didn't understand simple ones, like regular hair-washing or why a paper called 'The Effect of the Giant Thruster on the Spread-F Region' was funny.

She had liked her marriage too, up to a point, that being when her husband left her for one of their friends. She had a minor nervous breakdown from the surprise of it and from the yawning chasm that opened up inside her. One morning she'd called her sister from the bathtub, weeping into a washcloth, unable to speak. Her sister drove over from the town where they had grown up, sixty miles away, and sat on the closed toilet lid with her legs crossed, sorting through a shoebox of pharmaceuticals she'd brought with her, looking for divorce pills. By this time, Joan was out of the tub, sitting on the edge, wrapped in a towel.

'Here we go,' her sister said. 'These make you feel like melting butter.'

She took one pill for herself and gave one to Joan, and they ended up sleeping the whole afternoon, sprawled in the same bed, like when they were kids.

She had liked her friends in Iowa, not up to a point but forever, the women who supported her through her divorce, the same women she had supported through theirs. Their comments ranged everywhere from bossy ('Think about yourself, not about him') to unrealistic ('You will never regret this but he will') to hopeful ('This is your get-out-of-jail-free card') to mystical ('The Hanged Man actually is a positive card') to useful ('Where do you keep your booze?'). They helped her move all the stuff he'd left behind to the garage and then made a bonfire in the backyard of the farmhouse and milled around declaring it her year while she shivered in a lawn chair with her knees drawn up, wearing a cruddy down vest liberated from one of the boxes.

And then someone else took over the space journal and she found herself working for a professor emeritus who spent his days in an office on the top floor of a building named after him, puttering around and giving orders to his half-retired secretary, an elderly woman known as Mrs. P. who wore dark glasses for an eye condition and loud perfume. Every morning there were more e-mails from scientists asking about the status of their papers, queries that the professor emeritus took long hours to ponder and then answered in circuitous letters filled with courtliness and spin that Mrs. P. laboriously typed and mailed out, using her own roll of stamps instead of the franking machine.

Joan got sick of it eventually, the divorce pain, the chasm, the switching from the old editor, who did things like ask her what she was reading, to the new editor, who did things like ask her to bring him coffee. The first time, she had said yes because she was taken by surprise, the second time because she wanted a cup for herself, the third time because she felt solidarity with Mrs. P., who would have to go up and down the stairs in her place, and the fourth, fifth, and sixth times because his name was in the dictionary.

One of the guys had rigged it so that when she turned on her printer each morning, it would chug out a piece of paper with a daily quote on it. Once it said, *Politicians make strange bedfellows*, and she had folded it, put it in a university envelope, and mailed it to her ex-husband, who was a local politician. She used the franking machine. Another time it said, *Sometimes you find yourself in the middle of nowhere, and sometimes in the middle of nowhere you find yourself*, attributed to Jerry Garcia, her old favorite. One morning, it said, *Traveler, there is no path; paths are made by walking*, and instead of recycling it, she put it on her desk and looked at it. *Traveler, there is no path; paths are made by walking*. Anonymous had said it, and she was right.

The Russians arrived on time, stubbled and hungover, two of them in the cab of a cross-country moving truck. They were sipping from large cups of coffee and greeted her elaborately and – she thought – ironically. The packing materials that were supposed to be in the back of the already half-filled truck weren't there, but sitting on the corrugated floor were two more guys, smoking and eating crusts out of a battered pizza box. The crew convened in a corner of her living room for twenty minutes, drinking their coffee and discussing in Russian how to pack a whole house with nothing but a phone book and her own laundry baskets. When she approached, one said, 'Lady, this isn't for you to worry . . . we will have for you to worry later.'

The Iowa City house was ornate and crumbly with high ceilings, pocket doors, and a resounding, barren echo. Almost everything of value had been given to the ex, and nearly everything else had been dragged to the curb for university students to pick through. They rode up on bikes and later steered carefully away balancing crockery, birdcages, vintage vinyl (James Gang, Grateful Dead), garden rakes, faded quilts, antique egg crates. The rest of it went to the dump. She and her friend Sara, stoned and eating potato chips, drove a borrowed pickup truck to the landfill, where they hurled her belongings onto the spongy ground, Sara bursting into tears finally, saying, 'Even this? Even these?' as she threw objects and boxes of objects over the side. When they pulled away, an idling bulldozer came forward and pushed a wave of dirt over the whole mess as Sara leaned out the window, spellbound and dismayed.

So Joan had erased her past, but still, the paltry present had to be packed, so she drove to the grocery store and filled her hatch-back with a stack of soiled produce boxes and some flattened cartons held together with twine. Back at the house, the head mover produced a large roll of tape from the cab of the truck and held it triumphantly above his head.

A shirtless blond guy in dress pants was packing the entire con-tents of her kitchen using the yellow pages. He placed one page between each of her plates, like a bookmark. 'Why are you even bothering?' she asked him.

'Lady, we must pack,' he said, gesturing dynamically and rolling his eyes. 'Lady think she can move without pack.' In her bedroom, one guy was half-heartedly dumping shoes and books into the same flimsy box while another stared pensively into the drawer of her bedside table.

As soon as they had jammed her stuff onto the truck, the movers drove off to their next destination, wherever that was, all four of them in the cab. She handed her house key to the real estate agent and said goodbye to her friends, who stood in the street and waved after her, a row of women with bright frightened smiles on their faces, just like the one on hers.

It was August and hot, and she left on Highway 6, a narrow two-lane that ran through the treeless, endless landscape of corn. The sun and wind blasted into the driver's-side window, and fifteen minutes out, there was an accident on the road. Her car was the third in line, stopped by a motorist waving a white dress shirt. Just beyond him was the wreck itself, a sports car resting upside down in a ditch and an SUV lodged against a crumpled guardrail, its unbent grille glinting fearlessly. She couldn't look at the accident, so she and the dog got out and stared behind them, watching the line of cars increasing one by one, clicking into place like a row of dominoes.

Eventually, a chopper appeared, dangling from its propeller, and settled awkwardly on the pavement up ahead. It took on cargo and then spun up and away, veered over the cars, hovered uncertainly for a moment, and then swept westward. Traffic resumed, chastened, crawling across the landscape in a long slow line, like a caterpillar consuming a leaf.

In the late summer and early fall, Ithaca truly did live up to its bumper stickers – it was gorges. The park's narrow passageway opened onto her chasm, externalized so she could walk through it and come out the other side every afternoon. Her rustic house with its set of big glass doors looking out on the trees, the little dog sleeping in the crook of her arm at night, the part-time nature of her job allowing her to get up every morning and drink coffee while making drawings of her dreams, the good parking space at

WHAT YOU SEEK IS SEEKING YOU

work, the bad people down the road who bred Dobermans and had mysterious gatherings that included scores of cars parked willy-nilly along the gravel. She decided to like the bad people because they pointed their guns at the ground when she drove by and also because she was afraid of them.

The premium parking space at Cornell was secured for her by the new boss, Ed, a man so kind and thoughtful that she suspected he might be paying some kind of monthly freight on it. Those were the two perks to her job – the parking space and Ed. Otherwise, it was deadly, sonorously dull, forcing people to crawl out of sleep in the morning and draw their dreams.

The social psychologists all seemed like perfectly regular, nice people, far enough away from the spectrum that they could study it. They wrote long laborious papers proving that people who lived alone and had few social contacts were lonelier than those who lived with others and had a social life. Conducted extensive NSF-funded experiments instead of just calling her.

Her Iowa friends didn't abandon her. A couple of them checked in every day or so, just to talk about nothing.

'How's the Pink Eddie factory?' Mary would ask. Ed occasionally wore a pink polo shirt with his khakis. 'What's new in squishiology?'

It was a soft science, true, but civilized in a way that astrophysics hadn't been. For instance, nobody in squish ever stared too long into a telescope and fainted. Nobody ever brought her inappropriate gifts or accidentally wore his wife's blouse to work. Nobody, in fact, ever did anything, including her.

'What's your plan for the weekend?' Pat would ask each Friday.

Her weekend plan was mostly: on Saturday draw, hike, go to the co-op, get Thai takeout, watch a movie, read; on Sunday draw, hike, go to the mall, get Thai takeout, watch a movie, read. The mall was in Syracuse, the nearest city with sunlight, and she would drive the interstate for an hour-plus until she saw the mall's carousel roof and then wander around Lord & Taylor in her hiking boots looking at clothes until she felt like herself again. Then she would drive back. Once Pat had to remind her that they were coming up on a three-day weekend and she broke down in tears right at her desk. It turned out okay, because she cleaned her fridge on the third day and then drove twenty miles to Taughannock Park, which had its own falls, a tall narrow ribbon of silver that emptied into a deep pool at the bottom. She found a ledge and read her book, checking the time every ten minutes or so, while Sheba walked around on the mossy rocks. After one hour they got Thai takeout and went home.

It started snowing and wouldn't stop. It didn't always accumulate, but it always snowed, sometimes invisibly, just the feeling of straight pins being hurled at her face. Men in camouflage began materializing in the park. One time she saw a thermos, silver with a blue plastic cap, hovering in the air before realizing it was strapped to a hunter holding a crossbow and leaning against a tree, observing her.

'I wouldn't let your dog get too far ahead,' he said as she passed.

One of the dreams she had drawn was of being pierced through by an arrow. In the dream, it hadn't hurt, but she couldn't pull it out because it was barbed, like a cupid's arrow. In the drawing, she was sort of hunched over it, wearing a nightgown, and had a black bar over her eyes, the way they did in old girlie magazines. She had thought the dream might be trying to tell her something, which it was: like, stop going to the park.

She threw herself into piecework at the Pink Eddie factory, sending the papers out to reviewers at a blinding clip, retrieving their responses and walking briskly across campus to share them with Ed, even going to dinner at his house with his wife, who was warm and lovely, and a postdoc from Korea and his wife, who also was warm and lovely although she barely spoke English and once when she thought no one was looking, she glared at the coffee table and ran her hand through her hair in a mad-housewife way.

Right around then the snow started accumulating, banks of it, stiff like packing material that creaked when she walked on it. The gray smoke from her chimney dispersed into the gray sky and she countered by buying an elaborate set of bright markers. They stood upright in their own plastic lazy Susan, taking up half her drawing table, every possible hue of every primary color. Somebody sent her a boxed set of *Beavis and Butt-Head* DVDs and she watched all of them in a row on a dim Saturday, then threw up her pad thai. Another time she tried to walk her dog on the road and was accosted by the Dobermans. Sheba, despite being mostly blind, was still willing to kill them, spinning in circles and making exorcist noises. The Dobermans followed, their hackles raised, growling.

'Can you please call your fucking *dogs* off?' she cried to the people who were standing in their yard watching.

'Muffin,' the woman said after a moment. 'Trina.'

The dogs took a few more stiff-legged steps and then turned and trotted back toward their house and up the driveway.

It was around this time that she began to think about making some friends.

Before she could formulate a plan, her father came down with a terrible flu that turned out to be cancer. For a few weeks, her sister ferried him to radiation and chemo, calling to report the details – the Sharpie diagrams drawn on his skin, the gruesome melted-chalk taste of the Ensure he drank from a bent straw, the waiting rooms with TVs blasting, Ellen dancing ghoulishly across the screen while patients shivered under afghans, receiving their poison.

Joan called him every day after his treatments, making her voice buoyant, and then again in the evening to see what he was

having for dinner, even though he always said the same thing:
'One of these milkshakes.' Near the end of every conversation, as
before, he would ask, 'How's your little dog?' He never called her
Sheba, even to her face.

The day he didn't answer she got hold of her sister, who drove
over to find him collapsed on the floor.

'It's not going to work out,' her sister whispered into the phone
that evening from the hospital corridor.

Within two hours, Joan and the dog were in the car, first creeping on snowpack through western New York and then driving fast
on dry pavement all through the night. Loud music and sparkling
stars until it was dawn in the Midwest, and they could slow down.

They had him sitting in a chair, but he was slumped over, eyes
closed. He looked smaller, burnished, and so intensely like
himself that for a moment, standing in the hall, Joan didn't recognize him. Next to him was Connie, one of his girlfriends, wearing
a sweatshirt with a big plaid heart appliquéd on the front. Connie
was looking at her shoes, turning them thoughtfully this way and
that. She reached down into her bag of knitting, took out a long
blue needle, poked at the sole of one sneaker, dislodging something that she then picked up with a Kleenex and deposited in the
wastebasket. While up, she tidied a stack of newspapers and then
opened the drawer of the nightstand.

'Boy, they give you everything you need,' she said. He roused
himself to agree with her and shut his eyes again.

'Looky who's here!' Connie cried.

Joan started to feel a little unhinged when she knelt to hug
him; he was ectoplasm. He raised one hand slowly, ran it rumi-
natively over his face, and then set it gently in his lap again. His
legs looked severely compromised without trousers, wavery and
slightly see-through. A phone rang loudly and everyone flinched.

'It's turned way up,' Connie said. Her ride was calling from the lobby.

They walked to the elevator while a stout, uncheerful nurse tended to her father. Joan and her sister liked Connie the best out of all their dad's girlfriends because she was the most like their long-dead mother – she enjoyed partying but kept her wits about her. She was going to bingo that night but would come back and sit with him the next afternoon. The elevator doors opened and Connie gave her a quick, hard hug before stepping in. They were both crying.

The nurse had helped him back into bed; the covers were pulled formally up to his shoulders and then folded back. He was staring out the window to his left. From where Joan stood, the window looked out over a field of Mercedes-Benzes and BMWs, the doctors' parking lot, but from the perspective of the patient, it was just blue sky and gorgeous pillowy midwestern clouds.

'Look at that sky, Dad,' Joan said. He continued to gaze, his jaw moving imperceptibly, as though he were chewing something very small. She pulled up a chair and watched with him. The blue, the clouds, the occasional gliding bird. At some point she took his hand. He nodded as though she'd said something and continued gazing.

Her best friend from childhood drove over from Chicago for the funeral. They spent the night before making popcorn and drinking from the parents' liquor cabinet, just like in high school, and then later slept in the twin beds in Joan's old bedroom, whispering in the dark the way they always had even though there was no one to hear them now.

Before they'd turned sixteen, they had made their dads drive them everywhere at all hours, and their dads had done it without complaining, even though Liz's had only one arm and Joan's was occasionally inebriated.

'They were the last decent guys,' Liz whispered.

One afternoon, while Connie sat with their father, Joan and her sister went back to the house intending to go through it and figure out what to do with things. Joan had opened the drawer of the buffet in the dining room where they kept the communal combs and brushes, bobby pins and barrettes, and in the very back she found a brush with their mother's hair preserved in it from long ago. Before death; before chemo, even. The hairbrush defeated them entirely, and they decided to find someone to come dismantle the house and sell what could be sold.

After the service, after everything, Joan gathered two boxes of stuff from the attic, found Sheba, then called her sister from the phone in the kitchen, lighting a cigarette and staring out the window the way their mother used to do.

'That was fun, experiencing another death with you,' her sister said. 'Let's do it again soon.'

'Next time it can be mine,' Joan said. 'Just kidding.'

'You need to make friends out there,' her sister said. 'Liz agrees. We discussed you.'

'You don't disgust me,' Joan said. Outside, a black squirrel was sniffing around under the tree.

'I mean it,' her sister said. They were both their mother now.

The black squirrel came to the sliding glass door and put his front paws up on it, peering in. After they said goodbye, Joan filled all the feeders for the last time, found a jar of peanuts in the cupboard, and emptied it around the base of the tree.

'I filled your feeders, Dad,' she called into the empty house, then got in her car and drove back to Ithaca.

Once she got back, she quit smoking, except for a couple of times a day when she went down to stand in the alcove with Alana, whose sister had died during the three weeks Joan had been gone.

They shivered companionably, backs against the cold stone of the building, not saying much, just watching the smoke as it hurried away from them like everything else.

She started going to a yoga class where everyone was more flexible than her and to a meditation class run by a super-crabby monk in a messy living room.

'I have to move shit off the rug to put my cushion down,' she told Pat.

'Can't anyone say they're monks?' Pat asked.

'I think they're real. They all live in that house and wear gowns,' Joan told her.

Everyone in the meditation group, including her, seemed a bit off in some way, but she liked closing her eyes and imagining the path through her park for forty-five minutes every Wednesday night. This foot, that foot, this foot, that foot. She liked the Rumi quotes in dime-store frames hanging precariously on nails here and there. LOVE IS THE BRIDGE BETWEEN YOU AND EVERY-THING. This, that, this, that, until eventually there was nothing but the gray sky of her mind and the faint odor of the carpet.

Someone who worked in her building showed up at yoga class, a pale woman with bobbed hair like a flapper's and dark lipstick. It was her clothes that Joan had noticed more than the woman as she went up the stairs past the journal office in the mornings: billowy slacks and tailored dresses and narrow skirts with crisp blouses and once, in the fall, a soft belted jacket with felt flowers appliquéd on it, which sounds terrible but wasn't. The last thing Joan would see after the outfit went past were the shoes – flats, ankle boots, or, sometimes, a pair of slender wingtips that looked like men's shoes except for the heels. The woman was quietly hopeless in yoga class; when they bent over to touch the floor, she was still basically upright.

FESTIVAL DAYS

'I refuse to do the sun salutation until there's a sun,' Joan whispered to her as they were watching the others do headstands.

'I just had to get the fuck out of my house,' the woman whispered back.

'Could we maybe do a tripod?' the teacher asked them gently. She was in her early seventies and wore harem pants and a lavender leotard. She moved her topknot out of the way, put the crown of her head on the floor, balanced knees on elbows, and smiled at them upside down.

YOU ARE THE UNIVERSE IN ECSTATIC MOTION. One of the Rumi signs wobbling on its nail.

Once in the tripod, Joan raised her legs slowly and balanced there while the teacher stood behind her, just barely touching her ankles.

'I met someone,' she told Mary the next day. 'A woman in my building. Her name is Deirdre, she's a technical writer, and when I asked what that meant, she goes, 'Well . . . it's technical' – i.e., sense of humor.'

'I thought you were going to say a guy,' Mary said. 'But this is very good.'

That afternoon on her way out, Deirdre stopped in Joan's office and invited her to go to a party over the weekend. Her neighbor was having it and Deirdre wouldn't really know anyone there except him.

'Who is he?' Joan asked.

'I'm not sure, just this guy scientist,' Deirdre said. 'He's kind of' – and she made a waving gesture around her head. 'He has a lot of plants in his house is all I know, and he rides a bike in the snow.'

Joan was too shy to go to a party where she knew only one person slightly, because what if nobody talked to her. Then she

156

remembered she was in Ithaca, where nothing mattered. 'Okay,' she said.

On Saturday afternoon she loaded wood from the shed with Sheba and then they watched a movie, curled up together on the sofa while it snowed. When they woke, the sky had gone from tarnished spoon to black and Joan didn't have time to make herself look any better than usual.

It took forever to get the snow off her car, and she ended up leaving it with a tall crown on top that looked like a haircut from the eighties. She slid sideways down the big hill and then fishtailed into town, arriving at the address exactly when everyone else did. Somebody immediately parked behind her.

The house had a wide porch and carved front doors with bubbled glass, like an old Iowa farmhouse. The walk had been shoveled haphazardly and they picked their way up the steps and onto the porch and then a tall guy in a thick sweater banged on one of the doors, pushed it open, and they all herded inside.

There was an awkward stamping of snow off boots and smiling; everyone had hat hair and was trying to do something about it.

'I'm Deirdre,' Deirdre said to a portly guy with a bushy beard.

'Ari,' he said.

'Chris,' said a woman with short red hair, unzipping her coat. 'This is Diane.'

Diane said hello and then the tall, sweatered guy said, 'Thor here.'

'Joan.'

The foyer was clean and empty, with apricot walls and a neat rag rug.

Just beyond was a kitchen where she could see big bulbs of garlic hanging in a bunch over a butcher block, bright crockery on the open shelves, and a ladder-back chair with what looked like her mother's homemade noodles draped over its rungs. In a room off to the right were pots of ferns and orchids, a ficus tree with lights sparkling in the leaves, a scarlet begonia blooming next to a guitar in its stand, and a big gray sofa. There was music in the background that she recognized – her old friend Jerry Garcia.

Diane asked what they should do with their coats. Ari pointed toward a closed door.

Once in a while you get shown the light. Joan felt the warmth of the house and the people radiating through her like home. It was the universe in ecstatic motion. There were two doors, actually, and she stepped forward and opened the right wrong one.

Now

THE DAY IS FINALLY HERE. Not the day I give the talk but the day I write the essay that is the talk. I've done everything else possible, several times. Reading, sleeping, musing, reading, hanging out with people, sitting outside in the lawn chair and the heat, feeding the birds cracked corn on the stone wall, witnessing a very gentle fight between a chipmunk and a mourning dove – choosing sides because the mourning dove was taking one tiny grain at a time while the chipmunk was vacuuming the length of the stone wall like a carpet. Reading some more, and then more, driving the dog around slowly on our country roads for an hour each evening so she could smell the night air. Letting other cars pass us in the dark, listening to Terry Gross ask people questions and then to their answers. Dion, he of the Belmonts, surprised me with his keen mind and his obsessive love and encyclopedic knowledge of not just doo-wop but all music. Why would it be surprising that Dion knew a lot about music? Think it through, Jo. Pay attention. Remember when Sherman Alexie said that thing and you pulled over to write it down on a receipt and then forgot the end of it and had to listen to the whole interview again the next night so you could pull over and write the second half – *of one sentence.*

Remember what X said and how it annoyed you enough that you thought, *Oh, please. This is why the world* hates *a memoirist.* Remember what Bruce Springsteen said and how it thrilled you enough that you thought, *This is why the world* loves *a memoirist.* Remember what Astrid something, the woman who created the look for the Beatles, said, and remember how it made you think of John Lennon, who had a guy crush on Astrid's boyfriend Stuart, a young man who politely refused to be in the Beatles. He wouldn't have lived to regret it, Stuart, even if he hadn't died soon after of a brain aneurysm. Stuart was that certain an artist.

Forget, of course, everything Terry Gross said, because she is so good at her job that she isn't what anyone remembers. I like people who are good at their jobs but I'm not one of them. Which is why you'll notice that everything I did this summer until today – the day of writing the Alaska talk – did not have the word *writing* in it.

But now I *am* writing, because it's on my calendar and it's in my mind, though what Dion has to do with Alaska I don't know. He sounded like someone's dad, old now but still young in the way that rock-and-roll guys stay young. I remember something else: how my own dad was not a rock-and-roll guy but looked (in his younger days) like Buddy Holly.

And there it is. If you muse long enough, you get to it: I wanted to go to Alaska because that is where my dad spent his war years, the only time in his life that he traveled anywhere farther than a fishing cabin on some midwestern lake. A small-town dirt-poor Illinois boy who got sent out with one brother or another every afternoon to bring back dinner for the family. Tramping through cornfields and woods with a shotgun and a couple of dogs, always dogs, and then tramping back with a squirrel or a rabbit for dinner. Using bamboo rods to catch walleye out of somebody's pond or out of the Edwards River. My dad, who learned sports at their rural school from a teacher – Miss Laura Smith, who tucked her long skirt into her bloomers and taught my dad and the other guys to pole-vault. He said, 'Boy, she could do the long jump – you oughta seen her. And she taught me to sprint.'

He told me that years later, at Laura Smith's funeral in the little town – a town so drab and meaningless, stunted, that the only funeral parlor was called Crummy's – there were rows and rows of men in their stiff good clothes with weathered faces and white foreheads (the telltale sign of a farmer at a funeral) paying their respects to the coach who had taught them layups.

Anyway, my dad got called up for World War II and was sent to the Presidio in California for his training. I loved the word *presidio*; it sounded like a foolish leader or a musical instrument. And lots of things happened to him there. He was crudely circumcised, for one, carried to and from the mess hall for days afterward by his horrified and sympathetic buddies, and he was laid up in a ditch during a training maneuver and left there ankle-sprained for twelve hours in the hot sun, provoking forever after the question he would always pose to me: 'Honey, does your dog have plenty of water?' He couldn't even fire his gun to announce his dilemma because they were training with wooden rifles.

See, I know the stories very well; I listened to him then the way I listen to Terry Gross now.

He grew very close to the men in his unit, the guys who winced over his sore dick with him and crouched in small groups smoking cigarettes to have their pictures taken, but before they were all sent to the European theater, he got plucked out of the mix and made to go to Alaska.

This disappointed him terribly – he wanted to be with his buddies – but it most likely saved his life. Laura Smith, actually, saved his life. Some general was worried that his men stationed in Alaska were withering away from boredom, so he flew from base to base to recruit a basketball team. Which is why Beard, with his long legs and his Buddy Holly glasses and his small-town ball skills, had to take leave of his unit and get on a ship that toiled its way to Kodiak Island, the men vomiting over the steel sides and into the churning waters.

So this is how you write. You let the writing lead and you simply follow, letting the memories and the images and the language take over; you're the writer, you get to decide, and a talk is whatever you want it to be. You can decide that Laura Smith, with her wadded-up skirts and her ability to hit students *hard*, as I was told, is no longer just dust in the Viola Cemetery back behind Crummy's but that she will and should make her way onto a kind of stage in faraway Anchorage, her name and her accomplishments invoked to people born long after her last layup, people who would have no reason to know or appreciate her or know the hard men with their pale foreheads and their silent sons, those boys who rode tractors while other kids were splashing in city pools, who rode tractors while other kids were being put to bed, who were being woken up at dawn, who were walking in the woods like my father, taking aim at some squirrels and letting others live. This is the power of writing, that joy of recounting, not even my own memories, but someone else's. Imagining Jeff Crummy as a boy, his father the town ghoul but also a kind of tycoon because he owned a booming business. Crummy's, with its shining mahogany tables and powder-blue carpet, was where my father's own funeral was held but where mine will decidedly not be.

A few minutes ago I got up from writing this to make a cup of tea and stare out the window at the birds. And while I was doing that I was thinking about one of the lines up above (before the funeral-home stuff, where, by the way, I made up the details of the blue carpet and the mahogany tables), the part about the men puking over the side of the ship. It made me remember something I saw on television with my father long ago – we were watching a documentary and there were men on boats sitting crammed together on their way to Normandy Beach and their own deaths.

Those first boats were filled with cannon fodder who were aware they were cannon fodder. And some were praying with the chaplains, who were standing up with crosses in their hands, and some were staring starkly, and some were so frightened their faces were in rictus states, and some were so sorrowful, so grief-stricken, that you couldn't keep looking. Facing their deaths, their deaths were visible on their faces.

That's what I was remembering while waiting for the tea-kettle. Those boys – and many of the boys were men – exist now only in documentary form and maybe in the minds, sometimes, of the people who saw the footage. It seems almost too private, like viewing autopsy photos, to have seen them in their last moments, reckoning with their own souls, fighting their own natural impulses to resist, to be like Henry in *The Red Badge of Courage*, to flee instead of fight. Henry, a young boy sent to the front lines of the Civil War, going from the farm fields to musket balls and hand-to-hand combat without ever having shaved, carrying a ration of jam his mother packed for him.

Anyway, that's what I was thinking while I made my tea, and now I'm back in my seat, computer on lap, listening to the flap of the shiny strips I've taped to my windows to keep the birds from flying kamikaze-style into the glass.

And, see, there's a whole other essay in that – the planes spiraling down from the sky, aimed at a warship, missing it by the equivalent of inches, the pilots not bothering to ditch, because why. It's an ocean. Their souls being yanked up and out of their bodies the way a parachute yanks its cargo upward when it opens.

*

There was nothing happening in Alaska when my dad arrived. He played basketball and cards and worked as a secretary for a higher-up, teaching himself how to type so that he could have time free to roam, since there wasn't much to type about. And that's where his real war stories begin.

Beard with a rifle – he always acted it out – aiming straight down into a stream teeming with salmon rushing upriver and shooting. 'Honey, you could fire right down into them and they wouldn't turn.' The rush of spawning silver, the tall man standing, firing his gun into the water – isn't that crazy? And yet he never lied that I knew of, never even exaggerated the way us other Beards do. He spent the days wandering on his island and beyond, seeing bears and elk and fishing and filing away a lifetime's worth of images to bring back to the land of dun, spelled both ways. Nobody died except one guy who apparently went off a cliff in the fog. The men searched and searched for him, heartsick and frantic, but all they found was his bag at the bottom of a cliff. A musette bag. And it's funny, because I didn't know that word and whenever he told the story – 'Honey, all we found was his musette bag' – it became linked in my mind with music.

My dog in the back seat, the scents like music to her nose during our night drives, Dion's doo-wop, and a book I read over and over as a kid, *Jenny Lind and Her Listening Cat*, which had illustrations of a little girl just like me, a blue ribbon in her hair, and her beautiful gray cat, sitting with paws perfectly together. Jenny Lind would sing to Kisse Katt in their little Swedish house, quietly and modestly, not knowing that she would grow up to be the most famous woman in the world for a while. I loved that book; Jenny Lind's otherworldly soprano unfurling in the cold Swedish air, the devotion of Kisse Katt, the two of them at night gazing out their attic window at the northern lights billowing in the sky.

Neil Young pulled a song from his own music bag that I sang along to when I was younger, about the aurora borealis and about indigenous people being shoved from their land and their tribal ways.

I saw the aurora borealis once, driving on a highway outside Ithaca with my friend Sara; the sky became animate, bright curtains floating and changing color, a gauzy hem lifting and settling, then lifting again. Sara reached over and turned off the music and we were silent, the road droning beneath us, until it was over.

'Do you know what that was?' she asked me in a hushed voice.

'I think so,' I said.

Pure sensory experience. Who knows what it meant for Sara, but for me it instantly retrieved the fifty-year-old memory of Jenny Lind, the cold window of her garret, the soft gray cat, the blue ribbon that shone like satin, a clear soprano voice made suddenly visible in the black sky, her vibrato moving the drapes of time and space and color and light.

Neil Young's song wasn't really about the aurora borealis; it was about indigenous people being shoved from their land and their tribal ways. My dad was known on the base for being an outdoorsman, a guy who got so excited at the miracle of salmon spawning, a guy who knew just where to be to watch the bears fishing, a guy who could lead the trackers as they searched for the forever-lost man. And so one morning someone woke him very, very early to say there were Inuit in a boat asking for Beard, and when he dressed and went out, they said they were there to take him to watch the annual seal harvest.

'Honey,' he told me, palms upturned. (It was always the same.) 'It was an honor and I couldn't say no.' So he went with them. Once I told him I was planning to see a documentary in which there was footage of baby seals being killed. He said, 'Don't watch that.' Uncharacteristic for him to say *don't* anything. When I pressed him on it, he said only, 'It's very, very tough.' So I didn't watch.

But he had, all those years ago, 1940-something, and felt privileged to do so and then ill afterward.

'It was the boat,' he told me.

I think of it now, that documentary that I never saw, in the same way I think of the Normandy boats and the private faces of the privates – some things belong only to the people who are experiencing them. And by people, I also mean seals.

Lunch tastes better when you've been writing. Same hummus as yesterday, same baby carrots, same unacceptable thing that I don't like to tell people I eat. And yet it all tasted delicious like the way food tastes when you've been hiking all day and finally figure out how to get the stove to light without blowing yourself up and you make the freeze-dried plate of slop that you bought at REI and even though it's unidentifiable vegetarian gore, it tastes ravenously delicious, and then you toast marshmallows that have been smashed flat in your pack but slowly, through the first course of the meal, expand back up to near-normal proportions so you can char them on a stick and eat the golden-black crust and then char them again. That's what lunch tastes like when you've been doing your writing.

Pringles are the thing that I usually don't admit to.

I don't know how long this should be, but I could keep going forever, linking one thought to the next, one image to the other. Ha – I can see the faces three weeks in the future and the collective look of horror at the idea that the speaker's sheaf of papers might be endless, self-perpetuating. The sheaf is not, but the story is. And I hope you'll notice also that there *is no story*. It's simply thinking, focused thinking, with words attached to memories attached to images and the images linked to form the elusive, still-blurry idea at its core. I can't yet separate it from the background.

Once at Yellowstone I sat on the ground to focus my scope on a pack of wolves off in the distance, and one of the scientists I was there with said in a snobby, disgusted voice, 'When you're on the ground, to a bear you look like an animal struggling.' Same shitty guy who acted surprised when I was the only one who could rock their Jeep out of the snowbank. *Just because you live in New York doesn't mean you weren't born in the Midwest, fuckwad, where the wind is so cold you scream silently walking from your house to the car, battery under your arm, between snowbanks as tall as your tall father.*

And there we are, back to the subject at hand? My father, telling me about the Kodiak bears, how he and his buddy saw them using their claws to spear a fish and then sharing it, back and forth. 'Claws this long, honey,' he said, crooking his finger.

Weren't you scared? I asked him.

'Well, we had our guns,' he admitted.

The pack of wolves in their radio collars, picked off one by one in the shoot-shovel-and-shut-up atmosphere outside the park. My own father, heading out each winter on a daylong hunting expedition with our dog, a little terrier otherwise found sleeping on the heating vent. Coming back with rabbits and squirrels, turning me into a vegetarian at a very young age. Once he fell through a lake that he thought was snow. We were round-eyed, listening to the story of our dad dropping through the ice, the terrier barking wildly at the hole, bubbles rising and him reaching upward for the edge and hauling himself out, building a fire and stripping naked – our dad naked! outside in the snow! – to dry himself and his clothes before he could make the long walk back to the car, carrying Yimmer, as always, because she wore out halfway through. And then another time, a few years later, him coming home from hunting and handing the gun to my mother.

'You might as well sell it,' he said grimly, 'because I'll never use it again.'

What happened that day that was so terrible he never hunted again after a lifetime of hunting? Something with an animal, we knew that, but when we asked our mother, she said to drop it, and the gun went away, and my father became the man in the neighborhood who had squirrels as pets.

'Ope, there's my black one,' he'd say, getting up from his chair to go outside and hand it a peanut.

Okay, I'm drifting downstream now on what seems like an endless supply of words, memories, waiting to catch a branch. I should stop and read the Denis Johnson story that my partner keeps telling me to read before Alaska – I listened to him laughing in bed one night while he read it, and I like funny, but I loved Denis Johnson, and right now it's too soon for everything but 'Now,' which, if you don't know it, is a Denis Johnson poem that describes soul-examining depression, triggered by hearing middle-of-the-night foghorns on the San Francisco Bay. It begins:

Whatever the foghorns are
the voices of feels terrible
tonight, just terrible, and here
by the window that looks out
on the waters but is blind, I
have been sleeping,
but I am awake now.
In the night I watch
how the little lights
of boats come out
to us and are lost again
in the fog wallowing on the sea

I used to read it to my students just to remind them that there is beauty in darkness, but now ('Now') it just makes me think of Wesley, my beloved writer friend, standing on the railing of the Golden Gate Bridge holding a cable stretched high above the water. The fog wallowing on the sea, the fog of war that made the man step off the Kodiak cliff, carried away without his musette bag, alone. Wesley alone, trembling.

> And so does my life tremble,
> and when I turn from the window
> and from the sea's grief, the room
> fills with a dark
> lushness and foliage nobody
> will ever be plucked from,
> and the feelings I have
> must never be given speech.
> Darkness, my name is Denis Johnson.

The terrible despair, and yet he survived it, as most of us do, living to die decades later. Wesley, never plucked from the dark foliage. My father, plucked from the unit of men; the other men, the Japanese in their hospital beds on some Aleutian island – Attu or Kiska, I can't remember – unable to fight or flee, plucking the pins from the grenades that were graciously given them during the evacuation and, as my father showed me over and over through the years, pressing them to their chests. Dying by their own hands, like Wesley. He let go and we hang on, and both are beautiful and stupid.

And maybe it's meant to be blurry, maybe the background is more important than the sharp outline of the wolf that emerges, gradually, as the lens is turned. The dark lush foliage, the sweet soprano sound of the northern lights, the low notes of foghorns on the bay, the way the artist laid a narrow strip of white to make

Jenny Lind's ribbon look like satin, the ivory fur of the harp seal babies, the rush of salmon leaping upstream to their deaths, the kamikaze pilots plummeting to theirs, the icy sky at night over Neil Young's Canada, Pocahontas and the smoke of muskets and the sound of grenades muffled by the embrace of arms, the squirrels receiving a bullet or a peanut, the chipmunk fighting the mourning dove, the faces of the men on the boats as a wave fell and they caught their first glimpse of Normandy's sand, a woman in a lace-collared dress in 1932, rucking up her skirt and taking a running start for the long jump, the way we all must do as writers, following our own legs as they stride across thin air to deliver us with a soft thud on a pile of sand somewhere.

Here, and now.

Festival Days

In the festival's terror
The village
Has become impoverished, indifferent
Like trees in fall.
On women's shoulders
Naked boys sit,
A little shy,
Hiding their members in their thighs

– Nand Chaturvedi, 'The Cruel Festival Time,'
translated by Katherine Russell Rich
and Vidhu Shekhar Chaturvedi

THE FEVER-DREAM PRIMARY COLORS of this Arizona rental, purple and green and blue and red, and the American Indian rugs and Moroccan rugs and the determined ceramic tchotchkes glaring from every surface. I thought it was nightmarish at first and it reminded me of something but not until this morning sitting on the bed did I realize that it reminds me of the Best Exotic Marigold Hotel. Staying there in India, with Kathy. How kind our driver was to her, ferrying us across the countryside and so carefully attending to her needs while Emma and I were basically green from dogs-getting-hit-by-cars phobia and hunger. Although Emma had thrown in the towel instantly on hunger and was glimpsed grabbing fruit (fruit!) and other inadvisables off the very first hotel's buffet table, and when I tried to stop her, she snarled, '*I have to eat these,*' which startled us both into laughter and then of course she and Kathy, who ate everything because she was throwing up all the time anyway, got massively sick and I lay in my quiet elaborate bed with nets and gold tassels reading Jonathan Franzen on an e-reader and listened to them puking up goat guts and watery yogurt in stereo.

The day we arrived at the Best Exotic Marigold Hotel, there was a big ornate plywood sign outside that said ALL ELDERLY ARE WELCOME and we were like, *What the fuck, now this?* But they remembered Kathy from a previous stay, the two young guys who ran it, and they loved her, and she walked with her canes while Emma carried her satchel and they showed us to our rooms, and I went into mine, where the guy had put the suitcase on the bed, and as I unzipped and opened it, a little gray mouse came from nowhere and jumped in. When I went to turn around and leave, I noticed on the floor – which was beautiful old cracked tile with a thick Moroccan-style rug, just like here in the Arizona desert – that there was a little toad I could have stepped on. I picked it up and carried it out to the patio. Then I went over to Kathy's room and told her about the mouse but not the toad. I said, 'Do you think I should tell Emma?' and she said, 'No! You shouldn't have told me!' and we fell into hysterical fits on her big lumpy bed, which probably had its own resident mouse.

She was adamant that we had to eat the hotel's food because the two young guys – both married, both with children, both in graduate school – were really excited about making dinner for us, telling us all about the movie that had just filmed there and about how they were having townspeople come to entertain us, their only guests, with music. So all along I had been drinking Cokes out of the can and eating hotel food from room service – frozen egg rolls and pizzas that they microwaved for me – but now I had to really give in and let go. The meal they made was the best I've ever had in my life, little bowl after little bowl of delicious vegetarian dishes that we didn't even try to identify, and they made it all, so varied and filled with fragrant spices, in a kitchen off the patio. Afterward some men from the town came and played music for us – Emma, the good sport, danced – and then they put us to bed.

I huddled under a bunch of exotic-marigold blankets that smelled like mice and incense, still reading Franzen, my imaginary friend, and suddenly *blam*, terrifying me, and then *blam*, terrifying me again and again. All night. A horse and I shared an ancient wall and every time he had a bad thought or noticed for the millionth time how small his stall was compared to how large the world was, he would send a hoof out and punish our wall.

Next morning I got up really early and it was beautiful outside, warm and everything blue and sort of ruined-looking, the little courtyard with its rusted wrought-iron table and broken clay pots and feral cats peeking out from the foliage, and I saw a narrow crooked set of steps and climbed up and stood on a crumbling balustrade and looked at the blue, blue sky and a flock of green, green parrots through the crumbling archways. When Kathy came out on her canes I said, 'Hi, I'm up here,' and she who could not climb said, 'Tell me what you see,' and I described everything because I could see the whole little town, all the backyards, and how some people had goats tied on their roofs and other odd and (to me) terrible little details. I was standing up there when Emma came out and I talked to her too.

Emma and I were so sad about Kathy and communicated it without speaking, and our sadness, our worry, and our silent understanding became like another person on the trip. While I was up there, after framing myself under a broken arch against the sky so Emma could take a picture of me, I wandered along the back edge and looked down and saw – holy shit – the open-air kitchen in which the guys had prepared our dinner the night before. It wouldn't be possible to describe even for me, the describer, but it was as squalid and rudimentary as anything I have ever seen, and I called down to Emma, 'You have to come up here,' and so she obliged by climbing the little stone steps and I pointed down at the kitchen and she had a mute, smiling conniption while Kathy gazed peacefully up at us from her iron table with the broken clay pot and its tattered pink geranium. The silent person between Emma and me was freaking out, but not us. We were perfectly calm. We had the kind of look on our faces that my sister had when the team of doctors told my young nephew that he had cancer and it might be a kind that little kids don't recover from. He had refused to listen to them and stared only at his mom, whose eyes were fixed on the doctors, her expression not worried at all, smiling almost. When the doctors filed out, my sister said, 'Okay, Aunt Jo Jo and I are going to the cafeteria for malts. What kind do you want?' And this little boy who refused to look at or trust the doctors but trusted his parents utterly said whatever he said, chocolate. And when we got down the hall, Linda fell like a tree.

I got sick later from that kitchen; that delicious incredible Indian food was full of microscopic critters my body hadn't met before. This American Indian house here in the Arizona desert is full of critters too; in the yard is a small sign saying BEWARE OF SNAKES.

From the ruins up on top of that balustrade, Kathy down below in her rusted chair, and Emma with her phone, framing me under that ancient broken arch with nothing but blue sky around me – in that rare moment I got to be the higher power, looking down on mice and friends.

So the Marigold Hotel with its giant plastic flower affixed to the crumbling patio wall, me up early after the night of the trapped horse sending out his foot, like sleeping with a man who wants you to know that the bed you're clinging to the edge of is, in fact, his. Not that he wants you to feel bad about it or anything, just that he did buy it, and he did get the people down in the city to put it on a truck, and he did flee the house when they arrived so that you could be the one to watch them assemble it after cringing over how they were going to get it upstairs. They had to hike it onto their shoulders in order to wrangle it up the stairway, along with the big broad headboard that I recently almost painted PLEASE DON'T FUCK HER IN THIS BED on but then didn't, because I don't like to mar wood. I watched them inch-by-inch themselves up the narrow stairs in the upstate house with its low ceilings and hand-hewn railings, the same way (back to India) that I watched Kathy in another grand castle-something hotel, the one with the ancient paintings of elephants and camels all over the stucco walls, and her refusing to be left behind when the elevator ran out of floors and we found ourselves in a big empty ballroom with a stage and chairs and a narrow opening that seemed carved into stone with shallow, slippery steps. She wanted the roof, where the sun was, and a view of Udaipur or whatever midwestern-type Indian city we were in that day. She handed us her canes and then, with Emma going first, crawled up the steps, slowly, me behind her, Kathy determined, not joking or sighing, just working. One step at a time, until suddenly we came out into bright sunlight onto a rooftop patio with potted plants, chairs draped in dyed fabric, and a lone woman pushing a broom.

We could see everything once again. The whole town and its people, all the roof-life of the town's citizens, four girls nearby who screamed when they saw us and started laughing and pointing because we had suddenly appeared slightly above them, out of nowhere. Even we felt like apparitions at that point, in our gauze shirts with our queasy stomachs. Kathy sat in one of the bright chairs while Emma and I roamed the roof, waving at the girls until they got tired of us, and then we sat down too. The woman continued to push the broom, although the roof and every other inch of the castle-something hotel was spotlessly clean. Not just clean but polished, the leaves of every succulent plant shining with some kind of wax. The man down below who was working on the lawn was in white with a purple brocade vest, cutting the lawn with a pair of scissors. Labor being so cheap, people being so plentiful.

A night or so later, at a cozy private guest camp on a waterway, surrounded by wading birds and lily pads with frail-looking toads sitting on them, we listened to a series of distant shouts as we ate our respective dinners of Greek yogurt (that was me) and fried somethings (that was them). Kathy asked in Hindi what the shouts were, and the Colonel, a royal of some kind, explained that in the surrounding fields, deer would come in the night and try to eat the crops – his crops; he was the landlord of everything around us for miles – and so every few acres a person would be stationed to scare them off from dark to dawn. Cheaper than a fence.

So we were up on that bright daytime roof with the woman pushing the broom and shyly refusing to look at us, and Kathy asked her a question in Hindi, something along the lines of 'How are you?' The woman became delighted because she had never met a white woman who spoke Hindi, and they began a kind of lilting conversation, with Kathy telling us along the way what she was saying and what the woman was saying. The woman was beautiful, dressed in street clothes, not a uniform, one of the thin bright dresses that we kept seeing in the brown landscape when we were being driven around. Dun, dun, dun, and then an elegant fluorescence sweeping past, a woman with a huge jar or a bale of straw on her head wearing a sari so bright that it would be acidic in American light but in the soft light of elephant-India it glowed like phosphorescence in the ocean, those tiny sea creatures that when you move your arm through the water leave a trail of fireworks.

Once I went to watch fireworks with M., and as we were lying on the dark grass in the summer heat, our friend Nancy on his other side and all of us giddy and goofy – especially him, with an audience of two ladies who were in good moods and shorts – he named all the fireworks as they exploded and fell. I can only remember now the Countess's Necklace, but they were funny and made me happy to be with someone who could amuse me when fireworks, which always make me sad, were rising into the dark and causing me to dissipate with them.

The summer after Kathy died, Emma had a fireworks party at her house, and we all went, lots of people, to watch them over the Hudson. And strangely, we couldn't see them at all, just giant puffs of smoke and the concussive sounds that would follow. Emma and I running from dark hill to dark hill trying to see them, but the whole event was invisible to us, and I kept thinking, *It's like Kathy; we can all feel her, but we can't see her, we just have to know that she's out there sending out her sparks while all we get is the smoke.*

Back on the roof, sitting in those elephant-print chairs, Kathy talking to the shy young woman with the broom who was aston-ishing in the way that so many Indian women seemed to be. In America the hyper-beautiful are monetized into movie stars or married to moguls, but here they were also pushing brooms or balancing their bales or begging. Once when we were in a car being driven through the cacophonous Delhi traffic, an older woman came to the passenger window where I was and begged with her eyes, holding out a palm and murmuring something. She looked like someone's grandmother, her hair white and slightly bouffant and a silk scarf tied around her neck like an old-fashioned stew-ardess. The driver snarled at her but I reached into my pocket and got all the money I could find, many bills that probably amounted to five dollars, and thrust them at her. I could no longer bear not responding, could no longer bear having to look away, could no longer bear the feeling that the beggars were the equivalent of flocks of pigeons in a Roman square, rising up en masse as tour-ists moved among them to see the fountains. So I gave her all I could grab and when the driver admonished me, Kathy leaned over and said, reassuringly, 'That was good to give her money – she was a widow . . . when her husband died, they turned her out into the street.' And then she told the driver in Hindi to shut the fuck up in her light lilting failing voice.

When it was time to leave the roof – we were heading to the guesthouse that day, the one among the reeds and toads with the royal who bellowed at the boy bringing me my yogurt on a silver tray because he had peeled the foil lid neatly back – I went first to keep Kathy from tumbling and then she sat to descend the stairs, working them one by one, first feet, then butt, then feet, and Emma coming last, with the canes. I got to the bottom, ducked my head, and stepped into the empty ballroom that was no longer empty to face rows and rows of chairs filled with Chinese men in suits, affluent-looking but not like businessmen; more like a religious cult. Everywhere men in rows, each holding some kind of prayer book, and the podium was now banked by flowers and occupied by a man who had come to a halt in his sermon as a woman – me – appeared next to him.

Then came Kathy laboriously crawling, and the men in the chairs could see just her feet, which she was picking up manually, by her thighs, and setting down, then moving to sit on the next step, then manually putting the feet one step lower, et cetera.

And so she materialized in the room, legs first and then her face, concentrating on the task of not falling, and when she looked up she saw that we had descended like Spider-Man into the theater of whatever this was. I saw her pulsate with shame for a moment on the last step, her dead legs asprawl, her face radiating something both false and beautiful, like the big plastic flower on the wall of the Marigold Hotel, and then she grinned. Big and real. In her handmade Indian hat that made her look eccentric and hip, in her gauze shirt and yoga pants, letting Emma and me haul her to her feet and fasten the canes to her forearms. She smiled so radiantly and so wickedly, and we walked, *click-click, click-click*, down the flower-banked aisle, *click-click*, past the pious-looking nervous men who stared not at us but at their books, their laps, the vault of the castle-something ceiling, and past their leader, the man at the podium who waited until we had gone through the doorway to the elevator alcove before he resumed his sermon.

It always seemed like we were trying to hold on to her, grasping smoke, watching her disappear, but in that flower-festooned moment, Kathy emerged corporeal, the stone wall giving birth to her, feetfirst.

*

The thing that I didn't want to say and still don't but of course will is that a roomful of pious men is frightening to me, whatever message the guy at the flower-festooned podium was booming out in his patient and insistent way. As we clicked past them, their palpable repression met my self-consciousness and Emma's worry and it was like walking through damp cheesecloth or someone's sodden sorrow. And poor Kathy, always the target of everyone's frantic bleak horror, but still she had mirth on her face, and as soon as we stepped into the elevator she would put the whole thing to rest with some deadly comment like she did everything else. If she had still been alive when M. left me, for instance, I know her exact words upon hearing the news – which I would have delivered to her first, just for the sheer jolt of it: '*I knew it!*' she would have said, and later she would have told Emma how she had never trusted him, but she wouldn't have told me, because of course she was too diplomatic for that and because she was too astute to show her hand before the outcome was determined.

Yesterday, on a rocky path up through the Arizona saguaros, Mary got me to call out for help to my higher power, but right now I feel connected to my lower power. When M. told me how he and P.R. got started, I said to him, *Thanks for going to the place I love best in the world, the place where I go to do my work, the place that feels like my grandmother's house when I walk in the door . . . thanks for going there and trashing it.*

I was connecting to my lower power, trashing it being just a figure of speech and not even a particularly good one for a writer. Also not fair to the place, which is an elegant old art colony with fountains and woods and a pond where men go to fish for bimbos. I only say that because of her fur coat.

*

180

Roomfuls of pious men, male writers, the National Book Awards or some other publishing event that I attended as M.'s plus-one long ago, and there was Kathy as her own plus-one at the same thing. Kathy in some beautiful gold-threaded getup, standing on her own sturdy legs, no canes, no wig, no walker, looking gorgeous and wicked, drifting past my table every once in a while to report some gossip or point someone out. Nancy was there too, and the three of us at some moment were packed into the ladies' room trying to get our makeshift outfits to look more like what the other people were wearing, tugging and tucking and squinting with our mirror faces and then giving up to go back out and be what we were and what those of us remaining still are: wallflowers and observers. And then the rumor suddenly rose like a wind, that the Famous Writer's beyond-beautiful new wife was there. A human version of the amazing delicate blooms Mary and I keep finding on our walks through the Arizona desert right now, the tiny, tiny petals edged in fringe, or the ones that look like miniature stars, or the little sprays of daggers that you have to photograph close up in order to distinguish the petals, or the ones that look like clusters of purple air, they are so insubstantial. The Young Wife's reputation preceded her, and so Kathy and I decided we would detour over there and more or less innocently walk past her – just browsing – and see for ourselves what all the fuss was about.

First of all, she wasn't real. Or she was real in the way the purple-air flowers are real. Narrow, willowy, utterly dramatic, in an evening gown that was the color of the sunset last night over the Tucson Mountains, pink-white and yellow and diffuse, like sunlight and starlight at the same time, and it sounds like hyperbole, but it's true. She looked like she was made of honey.

'The truly beautiful don't have pores,' Kathy explained afterward, meaning the ones who appear in magazines and on TV shows and in movies and on rooftops pushing brooms. We brushed past, behind her, and we saw she was smaller than us but also larger somehow, narrow but tall, and her husband sitting next to her, hooded eyes and broad shoulders, was holding forth to someone or everyone, but nervously, like a man who was being pursued. Aware that he had charge of this creature who was so much more than he was. Beyond young, beyond lovely, beyond him. A porcelain figurine that must be dusted with a paintbrush and that you will absolutely drop at some point, not because you're clumsy, but because that's your destiny.

She dropped him instead, or they dropped each other, and the last time I saw a picture, it looked like her face was altered. The exquisite features were relaxed and sunny away from the Famous Writer, who looked, in that moment still frozen in my mind, like he was coiled around something, nodding as he listened, watching as the current of people moved past, and past, and past.

So – the Young Wife and the large room filled with the deafening sound of tableware being handled by the writers and the not-so-writers. Me. And the large room in India filled with the repressed men staring at their laps – *the laps of men* – and Emma, long after India, in a diner upstate, explaining to M. over coffee what it means to a young woman to attach herself to a much older man. M. across the booth, listening to my friend reason with him on my behalf.

And many years before, back in Iowa struggling with writing, smoking my Vantage cigarettes on Mary's couch, the fabric blue-and-white ticking, like a mattress or a bomb, and her fake-hypnotizing me and me climbing downward internally into my mental cellar, opening the door, and seeing my young mother asleep in the middle of a summer party, one leg flung over the arm of a chair, her face pretty and sunburned; even in black-and-white, you could see the sunburn. The vision came from an old picture taken in a fishing cottage before I was born, aunts and uncles drinking beer and playing cards and my mother missing the party. Kathy, missing the party. Both of them dying in the very middle of their lives. Kathy waltzing past the Famous Writer. The Young Wife's dress that was like a vivid sunset made of some kind of iridescent nylon, like those wavering images crossing the dun-colored roads, fluorescent and curved. The Arizona skyline at sunset, with its pattern of crescents, clouds in the shape of quote marks, framing some thought that I can't even bring myself to say. Almost geometric, they looked, and decorative, like P.R.'s paintings, or like something made at the county fair by a child.

The local county fair. M. already burned out on it by the time I came along, all those years of watching his children run loose there while he wandered the aisles of exotic poultry and the food booths that don't improve matters – fried dough, French fries, various meats on sticks. Cotton candy. I always said, *You are the best-looking man I know. I love the way you look.* I meant it, but nobody ever believes that stuff. Poor all of us, with our terrible self-images, and poor me trying to convey my true opinion: *I love the way you look.*

The clouds, turning my words into air quotes.

I loved the way he looked.

So the fair. The chickens, the cows, the parts that we loved together – the dogs doing their sheep wrangling. Him watching my face while I enjoyed the show. 'It's great how much you love things,' he used to say sometimes. When we would land in an especially fun hotel somewhere, with a beautiful view or a room-service menu with vegetarian options. 'I love traveling with you,' he would say.

I love you.

I always meant to say those words to Kathy, but there wasn't a time when I could because her goal was always to be alive and moving toward health, not alive and moving toward death. To tell her I loved her would have been like telling her she had to go into hospice. Which I did. The look on her face, lips pressed together, a head shake – absolutely not. And I kept coming at it from different angles, saying, Please just talk to this woman, she's a nurse, she'll make it better; being in hospice just means you won't have to take another ambulance ride, it just means they will come to you instead of you going to them. I said *hospice* with air quotes around it, little vaporous flourishes.

The famous writer with the porcelain wife, his head nodding as gracefully as a wildflower on a stem. Viperous, vaporous, lovers and friends, the betrayers – 'Hospice is only a word,' I said, and that word means a home nurse who will keep you from having to get in an ambulance – and the betrayed, Kathy, in her wig on her sofa, nodding uncertainly, her face twisted in a way I'd never seen before, utterly aware of what *hospice* meant, of the fact that she had placed her fate in the hands of someone who was delivering her into the hands of those who would deliver her . . . where? Air quotes over the Arizona sky, invisible fireworks over the Hudson, the concussive sounds of gunfire. A random gunman in his final burst of glory, the Countess's Necklace exploding in the black sky. An exquisite woman in a sunset-colored dress whose face has something different about it now.

'I love traveling with you,' he would say.

On the trip to India, at the Colonel's lodge, M. waiting at home, so far away he couldn't even be imagined, and just beyond the railing of the surrounding deck, through the binoculars, the most amazing birds, odd in the way foreign birds always are – balancing on the very tips of reeds, bending them, or skimming across the low-water spots, bright foliage that turned out to suddenly have a beak, or long thin yellow legs – and just behind me, coming out in the evening from her room, Emma, blond and American-looking, but in that elegant way of women back in the thirties on safari in Africa, lanky in high-belted trousers and a man's silk shirt, only she was on a deck in India surrounded by the Colonel's own birds and wearing a soft white blouse over blue jeans and an Indian scarf in a kind of bright maroon, puckered with handwork and perfect-looking. Worried, as always, and letting the Colonel's arrogant ministrations get on her nerves a little bit. It was later that night I heard the stereophonic vomiting from her room and Kathy's. So, the bright gold and red birds – there were green parrots too, in flocks, settling and then startling. The servants coming through to build a fire, to give us tea, to put pillows under our feet, to treat us kindly. Kathy clicking her way out, making idle chat with the Colonel, who was lowering his face every once in a while down into the basement galley to intimidate and harass the men who were sweating down there. She would sometimes turn to us and speak quietly and deadpan right in front of him about him, but he wouldn't hear it, his ear tuned only to a certain frequency of conversation, some combination of flattery and ornate respect and a female trying to appeal to him. He wasn't much older than us, and yet he took on the air of a beloved uncle, much adored, even though we didn't even like him. The Kernel, we called him.

Some other Raj type showed up that night after her dinner out to have us pay our respects to her as well. She was gorgeous and silver-haired, her sari draped so elegantly that I couldn't stop staring at it; how did it stay like that, flung just barely over her shoulder, the folds framing her stark collarbones and the battered silver necklace heavy with rocks. She showed up not because she wanted to meet us but because she wanted us to meet her – these royals, even the meaningless ones holding meaningless titles, still have a sense of duty.

After we were allowed to stagger off to our rooms, the other two attending to their puking duties and me in my heavy-blanketed bed with my imaginary friend and his companionable book, I saw another mouse – a small gray something that moved to and fro in the shadows of the room. And I heard the deer-shouter, and I could feel the presence of all those birds, and it came over me that here, in a hunting lodge somewhere in India, cold, with a hot brick down by my feet that had been wrapped in flannel by the servant, listening to the muffled agonies of my friends, I missed M.

'I love traveling with you,' he would say. Because we got along so well away from home, finding our way up and down various streets and countries, draped across each other on airplanes, writing about what we saw, or driving in cars, me in the passenger seat taking notes as he described what we were experiencing. His descriptions so startling that I would be in writerly awe, scrambling to record them, then later stitching the notes into a rough draft that he could look at to write whatever piece he had already sold in order to justify the trip.

But not in India. In India I was with my girlfriends, and we woke the next morning, both of them tottering, not even green but a pale, waxy yellow, into the sunlight on the hunting lodge's deck. In Kathy's room, where I went to retrieve something for her, I saw vomit pooled in her bed, *pooled*, and then a trail down the long hall to her bathroom, palm prints on the wall where she had staggered along. Nobody ate breakfast, and the car was coming to pick us up for Udaipur. Both of them were delicate, like the foreign birds on the reeds, swaying. Kathy thinking she might faint, but not really saying so; Emma, elbows on knees, staring penetratingly at the wood planks of the deck between her feet, everyone in her own, not world, but underworld. When the car came, we continued to sit. That day's driver understood. He knew us from before and Kathy from before that. And she had yelled at him once in Hindi. 'I just had to,' she explained. Otherwise he wouldn't take us where we wanted to go but where he wanted us to go. Whatever she said seemed to work.

186

They walked carefully to the car and got in the back seat, leaving me in the front, shotgun on the left side, a strangely precarious and foreign spot to be in. The car revved up and bounced onto the highway, and we began weaving through the mess, dogs trotting between us and the rocketing semis, Kathy and Emma breathing behind me, audibly, in all that commotion, and the yelled-at driver swerving us, over and over, into the oncoming.

'I love how much you love things.' Room service in an Italian hotel with such wide corridors that it felt like some kind of intricately patterned carpeted avenue, foreign, like all the foreign things – the tiny birds on the reeds that won't stop flitting inside my writing mind, swaying back and forth like the two people in the back seat, their queasiness made manifest by the veering around potholes and sacred cows. Don't get me started on the cows, downtrodden and starved. They may not get eaten but they also don't get fed.

They were skeletons with hide not even stretched over them, but tossed, like a filthy rug, heads hanging low as they moved slowly and inexorably through the cities and across the highways, refusing to acknowledge anything but the dirt in front of them, searching, searching, always searching for some morsel, a strand of green poking up through the packed ground. The dogs trotting purposefully along, more aware, in the way of dogs everywhere, of humans than of their machines – cars and motorbikes and even trains (a friend's dog hit by a train while she stood calling, urgently, urgently, and the dog wandering in a parallel universe, sniffing the ties, feeling the joy of not paying attention to that familiar voice on a beautiful, sunny, promising, leashless afternoon) – but the Indian dogs know to steer clear of humans. I saw a man on a motorbike veer close to one, a white-gray dog trotting along, wearing its ribs like a grotesque vest, and just as

187

he went by, the man gave it a good kick that sent it sprawling in the dirt.

Blam.

The horse sending out a foot every once in a while through that long night with me in my netted bed, cold, with my book.

The dog went flying and I looked away, couldn't tell the others because we weren't telling each other things except for that moment when Kathy reassured me about the widow at the window, the bouffant woman with the scarf knotted so carefully at her throat, begging for change.

Otherwise, we were seeing and absorbing, no comment about the staggering cows, the children running through traffic with their hands out, the seemingly whole litter of puppies that had been driven over on the road, a scene of such carnage glimpsed for a total of three seconds of my entire long life that I looked through it and beyond and not until this moment, a long time later, am I remembering it with any sense of what it was.

Don't try to distinguish the details, the different body parts or the mother dog standing just off to the side, her nipples hanging down like sorrow, her face impassive. All of them dead, and none of us even bothered glancing at each other.

'I love how you love things,' and the wide carpeted avenue of the Ritz, and the two of us ordering room service in Portugal instead of going out, and watching a movie that was so hilarious we were giddy, floating around the room clutching our guts, standing on our balcony in the dark, looking out at Lisbon, me from Moline, and him from Chicago. Him a man, and me just me.

Someone who didn't necessarily belong in Lisbon. (I didn't know where Portugal was when we decided to go there – had to secretly look at a map, which I then told everyone about, because it surprised me where it was, and I discovered that some other people whom you might have thought were vaguely smart thought Portugal was in South America.)

The Birdcage was the movie. Like my childhood, all those birds in cages, and me knowing it wasn't right but not being able to put my finger on it, like looking for Portugal in South America and not finding it. But finding Paraguay.

The canaries swinging desperately on their swings, lonely, singing and singing, while I fluttered around, wondering how to connect. I loved them, those creatures, the finches I would get, one pair after another, and keep until they died. Of loneliness, or drafts, or simply the fleetingness of their feathered life spans. *The Birdcage* in that hotel room, where we wheeled the ravaged room-service cart back out into the wide avenue and then closed our door on the world; the bathroom, too, was marbled and marvelous, with heated floors and seats and a sprawling tub where I could soak my body. 'Nooks and crannies!' he cried once into the bathroom at home – not yet my home; I was visiting – when I arrived and said I needed to shower before getting into bed with him. 'Nooks and crannies!' which made me laugh really hard, like *Birdcage*-hard. Or the other times when he would do whatever to amuse me – since we're on a showering theme, say, fill a pitcher with cold water and step into the bathroom and throw it into the shower. What you don't know is how odd that feels, to be in a hot shower, in that hot-shower psychic space, eyes closed, soaking in the sensation, and then a big dollop of cold water from above, startling you into the moment and into the smeared reflection in the smogged mirror of a man ducking back out. And you, naked and thrilled, wondering at what has happened and where you have found yourself.

The mother dog, naked in her confusion, standing with her nipples hanging down. The Lisbon bed, and then the shower with its heated marble, and the balcony with the lights sparkling all around us, the Indian rani, with her battered silver necklace embedded with stones. The Countess's Necklace, exploding in the various skies, over Udaipur, over Moline, over Paraguay.

The birds on the reeds, swaying, and the birds in the birdcages, swinging to and fro, singing in their joyous anguish.

'I love the way you love things,' and then the startling moment when the cold water splashes down.

The kicked dog sprawling on the Delhi street, the staggering cows, the scent of the poultry barn at the county fair, so thin and sharp it was like a dog whistle, unmistakable. Hen shit. The alien creatures in their stacked cages, bristling heads, fountains of feathers, odd herringbone patterns, scarlet rims around their eyes, detailed like the tiny flowers in the Arizona desert, rickrack around their edges, the yellow daggers protecting a soft furred stamen, the ones with petals so small and precise. The piles of painted rocks, only they aren't painted, they are petroglyphs somehow etched in a way that lasts a thousand years and counting, and nobody knows what the images mean. The artists still not understood, long past their time and eventually past ours. The county-fair Spirograph paintings that children stand in line to make, M. and me traipsing along the midway, arm in arm, and a barker shouting to him, 'Bring your daughter over!' Which was creepy at first, but then we realized it was the guy's way of flattering both of us. If that was ten years ago, then P.R. would have been just graduating from college, sharp-featured and aimless, like a nurse shark moving along the bottom of a cracked pool.

Male writers who end up with more than they deserve, and less.

Me moving at some point from the high-bouncing front seat, the aerie of despair, into the back to sit with Kathy, trading with Emma, who needed the open window, gulping the burned Indian air, eyes closed. The driver was doing it again, insisting on taking us where he wanted us to go instead of our destination, but this time I agreed with him. He wanted Kathy to go to the hospital instead of the hotel.

'Please, Kathy-ji,' he kept saying, turning around to beseech her while the oncoming traffic – cars, trucks, dirt-colored scraps of hide and humanity, fluorescent flourishes and, amazingly, fleetingly, a set of elephants wearing big square empty saddles – careened past us.

'No,' she said to the ceiling of the car, eyes closed, head tipped back, hands on her stomach. 'No,' and she said it cheerfully. Do not. Try to. Make me.

'Please, Kathy-ji,' I said jokingly.

Please, Kathy-ji. The elephants were monumental and dusty; they swayed back and forth as they walked, like the tiny birds on top of the Kernel's reeds, like the nauseated women in the car.

At the Dutchess County Fair, years before, Kathy had climbed into something called the Zipper and then waved at me from high in the air, upside down. 'I have the inner ear of a much younger woman,' she had told me. The inner ear and youthful flexibility being why kids could tolerate getting turned upside down and shaken but adults couldn't. I pictured her inner ear like a carpenter's level, with its bead of water and accommodating bubble. No matter how the world tipped her, she could right herself. Stage four went to stage three went to stage two went to stage one. And then back again, roaring, like a crowd in a stadium, like the Colosseum, or like the buzzing of bees when they are swarming. But at the Dutchess County Fair, sometime before the emperor turned his thumb down, before the hive was poked with the cancer stick, when she still had a shining cap of dark hair and two long sturdy legs and a desire to eat midway food, she got put in a Zipper cage, the bar lowered over her lap, some kind of shoulder harness click-ing into place, back to back with a boy of twelve or so, and the guy ran them right up to the top, fast, where they spun a few times – the Zipper's cage turning vertically and horizontally, if you can picture it – and then came to rest with their hands braced against the ceiling, upside down high in the air, and the boy vomited inside the cage, through the steel mesh of the ceiling, a glop, whereupon suddenly the guy jolted them back into motion, and the Zipper swept down, spinning, along the ground and stopped while the people on the other end got their turn to be terrorized.

Inner ear of a much younger woman notwithstanding, Kathy nevertheless bent over and gave a couple of delicate heaves behind a blue canvas tent after she came off. 'That was *really fun*,' she said.

Please, Kathy-ji, but she wouldn't go to the hospital because she knew what we didn't, that they wouldn't be able to help her there. She was happy to be sick with food poisoning, in fact; it was normal and banal and what happened to everyone who went to India – the normalness of it was thrilling to her, and the vomiting, let's face it, old hat.

An old Russian hat and a long fur, P.R. posing in front of Lenin's tomb. Compliments of Facebook. Of course I wasn't supposed to look, but it's hard to resist, the thin stink of curiosity linked with jealousy. Vamping in front of Lenin's tomb, what could be a better dog whistle for M., who comes from the loins of Communists, the romance of it, the thin stink of people who wouldn't be duped by the capitalist state into buying products that weren't needed, like deodorant.

His mother, when asked if she had any spare feminine-hygiene products, explained that she just used toilet paper. How do you do that when you're bleeding like, to use a cliché, a stuck pig? An image of which comes back to me from Kathy's own memory – her calling me from a research trip to India long ago, sobbing on a little street in a little town, saying that she had been walking and found herself in the midst of a group of men doing something to a pig, and then she dissolved again, hiccupping and gasping, and wouldn't say any more. Later she told me that what she had seen and what it had sounded like – a woman being slowly murdered – was the worst thing she had ever witnessed in her life.

Endless damage, endless blood. What a woman most wants when she is bleeding like a stuck pig is a fucking Midol, but what the actual stuck pig wants, of course, is to simply die, to be released from the suffering. But the body holds on, the terror holds on, the shrieks on a dusty city street, the woman who staggers past, hand against her mouth, then leans in a doorway, cell phone against ear, and calls me in my barn studio in upstate New York; she has to tell someone, and then I do too, my friend was so upset, so far away and upset, and I walk over to the house.

He's standing in the living room when I come through the front door, and the TV looks guilty. Afternoon baseball or CNN, or anything that isn't writing. The books he's written, elegant and beautiful and harrowing, are mostly about terrible damage that leaves someone's life tilted, upside down, vertiginous: a flare lodged in the throat of a man who is being cuckolded; a careening car smashing a disapproving father into paste on a Chicago street, like dog gore in India; a man beaten to death methodically and for no real reason in a clearing in the woods.

I love the way you love things.

I sink down on the couch, warm from where he was sitting a few moments before.

'Kathy saw something happen to a pig,' I tell him.

The damage that male writers do, to their characters, to their partners. The Young Wife in her shimmering sunset dress. Mia Farrow, shimmering in her rage, her daughter growing older in front of our eyes, turning stolid and bossy, making herself into a fishwife so we'll believe Woody Allen is at *her* mercy.

Brooke Shields with her lovely beetle brows, nothing between her and her stone-washed jeans. Jodie Foster in a picture hat and hot pants, nothing between her and the taxi driver who thought he owned her pussy and the tender, bemused girl that surrounded it. P.R. herself sprawled out on a living-room rug sometime in the '80s, with pushed-up bangs and little-girl shoulder pads, LET'S GET PHYSICAL in silver paint on her sweatshirt.

Let's get physical, with braided headbands lifting the perm-burned curls, all those '80s legs standing in all those droopy leg warmers, the giant wrinkled tree trunks of the elephants' legs, lifted like big leather columns, dragged through the dust, and set down again. One after the other after the other, their trunks swaying with them, feeling the ground gently, searching and searching, like the sacred, starving cows, moving along the ground, seeking the one pale shaft of green coming up through the packed dirt.

All those male writers, with their pale shafts, getting what they deserve, and less. Soon-Yi, posing for the man she knew as a father while he stares cartoonishly through his glasses, gulping and stuttering like the male actors he hires to embody his libido. The guy at the county fair, with his flattery and his chew: *Bring your daughter over!* P.R. in her stone-washed jeans, nothing between her and M.

Let's get physical. Kathy staggering along on the crutches that circled her forearms like a medical version of those wide silver manacle-like bracelets we wore when we were teenagers, trying to tan around them so we could have that pale stripe that made us even browner and even more white. Girls with their mana-cled arms, prisoners and not prisoners. *Bring your daughter over!* And Soon-Yi, the most lovely girl, according to Woody, like Mariel Hemingway, his high-school crush, though only one of them was in high school. Mariel with her pleading, uncertain, heliumed voice. A prisoner and a not-prisoner, both.

Arriving finally at the next hotel, pale yellow plaster walls with creamy arched doorways, open-air living, gravel walkways and large clay bowls floating with blossoms, Kathy-ji on the ground floor and Emma and me one story up, side by side, so we could walk out of our rooms and look down on hers in the temperate blue evening. Her coming right back out, crutches braceleted, to make her way up to where we were. The pea-gravel path impossible, the crutches couldn't maneuver it, and as she struggled, us standing back so she couldn't see us seeing her, two men rushed out of the office in their white billowing sleeves and drawstring pants, stiff embroidered vests, and despite her protestations, they put her in a carry chair and then bore her, like royalty, across the courtyard and up the flight of wide stone steps that she had planned to climb in her usual way – backward and butt-first. I saw then, as they were bringing her up to us, something I didn't see at all, or maybe only once, in the whole long time of her dying. As the men carried her across the pea-graveled courtyard and up the wide stone stairs to where her friends were waiting, she was crying.

On a train to nowhere, through some forested region, just a way to see the countryside and be ferried along with the locals, some of them children who jumped on in order to continue staring at us, Kathy resting back on the bony wooden bench, watching the treetops sweep by while the train climbed in its shambling way along a mountainside. Watching while being watched, and Emma and me farther down the bench, our fear sitting between us like a shaky friend. Swaying along the open windows to the train john, one car down, where I thought I might take a pee. Kathy saying, *Oh, that will not be an option,* but I went anyway, the children following, and no, it was not an option, the sight of it like scatological carnage, just an instantaneous glimpse before slamming the door shut again, but still burned into memory, like one of those black-and-white photos that you see in a true-crime book, a room with its innocent fixtures and then something dark splattered all over the walls.

Hard to imagine where to go with this next. From the bony bench to the fever and the scum-brown bowl, as Joni Mitchell said in her song about heroin addiction. Not the usual glamorizing of addiction, though the cold blue steel doesn't sound altogether unappealing, and of course Lady Release is what everyone is after in whatever way they can find it. Through the cold blue steel, if necessary, or through another song's even headier lyric about the swooning addiction of romance. *Love, the strongest poison and medicine of all.* Joni in her peasant dress and her tinkling bracelets. Kathy, slipping her forearms through the crutches in order to stand for a while on the train, hanging on to the window frame with white knuckles. I stand up at the window too, and then Emma, on her other side. Out the window is a plunging precipice, no ground visible at all, just leaves and branches, the tops of trees, and then slowly a gravel path rises up, and then a bench, a trash can, another expanse of wider path, and suddenly the train is at a stop and the passengers who board our car are monkeys – a whole troupe of them, blond with dark faces, like shaggy people with business to conduct. They sweep in through the open windows where we are standing and swarm us, holding out their black leathery palms, feeling inside our pockets, swinging through the car and then back again, in and out the windows, and then the train wakes up and begins moving at a crawl and the monkeys are eating our granola bars and the fruit that Emma had in her bag, and they're staring at us like very aged children, waiting to see if anything else develops while we pick up speed and the trees start moving past in a way that has a blur involved, and suddenly with one motion they all climb out the windows and we're alone again on our train. Like Joni all those years ago with her German wine, dreaming of watching his hairline recede, her vain darling.

*

Early years, late at night, sock hops in the bedroom lamplight, him playing all the music he wanted me to love. Sam Cooke, Iris DeMent, Steve Earle, Irma Thomas, Alanis Morissette. Alanis Morissette? I couldn't be made to admire that one, though it's funny in retrospect, both of us lip-synching about being a pill.

I love how you love things. Lying on the bed smoking a cigarette – that's how long ago this was – and watching him listen to music. My vain darling.

And yet. Our playbook of hilarious moments, accumulated over the years. Mostly his jokes, maybe two were mine – my one about butter, my one about word of honor. His famous Cold Spring joke that required me to pull the car over to the curb and put it in park, the two of us like people having seizures, no laughs coming out at all but simply twisting grimaces for at least a full minute while we writhed inside our seat belts, like a woman I once saw on an airplane. Across the aisle from me, wearing a Chanel suit and reading a magazine, the plane hadn't taken off yet, and suddenly her body went into convulsions and foam began pouring out of her mouth. I threw off my seat belt and stumbled over and tried to hold her down, and then the aisle filled up with the tall flight attendants, feverishly flipping through a spiral-bound book of laminated emergencies while I tried to keep her from hurting herself, just mostly moving her stuff out of the way and noticing the odd terrible detail – her feet, out of their pumps, balled like fists, her glasses sideways on her face with foam on the lenses – and at some point someone came down the aisle, a man who said he was a paramedic, and the flight attendants sent him back to his seat because a doctor was already handling it.

'I'm not a doctor!' I shouted. It's the only time I've ever raised my voice on a plane, and it was as frightening in itself as any other part of it. Once, coming back from Italy with M., who was in writhing pain from a back ailment, I had to, a couple of times, take out one of those emergency ice packs that you have to punch in order to activate the cold-making apparatus inside. Each time I did it, I went through a whole rigmarole to keep people from hearing it and thinking it was a gunshot. The narrow stainless-steel bathroom, the loud flush timed to coincide with the fist to the gut of the blue pack. The startling pop, like there was a shooter on the plane, some gunman who didn't like how paltry the peanuts were. The woman in the Chanel suit was taken off in a stretcher specially designed for an airplane aisle, and once we were up, the flight attendants offered me treasures from business class – a warm washcloth for the foam, a silver dish of sliced strawberries.

The Cold Spring laugh might have been the best, but there was also the wedding-dance laugh in my hometown that came later – almost at the end – M. the writer demonstrating to me his new dance move that involved a series of motions whose meaning I couldn't decipher no matter how many times he did it. Locking eyes with mine and shuffling his feet, he would poke the air with one finger and then poke the other air with the other finger. What? And then he explained, shouting into my ear, as the young people, my niece the bride and her midwestern hip-hop friends, floated around us in their lace and tattoos.

His new move was *control-print*.

The purple walls, the red walls, the Arizona fever dream of the house I escaped to with Mary after he went off with P.R. That bathroom with the perfectly calibrated showerhead, the weird feeling of reaching in and having to touch a jewel-encrusted wall while looking for the light switch in order to take a pee during *Nurse Jackie* binges, the parched yard with the sporadically placed plants and the BEWARE OF SNAKES signs that seemed metaphorical, though they weren't. The rattlesnake on the road, stretched across the other lane, and how the next day we were afraid it would still be there smashed flat, and thankfully it wasn't, and that mound of petroglyph rocks that had its own THIS IS A SNAKE AREA sign. But that vacation house is what I mean to remember, the wild walls and the big, hideous, mood-flattening painting that I had to hide so it wouldn't disrupt my dreams, how Alice calls every morning on her way to school in New Jersey to say, 'Honey, how are you?' and what a nice last name Dark is. And how I walk around and around that yard, nervous energy, soaking up the sporadic-ness of the planted cactuses and the little nubs here and there of the useless irrigation system poking through, and the hot tub we aren't actually insane enough to use, and then my favorite part – the Flintstone steps leading to the roof, where the whole desert becomes the theater and us the audience, that first taste of my end-of-day beer, which is always the moment when the anxiety starts to leach out of me, like sweat cooling on the skin. Sitting with Mary in those chairs with our tortilla chips and cold beer and the incredible Barbara Kingsolver scribble of mountains on either side of us, the evening train in the distance running on the tracks, so many cars, endless, desert-Southwest-long, a Joni Mitchell train, with its brakes complaining. *I used to count lovers like railroad cars, I counted them on my side. Lately I don't count on nothing, I just let things slide.* I've never let anything slide in my life, that's the sad truth. But our roof, with the scrawl of mountains and the blue mist sometimes and the vivid pink and coral stripes, the crispness of the air and the joy of listening to Mary's thoughts, that particular joy of knowing another person's past and present so completely.

So the roof, and my beer and her wine and talking and the scribble and the train that you could almost hear moving along the tracks, the way they do, the wheels on the rails, and the rocking sound. And in the mid-distance, the sprawl of Tucson and the interstate, the concrete connection Emmylou Harris sang about in a song I'll never be able to listen to again. How when she says the word *interstate* and her voice throbs, you realize that she can bring her emotions to anything, even something as bland, unchanging, and featureless as an interstate highway. Everything heightened, and her touring with Gram Parsons all those lifetimes ago, him killing himself on drugs and music while she had to stand there watching him disintegrate, dropping, as Tony Hoagland would say, through the layers of her care, down and down until she ended up alone on the edge of a canyon – this is from another song – watching it burn. A canyon, the washes where it feels like walking on a beach only without the water, any water, no water, and the cactus flowers everywhere, the scalloped petals, waiting all year to bloom just as Mary and I get off our plane and drive down the bland blond Arizona interstate to take them in, along with the rest of it, the morning when I woke so early and tiptoed to the kitchen for tea and looked out the window and there he was, scabby boy, tall and rangy, trotting purposefully from some harrowing night errand, like Gram Parsons at the end of a bout of drinking, heading home without his guitar or his shoes, staggering drunk . . . the coyote as a doomed country singer, or as the embodiment of loss, trotting through the dawn light, looking both guilty and defiant. Whatever he had done was already in his past, in his stomach, and he was just looking for a cool spot to sleep it off. The rattlesnake under the rock, the coyote stretched out beneath a friendly ledge, the sun a burning ball punishing everything for the sake of punishing. M. underfoot, the big blue arch of sky overhead, and the darkness falling in streaks of pink, while Mary and I drink.

The weird jewel-embedded Arizona wall, the jewels embedded in the elegant rani's necklace, her stark collarbones, her perfectly draped sari. The Arizona-Indian house with its scorpions and the India-Indian hunting lodge with its incredible accoutrements – the tiny bright birds flitting through the open-air living room, the telephones on each bedside table with a foot of cord dangling free, no jacks anywhere, the empty umbrella stand made from the foot and leg of an elephant, its leather eerily supple and lifelike. The down-at-heel Exotic Marigold with its own raja sitting in a lawn chair in a weedy field, keeping an eye on a worker, a young guy who was lunging the horse ineptly. Emma the horsewoman cringing and finally bursting out, 'You're doing it wrong!' as the horse, big and black, shapely and beautiful, huffed and staggered, the lunge line too loose, its pace too slow. The long whip licking its back delicately every few strides. 'They can get hurt doing it like that!'

The raja crumpling his newspaper just enough to look over it, cigarette dangling. No response from either man. Us turning on our heels and ignoring it, walking back inside the compound, along the ancient white plaster wall with elephants painted on it, the fresco images cracked and disappearing, the elephants' riders still fairly bright and distinguishable – the big boxlike saddles had been re-gilded somewhere along the way – atop the animals, imperious men in pillbox hats. A parade of elephants, their ponderous ghostly bodies fading into bare plaster, their legs gone the way of umbrella stands.

The grounds of the Udaipur hotel, shaved and magnificent, the cultivated shrubs and the men on their knees cultivating them standing up as Kathy and I go past. She greets them in Hindi and they reply, then they follow us slowly, hanging back, to make sure she gets up the ramp to the breakfast room, another man opening the door with a flourish, a white cloth over one arm like a maître d' from an old movie or a cartoon. Completely empty, a sea of linen and small jars of marmalade. I order dry toast and a yogurt, Kathy everything, including eggs. Tea, in a silver pot with a white napkin tied around its handle, and as soon as I pour it I know something is wrong.

Not an inkling, a knowledge. Suddenly I'm encased inside myself and something is in there with me, malevolent.

I have to go, I tell her.

And I leave her in the restaurant, Emma still asleep, with only the cartoon maître d' and the shrubbery men to get her back to her room.

Cutting through the low prickly grass, me and the thing, and across the pea gravel, up the wide marble steps, around the corner, and into my room, close the door and lock it, crawl onto the bed, me and the thing and the thing is getting bigger, forcing me into a corner of myself, on top of the spread, the pillow only half under my head, the bedside light still on from before, shining down into my eyes. Close them. No, open them. Closed, it's just me and the thing, whatever it is. Open, it's me and the thing and the light, bearing down. For hours I can't reach up and turn it off, can't raise the hand that would do it, can't shift my head enough that the light isn't shining in my eyes, can't do anything but lie there, trapped inside myself with the thing.

Once I think I'm going to throw up and am suddenly wringing wet, even the bottoms of my feet. I try to groan and can't; I try to roll over and I can't. I'm reeling without moving. Then it begins evaporating and the shivering begins, all internal, the barest movement. I still haven't turned my head. This is worse than death. This is all the suffering I've ever heard about or seen wrapped into the silent package of me. The beautiful thing about death, I realize somewhere along the way, is that it would *happen*, but this is somehow not happening, it's more like a place than an event, and all I can do is exist inside it. Time has stopped, I'm completely motionless, waiting, like an image in those old daguerreotypes of the men sitting against the backdrops, still and unsmiling, staring blankly into the slow process of being created, hats in self-conscious hands. Only I'm being uncreated.

Where are Kathy and Emma while it's happening? I know nothing of anything but the vivid light and the corner of the ceiling, the feeling of the pillow being half under my head, a ledge of cheek unsupported, the rich blanket wrinkled uncomfortably below a shoulder, the fact of the door being locked far, far away, across the continent of the marble floor. They went to visit a poet, I think, in a pedicab, and I see them – my friends in a small compartment being ferried through the streets, the monkeys with their leathery hands reaching into their pockets, the bouffanted widow with her composed smile and her stewardess scarf, the children pushing and shoving each other's hands out of the way to put theirs on top. The driver pedaling and pedaling, sandaled feet pushing down and riding up and pushing down again, the spokes, and then suddenly, a procession of bright shops, open to the street and filled with spangled wares, their owners smoking and calling out to the tourists in the pedicabs, the cows wandering slowly, not following the stream of traffic but weaving and halting, looking for anything, the scooters and motorcycles barely missing them, and then the pair of dreamed elephants with their empty box saddles, like the horse in JFK's funeral procession with the boots turned backward in the stirrups, the empty saddle carrying everyone's grief like a ghostly rider. The poet they were visiting was elderly and wise, a man on top of a mountain like in a *New Yorker* cartoon, and they were climbing the mountain – Kathy-ji crutching and crawling and Emma everywhere, behind her pushing and ahead of her pulling, and at some point I managed to roll over, away from the light, with my face turned toward the locked door and the window with its dark shade, around which was a halo of late afternoon light. A big, lit square that looked like neon at first and then faded into something less, by evening a pale frame around darkness. The room too was being uncreated along with me.

I saw the funeral procession with its horseless rider and its back-turned boots when I was eight, in the living room with my mother, who had set her ironing board up in there to watch and cry into a series of wadded Kleenexes. In memory it's all black-and-white, the woman in the veiled hat, the boy with his locked knees, saluting, my mother poking the iron into the corners of blouses and pleats, my canary in its cage, not yellow but gray. Everything gray. The light is gone now, the frame is no longer a frame, it's a shade and the room is an interior gloaming with just the puddle of lamplight now behind me, warming the back of my head.

And the night stays motionless, just me and the thing encased inside me, and the two of them somewhere else now, back from the poet's, at some point a soft tap on the door and my name, then nothing. The nothing grows larger and larger until the vomiting feeling returns, sweeping over and through me, upside down on the carnival ride, the Zipper, spinning with Kathy and the little boy, the three of us hanging above the Rhinebeck ground, and M. down below, looking up. He's holding something on a stick and suddenly I'm wringing wet again, my palms against the bed-spread, my hair, my eyelids, and then the Zipper swings down toward the ground so fast that I faint.

Inside the faint is nothing, but when I come to, the thing is pressing me against the cage, taking up all the room inside me, and the Zipper rises again, and when I look down the lights of the midway are blurred, like all colors of paint, and when the Zipper begins to spin, the paint is flung out, moving in a symmetrical design. Whatever he was holding on a stick is gone and he's no longer looking up but looking around.

My fingers through the mesh of the cage, the thing pressing me and pressing me until I open my eyes and the big square of the window has grown sepia-toned, its edges still dark, like an old photograph. I realize now the boy on the midway ride wasn't the one Kathy rode the Zipper with that time – he's a different boy, younger, a small, small child from a book of death photographs I saw once, only he was alive, arranged on a bed, his face a still mask of suffering, eyes fixed blankly on a ball that had been placed near, one hand with its small curled fingers resting next to it. The ball looked like it might be made of stitched leather, striped, a toy put next to him in his final hours, and then the camera set up too, the long process of photographing becoming part of the vigil. The rest were all death photographs – of babies in their coffins or in their mothers' arms, the photographer called in with his black-draped camera to record the faces the parents wouldn't remember otherwise, the toddler in a narrow casket leaned against the wall, his face already collapsing, a spray of flowers wilting over his fists. The small girl arranged in a chair, propped by pillows and a teddy bear, her eyelids painted to look like her eyes were open. What desperation in that grief-stricken family, to try to make her look alive for the only photograph they would ever have of her. Nothing, though, compared to the look on the boy's face, the patience of his suffering, eyes fixed on the striped ball as he waited.

The elephants at the circus, magnificent feet crowded onto a striped stool, balancing their tremendous weight against the fear of the bull hook, their dark eyes as impenetrable as the boy's, their trunks hanging delicate and expressive, as soft as soft penises, but more interesting. The sacred cows, endlessly grazing the concrete, looking for the pale shafts.

I'm in India and it might be morning – the shade has lightened now, no longer sepia but something else. I sleep for a while but I can still see everything, open eyes painted over my closed ones, and in the cage it's just me and the boy, spinning slowly, the leather ball spinning with us, and then the boy is gone and it's just me.

*

My sister collapsing against the wall and sliding down it in the hospital corridor, sitting on the shining floor, and me sitting next to her, knees up, staring at the opposite wall, tiled in Lutheran green. A nurse handing each of us a paper cup of water, which we drank obediently and then got to our feet and took the elevator down to the cafeteria. Then outside to a big field where she screamed as loud as she could and we took sips of our malts and then she screamed again. We went back in and up the elevator and her son was there with his dad, watching cartoons on the overhead TV, and he drank his malt and, many years later, in art school, made me a beautiful porcelain teapot with small strange cups to go with it.

The telephone is on the bedside table under the awning of the lamplight. I reach for it and dial Emma in the room next to mine.

'My door is locked and I need tea,' I say.

Minutes later a key is turned and an Indian man enters with a tea tray and Emma. She pours it for me but what I want is the sugar, and I empty packet after packet into my nephew's delicate cup. Not my nephew's, sorry. But it is Emma, and I'm sitting up now while she makes her own cup.

'I was sick,' I tell her, and it's true, I was, but I'm not now. Now I want that fucking lamp off and the shade open. The Indian light floods in, illuminating the marble floor, its black veins, the silver teapot with its knotted napkin, the linen hotel robe that Emma is wearing and that we both buy and bring home with us for reasons of flatteringness. Underneath it, I see London and France.

M. on a restaurant patio in Nice, early morning, before the plane to Corsica, plates of loose eggs and an assortment of fruit cut into cunning shapes. Little Eiffel Towers and Arcs de Triomphe.

'You could have a fever,' Emma says.

In Corsica, our crazy-handsome driver, like a movie star, who had lived in Brooklyn for a while but then returned to his native Corsica so his son could be raised in that culture. Me in the back seat staring out at the dense maquis. When I ask him what about the culture, he explains it simply, looking at me in the rearview mirror.

Vendettas.

Back from Arizona, a whole cache of her Kleenexes in a room I don't normally go into. There's a bed in there. I can't change any more linens, I can't clean up after her, or them. Why does she blow her nose so much? Why did she leave her underwear behind? Not really even underwear but something made only to be taken off and left in the sheets, a scrap of pale blue, discovered later, stuck to the side of the washer like a starfish. Me in my unpleasant skinniness trying to look fatter. I've lost a pound for every year we were together. Fell right off, almost gracefully, like stepping out of a dress. P.R. in our bedroom, stepping out of her dress. Blowing her nose. Blowing her nose. And for some fucking reason: blowing her nose.

I can't stand listening to the beating of my own heart anymore, the sound of aloneness. Not that everyone isn't, but most people don't have to be as aware of it. Though there are some, like David and a couple of other people, whom I connect to wholly through that silent idea, of existential solitude. David and I only have to look at each other to acknowledge it. In his office on our campus, where I am a civilian because of an ill-timed sabbatical, choking down a hard-boiled egg while he gazes at me, looking more like Dan Fogelberg than I can even tease him about. I can't stop feeling like I'm going to come unhitched from whatever tether is holding me here and just drift out his window and into the Westchester sky. What a terrible thought, to come unstuck from the world in Westchester, which already feels like limbo or purgatory.

Driving up and down those roads, lost, in the days before GPS and cell phones, and then now, in the days when I know that all those roads are P.R.'s neighborhood. Sadly, no one wants to hear me blame P.R. – first of all, she should be as irrelevant to me as I am to her, and second of all, I'm not listening to what anyone says. She came into my house and blew her nose and his, so to speak, in at least two of our bedrooms. I insist on claiming bitching rights on anyone who does that.

So David, with his kind eyes, in his office, looking like Jackson Browne because Dan Fogelberg is dead, patiently making me take bites of egg, suggesting that I go away for a while, do my writing the way I'd planned, hugging me as a graduate student waits.

And then driving without even knowing I was doing it the four blocks to the shelter, where I couldn't stand to be – all those dogs in all those cages – and the first dog out, humping my leg and then getting loose, poor Georgie, and me frantic and frightened, the thing I've always been afraid of in my years of volunteering, letting a dog get loose, and there it is happening. But she simply sat down, looked very sorry, and let me slip the lead over her head again. Started humping me once more. And then Doug and Ann rescuing me, and then all of us working with her, walking and treating her, teaching her how not to get aroused and overwhelm the humans. Until she was panting with exhaustion, not from movement but from the work of thinking, trying to figure out what we wanted and do it for us and from the work of having three people at once paying attention to her and being out of the shelter and into the sunshine and cold Westchester air of the parking lot. We put a pink collar on her, stout black pit in a pink collar, and I know she slept well that night, dreaming of the three people who wouldn't stop petting and praising her, handing her training treats, paying *attention* like what a dream, what a dream, Georgie Girl, actual humans looking at you. As though you matter, as though you are important, as though their

208

hearts, already broken in one case, are breaking for your effort and your unquenchable hopefulness. The bright sunny cold air of a Westchester afternoon with Jackson Browne somewhere in the background, running down a road trying to loosen his load, and downtown Yonkers and P.R. and M. over the telephone in a hallway somewhere, outside the real place of wherever he was, and me being spoken to as though I were illicit, as though I were the one blowing his nose and dropping the Kleenexes discreetly everywhere. For the mother to pick up, for the lady of the house or the maid.

End of day, or of writing day, almost – long terrible hours of twisting slowly in the cold New Hampshire wind, the noose tight, the toes just barely touching the ground, raw damp and the slowly revolving landscape of Eastern Seaboard trees with their evergreen fringe and their rough gray-brown bark, like the legs of the elephants in India. Me dangling above, not the abyss, but the cold, dark early-spring ground and above my own life, as mysterious and useless as the weird knobs on the trees outside this library window. This big soaring-light art-colony library with its *Mad Men* built-ins in pea-green upholstery, the crimson chairs designed to look like a cross between 1962 and the Jetsons. Everything low and ultra-designed, like my Barbie Dream House, back in the day when a girl could still dream about a house. The walls were cardboard, printed to look like shelves with books and chic modern vases; the furniture was cardboard too, punched out and then carefully folded into three dimensions, made to resemble this very nubbly green sofa I'm sitting on. Same bouclé fabric as Jackie Kennedy's pink-and-blood suit, the one she wore with a matching pillbox hat. My own pillbox not a hat these days but an actual box of pills, intended to take away the feeling I have right now, in this hollow-echoing library moment – anxiety, the veil between me and whatever this is that I can't stand feeling. Barbie as a bride in a long sheer veil, wearing a dress my mother made of brocaded white satin with pearls along the bodice – how did she get the pearls on there? My mother, named Pearl, making a Barbie dream-dress for her middle daughter who never became a bride at all, the daughter with the pale uncertain face and vivid imagination. The middle one, who has now been twice abandoned by a long-term man. Ken dumping Midge for Barbie, in both cases, and announcing it from his cardboard sofa. That daughter, me, could never imagine my way into Barbie's life – it would have required entering the dream along with Barbie, or along with Betsy Wetsy or Chatty Cathy, or along with that eerily human baby doll that I loved because it seemed for a while like an actual baby, almost alive and yet not. It seemed like a dead baby, which is why it put people off, and for that reason I was quite attached to it, poor odd baby. Barbie's dream, my dream, my mother's dream. Pearl, figuring out how to attach the pearls. Tiny holes in the beads to run a thread through and anchor them along the neckline. Barbie's mountainous neckline, that pronounced precipice. Me, dangling from my psychic noose, toes reaching for the damp New Hampshire ground, the yellowed winter grass, and yet still there's a little stand of daffodils, insistently vibrant in the gray-scape, which makes them somehow even more depressing in this rain. And not just to me – to everyone who is walking by here hunched over, the mitten-wearing artists who all seem to understand that I'm not one of them. I smile, I speak, I play Ping-Pong, I watch things on the big flat-screen, sitting in the dark paying no attention whatsoever, and then they put in a DVD of *Mad Men* and I sit in the gloom through that too, just looking at the dream houses and the dresses the women are wearing, the spongy polyester pantsuits the show has evolved into – it must be closer to the '70s than the '60s now in its lengthening plotline – and noticing the little annoying art-directed details. The way they smoke with a lot more verve and self-consciousness than people have ever applied to smoking, and I say that as someone who applied absolutely everything to smoking in my heyday. I smoked like a true madman, not one of these.

I'm sorry, Barbie, but your dream house was made of cardboard, the nubbly fabric was simply a picture of nubbly fabric, that button anchored into the plush pillow was the image of a button. Suzanne Button, my therapist, not plush but angular and real. Thank you to her and to everyone. Thank you to the New Hampshire ground, damp and black, under its bristles of last year's grass and its strange winter moss, for rising to meet my toes just enough that the noose doesn't completely shut me off. I'm not shut off, I'm open. A friend said, 'Your face is so . . . *open*, Jo.' And he meant it as a compliment, but it also scared both of us. Me long ago in Iowa on Mary's blue-ticking couch, me in Arizona on the cloudlike sofa, me in New Hampshire on this pea-green nubbly overdesigned built-in, me on the wall-to-wall carpeting of my parents' broken-dreams house, kneeling over Barbie's living room, bending her in half so she could sit on her cardboard bucket chair. Just like the crimson one over there that a man is sitting in, some artist-stranger who looks deeply immersed in his own panic and e-mail.

The sound of the librarian's quiet and purposeful heels on the sleek architect's dream of a floor, with its dark inlaid strips to point out step edges and its overall impression of rich pale paneling, a room so paneled that even the floor is paneled. And I can hear her walking around, not officiously but just like she has things to do and, yes, her shoes make noise, but she is used to it, this being everyday, her job being this, but also because people who decide to wear hard shoes on a hard floor every day are making the choice that they don't mind so much hearing themselves following themselves as they do their daily tasks. That, to me, is interesting. Different, as my mother would say. *Well, she's different*, about a person who wore something unusual or did something to her hair that impressed. (Never, probably, *He's different*, by the way, because it was already understood that *he*, in general, was different.) Hair that startled being different than hair that was, oh, maybe gently teased to give the bouffant a lift. But not 'piled up,' which was code for a woman trying to look better than everybody else or even just appealing. Like another mom who had super-slender legs that culminated in high heels and that were occasionally encased in black hose and who wore her hair 'piled up' on her head – actually, the technical term would be more like in a French twist, but even to employ the word *French* would imply such a differentness that it could never be uttered in our midwestern town.

Anyway, lucky for me, in the Barbie dream library, with its soundtrack of hard-soled librarian feet and the silent roar of the heating system, the pleasant nubs of the upholstered couch-bench, and the warm flannel of my sweatshirt's cradling hood . . . I somehow dropped off unassisted for the first time in weeks.

Such a nice phrase, *dropped off*, like my fantasy of the Kingston Bridge, of just standing on its ledge, the upstate wind buffeting me, the mighty Hudson reclining against its banks like a friendly blue-green dragon, waiting. How hard could it be to simply decide not to think and step off into the thin infinity that nevertheless feels more substantial – in the imagining – than whatever invisible future I supposedly have in front of me. The erased chalkboard of the rest of my life. A black background and then just swirls of things that have been taken away. My dog, my house, the ducks, the trees, the paths through the woods, the beautiful calm shelves of the study, all those books alphabetized over one long summer month, a letter a day for twenty-six days, surrounded by dusty pages and covers, getting more and more excited as I worked my way around the room. The red barn with the stall in it, the one where along the back wall various bottle ends were mortared into the chinks so a wavering colored light shines through just at a certain moment of the day, like the bottles and jewels embedded in the Arizona bathroom. The crocuses that refuse not to come up even though it's a cold-mud-and-bitter-rain spring, and the fence, with its wonky leaning against its own physics, here and there flattened, getting set back up on its feet each year so it can yaw and go akimbo again, the turtles and the foxes and the inexorable raccoon, making his way through the pond reeds at night, looking for what he can find and pull the head off, drink the blood of. The fisher, a crazy mammal, and the possum who stares into my motion-activated camera like it's a mirror. My studio with its aerie feel and its carved wooden flowers along the beams, its bent copper lights and its view onto a makeshift golf course, the haymow, the wetlands where the painted wood ducks swim in circles, the geese with their khaki babies each spring, and the hawks who sit in the tall trees and stare down. The heron. The bobcat. The dogs in their graves.

India, Arizona, New York City, Westchester, New Hampshire. Everywhere the veil of anxiety, like the statue I saw in a museum once of a beautiful woman, her face veiled – in fucking marble. The most incredible feat of artistic precision, to create a sheer veil over a woman's delicate features . . . delicacy shrouding delicacy, and out of cold stone. It was in one of those museums M. and I visited in Europe, or in New York, or in Paraguay. The funny little museum in Philadelphia when we went there on a road trip, eating some kind of exotic egg dish one morning in a hotel dining room, just the two of us and a sea of tablecloths, the place overbearing in its fanciness and yet the windows stared out into a barren street and a cavernous parking garage, like a de Chirico painting of existential emptiness. The museum we went to later that day was a crowded, converted house, but still venerable. I was driven my usual mad by the fact that the art was hung salon-style, the paintings stacked on the walls willy-nilly. They always claim there's a method to the madness in salon-style galleries but in fact the madness *is* the method, and who needs that when they're already teetering. Anyway, it was fusty, but we had fun and met friends that night for dinner, and I saw after all the years of hearing about the husband from the wife that in fact he really loved her, and teased her – *nobody* teased her, you would think – but also I noticed that he flirted with me. Which was fun and engaging, to have him relate in that way to me, just me, Jo Ann the Plain. And I don't mind being plain, I like the very word *plain*, which brings to mind tall grass, bending, and long flowing landscapes of same, like Julene's family ranch in Kansas, where years ago we stood in the clearing by the back door of the house she grew up in – its windows knocked out, its wallpapered stairways and parlors rained on and faded, horse-drawn buggies and flowers peeling down toward the warped floors in long graceful arcs. Like a doll's house, with missing exterior walls, only for dolls who were in despair, or London Blitz war dolls, and Julene and me standing in the yard, surveying the broken tractor sheds and silos, a rusty pump handle rising out of the prairie grass, which had overtaken everything like green water flowing in the breeze, and suddenly, from nowhere, a huge buck. He'd been sleeping, or hiding, in the yard, mashing the prairie flat in one spot, and he sprang up in front of us, big and brown and as male as it's possible to be, balancing his big rack on his head like the workers in India with their baskets, and leaped – one, two, three enormous bounds – and then disappeared, diving into the green waves and never coming up. He's still out there, and his brothers, swimming through the plains.

So I'm plain and I don't mind it, for that reason, and others.

*

Abandoned houses, abandoned women. Thank you, Sharon Olds, for *Stag's Leap*, and thank you to the friend who put me to bed in her spare room with a copy. Thank you, Alanis Morissette, for singing 'Thank you, India,' during our sock hops late at night. Thank you, weed. Thank you, humor. Thank you, Facebook, a woman vamping in front of Lenin's statue, in her full-length fur and red leather pants, your basic riotous pussy. My friend Greta, who kept her own counsel and didn't think it was that big a deal when a couple broke up due to a third party who was exceedingly young, suddenly yelling over the telephone, *Fur, are you fucking kidding me, she wears fur?* and then bringing me a pan of vegan brownies.

M., sternly, during a phone call: 'You need to stop calling her that. It's beneath you.' And then more pleadingly: 'But anyway, we *like* Pussy Riot, don't we?'

And me, sharply: 'Apparently we do.'

See? Humor.

I am allowing the hurt feelings to be ascendant for once in my life, not stuffing them down, the way we used to say back in group therapy. Where everyone was a woman, and everyone, even the leaders, sat in a circle in a subtly lit room, all of us lotused on our cushions except when we were beating them with bats. Those were the nineties, when you could beat the stuffing out of a pillow in front of a group of interested others while still secretly keeping your own stuffing intact. Where the women would stand up at the end and grasp wrists to make a human cradle for you, and you could, if you were brave, lie back and be rocked from side to side while you cried like a baby. Crying like a baby is a cliché, unless you're the one doing it. Now it feels like rain. Just rain that won't stop, the daylong, weeklong kind where the ground gets soaked to the point that the trees topple. And then when it's over, every-thing feels better, rinsed and sparkling. Allow the hurt feelings to be ascendant ('Your face is so . . . *open*, Jo') because it's better, one assumes, and it is also more realistic. The trees are toppled, yes, but now there's space to feel the new life, what it means to be free of someone else's judgment, of their categorizing, of the insistence that I be other. I am not other anymore. I am the actual one.

Which is the loneliest number.

On the Arizona desert trail alone, the way they tell you never to be, mountain-goating up stone steps, over boulders; my legs are feeling so good compared to the rest of me that I can't slow down. Hawks, vultures, a jackrabbit with parchment ears; the only sound my sneakers and my breath. The trail rises and me with it, sliding in the scree down the other side, regaining traction, and then suddenly just ahead, something that registers as a scrap of fabric, like a striped scrunchie someone had dropped, out of place against the trail.

The snake is exactly the same dappled-dirt color as the ground, but the rattles, black and white, stand out starkly, as they are meant to. The biggest rattlesnake I've ever seen stretching all the way across the trail, thick as my forearm, the head somewhere in a creosote bush, giving me leave to pull out my phone and call Mary, back at the rental house.

Other people's fear always takes my own away. I let her instruct me not to get any closer, to turn around, which I wouldn't have any choice but to do, but then I take a couple of pictures for later of just how enormous and palpable it is and how it's wearing a scrunchie. I move carefully to the left and suddenly see its head, mingled in with the creosote branches, and it's lifted, moving slightly, tracking me. Licking the air. This reminds me of something but in the moment I can't think what it is. Hooded eyes, the head nodding ever so slightly, like a jealous man or the snakes in India that live coiled inside baskets. Cruel confinement, but nobody cares because it's a snake, just like nobody cares because it's a cow, a dog, a litter of puppies smashed on a road, a starved cat carrying half a desiccated rat. Kathy on the phone that time: *A group of men doing something to a pig.*

Emma and Kathy want to spend a night in the glass-and-marble Lake Palace, but I stay behind in the room with its sepia window and its private courtyard where I can read my book and pretend to still be sick. I tell M. over e-mail, sent from the fragrant, lotus-blossomed office on the first floor, that I am cheaping out, but in fact I can't bear the thought of it. People on glass floors shouldn't use crutches.

There are e-mails from him about our dogs, the snow, my favorite duck named Ira whose wife died but who now, after months of feather-shedding grief, has a new wife he's harassing. Standing on top of her, pushing her head under water. The usual. I linger, reading and rereading, until the young woman behind the desk brings me a cup of tea. On the saucer, a tiny purple flower and a small spoon holding a cube of sugar.

'You are here with Kathy-ji?' she asks me. 'How is she?'

She's fine, I say. She's dying.

'Yes,' the young woman says.

But she wasn't then, not yet. In the evening I walk down to the lake through the grainy twilight and a man takes me across to the palace and another man helps me disembark and hands me off to another man who seats me in the gleaming lobby to wait while my friends are summoned. The men are all in crisp uniforms and I am wearing a sheer black dress and some jewelry. I know because there are pictures, and in them we all look happy, eating dinner in

217

a corner banquette under a chandelier, toasting each other with stomach-settling seltzers, holding our dessert spoons over some gooey shared mess that isn't sweet enough.

Emma walks me down to the water, and we wait for the boatman to appear out of the dark, small reflectors at our feet outlining the dock. She and Kathy had gone to a performance sponsored by the hotel during the afternoon, but there had been something off when they told me about it. The whirling dervishes, the bright costumes, lots of bells and beads, neither of them looking at each other or at me when they describe it, their voices careful, so that it seemed frightening somehow. Like speeded-up film in a horror movie, the helpless spinning person possessed by a sirocco. They did say they liked it, though.

'It was a *floor* show,' Emma tells me in a low voice. 'Literally. People were expected to sit on the *floor*! And so of course it was just . . .'

She trails off but I can see it. The cloud of dust whirling in its white sheet, the marble floor covered in cushions, like back in group therapy, the women grasping wrists to cradle and rock the afflicted. Emma and me, waiting for the boatman, the palace aglow behind us and the lights twinkling on the far shore, and in between just us and the black lake.

She wasn't then, but then she was. For a whole long summer she couldn't get upstate to her place down the road from me, alongside a different lake, green and brackish, but the house had a brightly painted front door and a key behind a broken piece of lattice under the deck. Me checking on it every few weeks, all the things she had unwillingly abandoned – the tall brass wading bird standing next to the stone fireplace, the nice sofa and chaise on loan from Emma, draped in sheets, the plastic cat bowls for the cats who died accommodatingly, one and then the other, right before she did, the dark family-heirloom painting that mysteriously disappeared later, along with her car, a late-model black Audi bought right before her legs stopped working. Every couple of weeks, wandering through and around, down to the lake where two summers before we had seen a bright blue frog, squashed flat on the path, and I claimed it had to be a mangled rubber toy from the dime store, because how could it be bright blue.

'I saw it before, when it was alive,' she had insisted, following behind on the path to the lake, where she dived in and paddled around, continuing our conversation. A neighbor appeared with his tiny twins and lowered them off the dock into the green water, where they bobbed, splashing their inflated arms, squealing. Kathy swam out of reach and then floated.

'They instantly peed,' she called to their father, who shrugged.

What painting? the family said after having casually confirmed earlier that it was at the lake house. It went the way of the bright blue frog, which couldn't have existed, could it? Even if somebody saw it.

I did swipe something once when I was there, a pair of fashionable sunglasses sitting on the table by the door. I really liked them, and fuck it, she was never coming back.

'You had a pair of sunglasses by the door and I finally just stole them,' I told her over the phone.

'Ha,' she said. 'Those were yours.' As in, they actually were.

So even then she wasn't, but then she was. One terrible ambulance ride and one even worse cab ride to the ER, where Emma and I had to push and pull her out of the back seat while she clung to the armrest. As soon as she realized what she was doing and possibly the hopelessness of it, she grinned. That was all, just a momentary resistance that unmasked the ferocity. We did that to her.

And then a few weeks later, coming home from teaching, two hours up the Taconic in traffic, arriving in my kitchen long after dark, exhausted and crabby, to see dinner laid out on the long farmhouse table, things I like to eat, and a half-frozen bottle of beer that I like to drink. I'm going to say there were flowers in a vase, though not with the stems cut the way I like them, because everything can't be perfect. Still, country bucolic, and dogs by the wood burner, Shep and Nell, with Rocket banished to a distance for covetously loving me too much, and also for loving the table when it had food on it. Little Rocketman, who ended up dying of an enlarged heart, so literal. The most beautiful dog ever, blue merle with brown eyes, some combination of border collie, Australian shepherd, and lunacy. We had driven all the way to West Virginia to get him after impulse-browsing on the computer.

'Are you going to take him?' the shelter woman had asked as soon as we got out of the car. She had him on a leash, still damp from his bath, trying to wear him out. We were there solely on a scouting mission, we were not committing to anything, we had coached ourselves on the long drive down. Be strict, this is not a small decision, et cetera.

'Yes,' we said.

So, the laden table and Rocket's red glare, the bombs bursting in air. Over India, over Paraguay, over the Hudson, Emma and I running from hill to hill, but all we could see were little puffs of smoke, like the wood burner on that cold night when the wind was gusting. Thank you for making me dinner, and sorry I couldn't eat it, because my phone rang and it was the hospice nurse.

If I wanted to be with her, I needed to come now.

Now? What do you mean, like *now*-now?

Yes, like *now*-now. It is happening.

How do you know that? I just saw her last night; you just *met* her yesterday.

Well, yes, sometimes it works that way.

What way?

The way that they either wait until the very end to go into hospice or they take hospice as the very end, and they go.

She wouldn't do that.

Well, if I wanted to be with her, I needed to come now.

The warm bright kitchen with the dogs on their cushions and the food on the table and the man sitting on the edge of his chair, watching my face.

But how do you know?

A long pause while the nurse is doing something else. Either thinking or shuffling papers or both. She resets the phone close to her mouth and sighs.

'There are signs,' she says. 'The lips have turned dusky.'

And a picture comes into my mind immediately, of Kathy's face, the stately shape of her head, the radiance of her skin the past couple of weeks. Luminescent. Poreless, like the woman on the roof in India. *Dusky* to me means bluish, the crepuscular light at that moment of the day when everything becomes unbearably beautiful, just for a brief, hovering handful of minutes, before it tips into darkness. *The lips are dusky*, I mouthed to M., who squinted. What?

'Her lips are dusky,' I said out loud in a flat voice.

The nurse was talking to someone else too. She was in a taxi, it seemed like, headed to her next miserable destination. She only wanted to remind me, before we hung up, about the morphine in the refrigerator. That I could be generous.

Emma was heading for the subway a minute after picking up the phone.

'Maybe better to get a cab,' I suggested.

M. was still at the table, the dogs were still on their cushions, the fire was still hypnotically warm, and I was back in my coat, making a cup of tea in the mug I had just brought in, the one that said LANDSMAN KILL TRAIL ASSOCIATION, with a drawing of a horse moving through a glade, a rider on its back.

You might think a *kill* is a bullet that lands where it was intended to, but where I live, it somehow is a stream, and the gurgles aren't death throes but the innocent sound of water moving over rocks. Only not always innocent because once I had to wade out into our portion of Landsman Kill and use all my puny strength to pull a poacher's beaver traps out of the mud. I threw them into my trunk, each one still biting a stick. I was driving to western New York the next day to go camping with a friend and somewhere along the way I pulled over and dropped them off a bridge into moving water.

Shep had gone with me on that trip, but it turned out that camping made him so nervous – the hot dogs, the trees, the vast sky – that we had to feed him toasted marshmallows all night to keep him from standing next to the car staring at the door handle. He crawled with me into the tent, though, with his lanky shepherd's body and square boxer's head, and fell asleep before I had my sneakers off. Snoring and slightly smelly and so exhausted by the adventure that he didn't even bother closing his eyes all the way. Sheppy, stop, I told him, nudging his shoulder. You look dead.

I'm tired of trying to describe things that aren't describable, so just trust me: when I swung back onto the Taconic and pressed the pedal, a wormhole opened up and my car entered it. Ninety winding miles in ninety minutes, everything black and sparkling with silence, no headlights but mine, no thoughts whatsoever except a constant telegraphing to the animals: *Stay back.*

At the West Side Highway, my phone rang.

You're *where?* M. said.

A dark beery bar in rural Illinois, some guy throwing picks at a dartboard, some other guy with his forehead on the jukebox, puzzling it out, some other guy bumping the lewd-lady pinball machine with his hip, and young me on a bar stool, balancing a saltshaker on a single grain, wondering if anyone would ever care where I was or what I was doing.

I'm wherever here is.

Once you get the shaker balanced on its beveled corner, you have to blow the salt off the bar so that it can look even more wrong, against physics. When I turned down Fourteenth Street, stretched out before me was a long, impossibly empty corridor of green lights, the nameless Illinois guy pulled back the pinball shooter and sent my silver car gliding through the intersections, one after another after another, until it came to rest in a parking space exactly in front of the building.

She was in her living room, sitting up in the hospital bed, the apartment darkened, candles flickering, a few friends that I didn't know moving about in the dark, her ex sitting glumly in a straight-backed chair, Emma standing in the bright kitchen with Daisy, the home-health aide. Behind them was the fridge with the morphine kit sealed in a plastic bag labeled with a skull and crossbones, drawn in Sharpie by me because it seemed like so many people were coming in and out that a mistake could be made. Kathy had seen me do it.

'You've drawn a skull or two in your day,' she'd noted.

In art class, every other still-life setup had a skull in it somewhere, just for atmosphere. The chalky ivory color of it, the faint temple dents, the tall, expressive teeth, the nose-hole vacancies. Still-life minus the life.

She was surprised to see me there when I was supposed to be upstate but took it in without asking.

'I decided to come over,' I whispered.

The darkness inside was juxtaposed against the lights across the street, an office building where at night you could watch various janitors moving through every floor, pushing big carts. Each cubicle was the same – pick up the wastebasket, tip it into the bin on the cart, put it back under the desk, look around idly, move to the next cubicle. Sometimes when you're desperately trying to preserve a life, it's good to look out the window once in a while and see what you're preserving. A version of it, anyway. Every few cubicles, the guy would do something different, like stop and adjust his earbuds or move his head rhythmically to what he was hearing or reach down into his pants for a second to set something straight. Then you realize: *Oh, right. Life.*

She didn't ask why everyone was there, she didn't ask why the lights weren't on, why there were candles burning, and she didn't relax either. 'Hi!' she kept saying whenever she made out another face in the dimness. We all just sat with her or drifted around, trying to read the spines of the books on the shelves, peering out the window at the office building, resting our hands on the bed – but not on her – whispering. At some point people started clearing out and it was just Emma and me, with Daisy in the kitchen reading a magazine, and Kathy asked for the lights to be turned on.

'So nice of you to come over,' she said formally.

Emma left to go uptown and I said goodbye too, but instead of leaving, I went into her bedroom and climbed on the bed. There were no blankets; all I had was my winter coat, but Daisy came in and put an afghan over my legs. For the rest of the night I drifted, hearing them out there, Daisy helping her get comfortable, the occasional cries and groans every time she had to be adjusted.

The night went on and on, and I kept my eyes closed against the sounds from the living room, but I didn't really sleep, just watched everything replay itself in my head. The moon shining off the limestone walls of the Taconic Parkway, my car moving through the wormhole behind a splash of light, banking around the curves, the guy upending the wastebaskets and rocking out to something in his head, the other guy from long ago rhythmically bumping his hip against the pinball machine, my tilted saltshaker balanced on nothing.

And because you can't make this shit up, it was that same night that the upstate winter wind improbably and nearly impossibly blew open the window on the duck house, and the raccoon, who swung by every night like a watchman with his lantern, sniffing at the cracks where the Mars light of the warming bulb shone through, balancing on the sill to check the window against its sturdy latch, on this one particular night, with its stillness and bitter cold and sudden gusts of wind, the window broke open, carrying the latch and two screws with it, and the raccoon climbed in and killed the ducks, even long-term Ira, who had survived other various lesser encroachments, but this time, no. This time they were helpless, tucked into the warm red bordello of the shed.

The next morning when M. went down to let them out he found the carnage, and later he told me about cleaning it up, the crime scene, and how he came across the little homespun brown female who had burrowed down under the straw and survived. The raccoon, like Richard Speck, had lost count somewhere along the way.

It was freezing in the bedroom and the day wouldn't come but who wanted it to anyway, the office building still and dark, its wastebaskets empty, Union Square for two hours completely silent and then the loud backing-up beeping of the first truck. When it seemed like I could, I went out to the living room in my coat, and when Kathy opened her eyes she didn't know what to think.

I'm just here to sit with you and have my morning tea.

'Oh, good,' she whispers politely.

After an hour or so Emma comes over too and we drink tea and coffee and talk quietly while Kathy listens, or doesn't listen. She is gazing beyond us, mostly, her hands open on the bed, like the little boy in the long-ago photograph, staring through the leather ball placed before him. At one point, Emma looks at me and mouths something.

She's so beautiful.

And it was true – she didn't bother with the wig because it was us, and that made her even more starkly gorgeous; her face was luminous again, the cheeks washed with pink, the eyes bright, the lips a dusky rose.

The hospice nurse shows up midmorning, looking harried and calm at the same time. We trade places with Daisy, who comes out of the kitchen to help take the vitals. She has poured tea for the nurse, and it's waiting on the table along with a plate of brownies someone brought the night before. Emma and I listen and stare at each other until the nurse returns.

How long do we think she has? I ask in a whisper.

About five minutes, the nurse answers in her regular voice.

Emma and I collapse into each other for a moment, stricken and panicked. Then the nurse leads us back out to the living room and positions us on either side of the bed. *Touch her,* she says, and we do. At some point Emma leans in and speaks quietly. In less than five minutes, we don't have her anymore. She's gone.

I left India a day before Emma and a week before Kathy, who stayed behind to attend a book festival in Rajasthan and give a reading. On my flight, somewhere on the giant, auditorium-size plane, there was a baby who couldn't stop crying. It was worrisome

226

after a while, the baby growing audibly weary, and eventually two flight attendants started moving up the darkened aisles, quietly asking for medical help. The man across the aisle from me woke up briefly to say he was a doctor and what was wrong. The flight attendant crouched next to him and said the mother was vomiting uncontrollably and the baby had a fever. The doctor waved her away and closed his eyes again. The flight attendant stood for a moment in the aisle, her face impassive, then moved on.

Four a.m. in Newark and there are only a few cabs and a lot of people. At the stand I tell a man I'm going to Eighty-Eighth and West End, our pied-à-terre, and he takes my money while another man stows my bags. As soon as we're on the highway, the driver announces that a mistake was made and it's going to cost more.

This, apparently, is what I've been waiting for. We yell at each other for about ten miles, him threatening to take me back to Newark and me telling him to go ahead, asshole, it's a fixed fucking *rate*. Stony silence as we cross the bridge into Manhattan and the streets begin slipping past. Every moment of your life brings you to the moment you're experiencing now. And now. And now. I've never been on the streets this early, predawn, and the driver agrees that it's eerie and perfect.

'They say India: I'll Never Do It Again,' he tells me in his Russian accent, decanting my bags onto the curb and accepting a tip.

The street is shrouded and cold and the bags are heavy. I drag them into the foyer and leave them at the foot of the stairway. The steps look endless from the bottom, I can hardly carry my own weight, but halfway up, our door comes into view and under it a narrow band of light. M. left a lamp on for me.

Then a shadow passes through the wand of light, and I begin crying because he's awake, in the living room, waiting.

We'll always be together.

Those were the words Emma would say a few months later, during Kathy's final moment, leaning in and speaking quietly.

The face of the marble woman, the cold chisel creating the folds of the veil – *We'll always be together* – and the stag rising suddenly out of the ocean of tall grass and leaping away.

Acknowledgments

THIS BOOK WAS WRITTEN over many years and in several places –
on the grounds of Yaddo and MacDowell, in the Sonoran and the
Mojave deserts, and in my barn studio in Rhinebeck. Always at the
other end of the table or the phone line was Mary Allen, listening
and offering writing encouragement, and always there were my
writing students, making me believe that I had something to say
and someone who might listen.

And finally, my lucky life would not be possible without Scott
Spencer, who brings love, humor, and his own brand of brilliant
artistry to every moment we share.

THE BOYS OF
MY YOUTH

For my siblings, Brad and Linda, and for Elizabeth White

Preface to the 1998 Edition

HERE'S ONE OF MY PRE-VERBAL MEMORIES: I'm very little and I'm behind bars, like a baby monkey in a cage. My parents have just put me to bed in a room with bright yellow walls. This is fine with me because in my crib there are various companions – the satin edge of my blue blanket, the chewable plastic circle that hangs down almost to mouth level on a piece of green cord, and a boy doll named Hal with blue eyes and lickable hands and feet made of vinyl. At this point in my life, I love Hal and the satin borders of blankets better than I love any of the humans I know. My mother puts Hal up next to my head as soon as I lie down, which is exactly where I don't want him. I smack him in the face.

'You don't want to hurt *Hal*,' my mother says sadly. 'I thought Hal was your *friend*.'

Hal and I have an agreement that he isn't supposed to come up by my pillow; if I want him I'll go down to his end of the crib. My mother snaps off the light and as she does so the night-light is illuminated, a new thing that I've never seen before. The door closes.

I can see the night-light through the bars of my crib. It is a garish depiction of Mary and Joseph and Jesus, although I don't know that then. Jesus is about my age but he looks mean, and the mom and dad are wearing long coats and no shoes. All three of them are staring at me funny. I start crying without taking my eyes off them.

The door opens and when the light goes on the night-light goes off. I stop crying and sit down by Hal while my mother looks at me. She puts the blanket back over me and leaves. Light off, night-light back on. More crying. This time my father comes in and picks me up, walks me around in a circle, puts me back in the crib with Hal, and leaves. When the light goes off and Jesus comes back on I cry again. This time both of them come in to look at me. My mother is smoking a cigarette.

'Don't ask me,' she tells my father.

About three more times and they give up. I am left to wail loudly, which I do for a while, until I happen to turn on my side, looking for the bottle of water they had tried to bribe me with. As soon as I turn over, the night-light miraculously disappears. The water is warm, just how I like it, and Hal's face is resting against the soles of my feet. I let go of the bottle and wrap the satin border of the blue blanket around my thumb, put the thumb in my mouth, and close my eyes for the night.

I tried to check out that particular memory with my mother when I grew up. I asked her if she remembered a night when I cried and cried, and couldn't be consoled, and they kept coming in and going back out and nothing they did could help me.

'I don't remember any that *weren't* like that,' she said, smoking the same cigarette she'd been smoking for thirty years.

So. Here's a recent memory, from two nights ago. I was riding through upstate New York on a dark blue highway, no particular destination. It was cloudy, the air was springy and cool, the dashboard looked like the control panel of a spaceship. Piano music on the tape deck, a charming guy in the driver's seat. I thought to myself, not for the first time in this life, *Everything is perfect; all those things that I always think are so bad really aren't bad at all*. Then

I noticed that out my window the clouds had parted, the clear night sky was suddenly visible, and the moon – a garish yellow disk against a dark wall – seemed to be looking at me funny.

In the Current

THE FAMILY VACATION. HEAT, FLIES, sand, and dirt. My mother sweeps and complains, my father forever baits hooks and untangles lines. My younger brother has brought along his imaginary friend, Charcoal, and my older sister has brought along a real-life majorette by the name of Nan. My brother continually practices all-star wrestling moves on poor Charcoal. 'I got him in a figure-four leg lock!' he will call from the ground, propped up on one elbow, his legs twisted together. My sister and Nan wear leg makeup, white lipstick, and say things about me in French. A river runs in front of our cabin, the color of bourbon, foamy at the banks, full of water moccasins and doomed fish. I am ten. The only thing to do is sit on the dock and read, drink watered-down Pepsi, and squint. No swimming allowed.

One afternoon three teenagers get caught in the current while I watch. They come sweeping downstream, hollering and gurgling while I stand on the bank, forbidden to step into the water, and stare at them. They are waving their arms.

I am embarrassed because teenagers are yelling at me. Within five seconds men are throwing off their shoes and diving from the dock; my own dad gets hold of one girl and swims her back in.

239

Black hair plastered to her neck, she throws up on the mud about eight times before they carry her back to wherever she came from. One teenager is unconscious when they drag him out and a guy pushes on his chest until a low fountain of water springs up out of his mouth and nose. That kid eventually walks away on his own, but he's crying. The third teenager lands a ways down the bank and comes walking by fifteen minutes later, a grown-up on either side of him and a towel around his waist. His skin looks like Silly Putty.

'Oh man,' he says when he sees me. 'I saw her go by about ninety miles an hour!' He stops and points at me. I just stand there, embarrassed to be noticed by a teenager. I hope my shorts aren't bagging out again. I put one hand in my pocket and slouch sideways a little. 'Man, I thought she was gonna be the last thing I ever seen!' he says, shaking his head.

The girl teenager had had on a swimming suit top with a built-in bra. I cross my arms nonchalantly across my chest and smile at the teenage boy. He keeps walking and talking, the grown-ups supporting him and giving each other looks over the top of his head. His legs are shaking like crazy. 'I thought, Man oh man, that skinny little chick is gonna be the last thing *ever*,' he exclaims.

I look down. My shorts are bagging out.

Bonanza

MY GRANDMOTHER MARRIED A GUY named Ralph, about a year and a half after Pokey, my real grandfather, died of a stroke in the upstairs bedroom of Uncle Rex's house. At Grandma and Ralph's wedding ceremony a man sang opera-style, which took the children by surprise and caused an uproar among the grand-children, who were barely able to sit still as it was. Afterward, there was white cake with white frosting in the church basement, and bowls of peanuts. My mother and my aunts were quite upset about Grandma marrying Ralph barely a year after their dad had died. They sat in clumps in the church basement, a few here, a few there, and ate their cake while giving each other meaningful looks, shaking their heads ominously. My grandmother, a kind woman, was way above reproach. So, it was all Ralph's fault.

He took her to Florida on a honeymoon, a place where no one in the family had ever been. There was an ocean there. They walked the beach morning and night, and Grandma brought home shells. She divided them up evenly, put them in cigar boxes, and gave them to each of her thirty-five grandchildren. The cigar boxes were painted flat white and glued to the top were pictures cut from greeting cards: a lamb, a big-eyed kitty, a bunch of flowers.

On that trip to Florida, I always imagine my grandmother walking in the foamy tide, picking up dead starfish, while Ralph sat silently in a beach chair, not smiling at anyone.

When we'd drive down to Knoxville for a visit, everyone would be hale and hearty, the food eaten, the iced tea drunk, the new rag rugs admired, and then we'd pile back into the car for the hour ride home. Ralph was always grouchy and harsh, with big fingers that he pointed at everyone while he talked. As soon as we pulled out of the driveway, my mother would look at my father and say, 'That old sonuvabitch, I'd like to *kill* him.'

I went to visit Grandma and Ralph for a week right after having learned how to whistle. I whistled at all times, with dedication and complete concentration. When I was asked a question I whistled the answer, I whistled along with people as they talked, I whistled while I worked, I whistled while I played. Eventually they made a rule that whistling was forbidden in their house. I felt bereft and didn't know what to do with my lips if I couldn't whistle. I would blow gently, without making a sound, while helping my grandmother get dinner. She must have felt sorry for me because she said once, kindly, 'Honey, you *can* whistle when you're outside.' But that was no comfort to me. Part of the joy of whistling was knowing that it was always available, you carried the equipment right on your own face. If I couldn't whistle *at all times*, then I didn't care to whistle outdoors. I couldn't wait to get home, where no one could make me do anything.

Grandma and Ralph both worked, so when I went to visit I had hours and hours each day to occupy myself. Grandma took care of senior citizens, some of them younger than she was, shut-ins and disabled folk who needed company and assistance with some of the necessities – cooking, talking. She was a volunteer. Ralph was a butcher and a sheepshearer. He drove a panel truck out to people's farms and killed their cattle for them. Eyes like pebbles, tanned face pulled into a knotty smile, bald head glinting in the sun, a foot-long knife blade aimed at unsuspecting furred throats.

Afterward he would use a garden hose to spray out the back of his truck. White walls and floor, pools and spatters of brilliant red. I glimpsed it once, without knowing what I was looking at. I remember thinking, 'That looks like *blood.*' It never occurred to me it *was* blood. The sheep, after being sheared, stood stunned, in masses, their sides heaving, long cuts and gashes on their pink, exposed skin. The wool stank like crazy and lay in mounds everywhere, gray and filthy. I was taken along on his sprees, sent off to play with complete strangers, farm children, while he went to work with his long knife, his buzzing clippers. I was known for being sensitive to the plight of farm animals and bunnies killed on the road, but I steadfastly refused to acknowledge what was taking place on those visits. I never figured out what was going on around me, even when it was written on the walls in red.

I went along with Grandma sometimes, too. I saw a lady who slept in a crib, curled like a four-year-old, so tiny. She stared out from the bars at me with blank blue eyes. My grandma helped her husband turn her over. Their living room smelled like pee and something else. We had a covered dish for the husband in our trunk and I carried it in.

The old woman had white hair that stuck up in patches on her head. I couldn't get over that she slept in a crib, and I couldn't stop looking at her. My grandma called out to her before we left. 'Eva!' she called. 'We brung Walter your noodle ring! But it don't taste nothing like what you made; I didn't have pumpernickel so I used white!' The words of grown-ups rarely made real sense to me. But Eva understood, and smiled faintly at us, her blue eyes staring through the bars.

'Oh, I got her smilin',' my grandma crowed. Walter walked us out to the car and stood while we drove away, a wide man in overalls and a pressed shirt. He waved to us by touching his temple gently with two fingers, and then pointing them at us. I waved back at him that way.

But mostly I stayed behind, at their house, and wandered through the rooms, picking things up and putting them back down. There were unimaginable treasures there, old things that you didn't know the purpose of, beautiful spindly-legged furniture, and things with exotic, lost names. Chifforobes and highboys, antimacassars and lowboys. Every surface of every wall was covered, and nearly every inch of floor space was, too. Only in the middle of each room was a cleared space for living, a more or less empty zone. Jars of buttons, every kind imaginable, home-made ones, bone ones, small pink and white ones ('Them're for a baby's dress,' she told me), enormous black ones. They were endlessly fascinating to me, all their colors and textures, the satis-fying *churrr* as they poured out of the jar and onto a table. I didn't quite know what to do with them then; they seemed to call out for some special kind of play, something that would lend itself to a pile of buttons. But I could never think of what to do with them next, so I would put them back in the jar, put the jar back on the table or shelf or closet that it had come out of, and wander on to the next thing. A small drawer in a small dresser, long thin tools with carved handles, a whole bunch of them rubber-banded together. 'Them're buttonhooks,' she told me, 'from when you had buttons on your shoes.' I didn't know what she was talking about, and set them back in their small drawer, closed it. On almost every surface there was an antique vase with a bouquet of flowers in it, set in the middle of a starched doily. Beautiful, exotic blooms, all plastic, all covered with a heavy layer of dust. 'They throw 'em away, just like they didn't cost money,' my grandma would explain.

I spent long days of blistering, stupefying boredom in that house, opening the refrigerator and staring into it forty times in an afternoon. Butter, milk, bowls with clumped food visible through their Saran Wrapped tops. There was stuff to eat to make you go to the bathroom, stuff to drink to make you go to the bathroom, and then several things to make you *stop* going to the bathroom. Nothing sweet whatsoever. She'd make a batch of cookies before I came and put them in the fat-chef cookie jar. I would eat all the cookies on the first morning, and then hunt relentlessly the rest of the week for something sweet. I would remember the cookies – greasy peanut butter ones with peanuts stuck in them, or chocolate chip ones with oatmeal – with a kind of hysterical longing. I couldn't believe I had eaten every one of them the first morning. What could I have been thinking?

I ate sugar cubes from the sugar bowl, one every hour or so. They were actually *too* sugary and each time I ate one I swore I wouldn't do it again. But another hour later would find me creeping sock-footed out to the kitchen, lifting the plastic lid of the sugar bowl, and selecting another.

Sometimes I would jump energetically on the beds, two twin ones that were in the room where I slept. I'd kung fu all the embroidered throw pillows onto the floor, and then jump and jump and jump, saying a Chinese jump-rope chant: 'Chicka-chicka China, sitting on a fence, tried to make a dollar outta fifty-nine cents,' until I was so out of breath I had to collapse on my back and wait for the rotating fan to turn in my direction.

Oh, the rotating fan.

The lovely rotating fan, something that moved of its own accord in the dead house during the long afternoons. I would set the rotating fan on a footstool in the long, narrow bedroom. My job was to feed Kleenexes into it and then pick up the shredded pieces.

By the end of one of those stultifying afternoons, I'd have an empty Kleenex box and a whole wastebasket full of soft pink confetti. Nobody ever questioned where the Kleenexes went when I was visiting, but once my grandma gave me another white-painted cigar box that was full of handkerchiefs, neatly pressed and folded. Every kind imaginable: flowered, embroidered, ones with Scottie terriers, ones with lace edges, the whole bit.

They ate terrible food, things mixed together that weren't supposed to be. Mashed potatoes with corn, pieces of white bread with gravy poured on top, peas and carrots in the same bowl. Ralph would have a dish towel tucked into his collar and hold a fork and spoon in his enormous paws. He'd get something on the spoon, a great gob of potatoes, say, and then open his mouth as wide as it would go, like a bird in a nest getting fed a chewed worm. He had deep creases on either side of his mouth, and as he chewed, gravy would run down the gullies in rivulets, land on the dish towel, and stay there. It was an amazing and horrifying thing to watch. I had a sensitive stomach and sometimes, sitting across from him – eyes carefully averted, fastened on the Aunt Jemima potholder hanging on a hook or on a pan lid with a screw and a block of wood jimmied up for a handle – just hearing him eat could make me gag. I was in the habit of rising from the table and walking around the kitchen every few minutes, breathing through my nose, deeply, to keep from gagging. Then I'd sit back down, pick up two peas with my spoon, and put them in my mouth. This is what my grandma said to me once: 'Eat your chicken, why don't you? And don't take the skin off, that's what's good.' They were trying to make me eat something with *skin* on it. At my own house, everyone knew enough not to say *skin* in relation to food.

My grandma, when she was cooking dinner, would send me down to the fruit cellar for jars of home-canned stuff. Then when I'd bring them up she'd open the jars and smell the contents thoughtfully; sometimes she'd have me take the jar outside to where Ralph was and have him smell it. He always said the same things: 'There ain't nothing wrong with *that*, tell her' or he'd bawl toward the house as I was walking back in, 'Maw, that'll be okay if you cook it longer!'

Once she served me red raspberries that she'd put up; poured them in a plastic bowl and put cream on them. As I started to dig in I noticed that there were some black things floating around. 'Grandma, there's bugs in this,' I said. She came over and looked into my bowl, head tipped back to see out of the bottoms of her glasses. 'Them're dead,' she told me. 'Just push 'em to the side; the berries is okay.' And I did, and the berries *were* okay.

At night we watched one show on TV and then had to go to bed, when it was still a little bit light out. They'd go in their room and my grandma would come out with her nightgown on and her teeth out to tuck me in. I'd be lying stiff as a plank under the bedspread and here she'd come, without her regular clothes on, with her arms and feet exposed, her mouth folded in on itself. 'G'night, honey-Jo,' she would lisp, pat me on the shoulder, and turn out the light. And there I'd be, while they snored up one side and down the other in the room across the hall. I'd tiptoe all over the bedroom, gazing for a while out the window, watching the sky turn black, the stars come out. I'd quietly open all the drawers of all the dressers in the room, take out things, examine them, put them back. I didn't dare jump on the bed, although sometimes I said 'Chicka-chicka China' to myself out of boredom. I tried counting sheep like on the cartoons, but I couldn't concentrate, couldn't for the life of me imagine what sheep looked like. I knew but I didn't know, just as I couldn't conjure up the faces of my long-lost parents and siblings. I was wide-awake, staring out at the vast Milky Way while the grown-ups snored on and on and the moon rose and sank.

The strange thing was, I always asked to go there. I don't remember them ever inviting me, or my parents suggesting it. It was me. From far away the idea of their house was magical to me, all those nooks, all those crannies, all those things to play with – the button jars, the lowboy with a little drawer full of marbles, the flower arrangements, the rotating fan. So, every July I got dropped off on a Sunday and picked up the following Sunday. By Tuesday I'd be counting the hours, sitting on the backyard glider, staring at the black lawn jockey and the flagstone path that took you to the garden, the broken bird bath with a pool of rusty, skanky water in it. Their yard had as much stuff in it as their house did, only the yard stuff was filthy, full of dirt and rainwater.

The last time I went there my parents drove off on a Sunday afternoon as I stood on the gravel sidewalk and waved, already regretting my visit. My grandma fed us, dinner was the usual ordeal of gravy rivulets and tainted food, and then they turned *Bonanza* on. I lay on the living room floor, in the cleared-out space in the center; on either end of the couch were Grandma and Ralph. She was knitting an afghan and he was sharpening a stack of scissors.

We were watching my favorite show. The dad, Ben, had a buck-skin, Hoss had a black horse, and Little Joe had a pinto pony. They had Hop Sing for a servant, in place of a mom. Back home my little brother would be humming to himself through the whole show, 'Umbuddy-umbuddy-umbuddy-ummm Bonanza,' and everyone would be telling him to shut up. My mom would be smoking her cigarettes and drinking beer out of a bottle, my dad would have his socks off and be stretching his bare toes, drinking his beer out of a glass. My sister would be trying to do homework at the dining room table.

Here I was with Grandma and Ralph, staying up one hour later than I would the rest of the century-long week. Little Joe falls in love with a schoolteacher who comes past the Ponderosa in a buggy. He kisses her a long one, it stretches out forever in the silence of the living room. There isn't a sound from behind me, on the couch. No one is moving while the kiss is going on. It's horrible. I look around the room, at the pictures that cover every inch of wall space, my aunts and uncles and their families, framed sayings from the olden days, plaques with jokes about outhouses, a pair of flying ceramic ducks with orange beaks and feet, and on and on. Too much to look at. The pecking-hen salt and pepper shakers, the donkey with a dead plant coming out of his back, the stacks of old magazines under tables and on the seats of chairs. Underneath me are three scatter rugs, converging their corners in a lump under my back. Rag rugs, one of them made from bread wrappers. Hoss Cartwright saves the schoolteacher when her horse shies and now she's in love with him. Little Joe tries to punch Hoss out.

Behind me my grandmother's knitting needles click together in a sad and empty way, Ralph's breathing is audible over the scratch of scissor blades on stone. In the dim circle of light that I lay in, my head cushioned on an Arkansas Razorback pillow, I feel completely separate from them because of the simple fact that in seven days I will be rescued, removed from this terrible lonely place and put back in the noisy house I came from.

It occurs to me that Grandma and Ralph have nothing, they don't even enjoy *Bonanza* all that much, they just turned it on because my mom told them to let me watch it. There can't be anything for them to enjoy, with their long empty days, full of curled-up old ladies and dirty sheep. They don't even drink pop.

I am crying on the floor, the tears go sideways and land coldly in my ears or on the velveteen pillow. I can't bear, suddenly, the way the television sends out its sad blue light, making the edges of the room seem darker. A coffee can covered with contact paper holds red, white, and blue Fourth of July flowers, taken from a dead person. I wish suddenly that my grandma was dead, so she wouldn't have to knit that afghan anymore. The rest of the year, while I'm gone back home and am playing with my friends, this is where my grandma is, her needles going, her teeth in the bathroom in a plastic bowl. My ears are swimming pools, and I feel trapped suddenly inside the small circle of light in the center of the room. I'm tiny Eva, watching Little Joe Cartwright through the bars of my crib, I'm a monkey, strapped into a space capsule and flung far out into the galaxy, weightless, hurtling along upside down through the Milky Way.

Alone, alone, and alone. Against my will, I sob out loud. I turn over and weep into the Arkansas pillow, wrecking the velveteen. Suddenly my grandma's hand is on my hair, the knitting needles have been set down.

There is telephone talk, and muffled comments from Grandma to Ralph, from Ralph to the person on the other end of the phone. My nose is pressed against the pillow and I'm still crying, or trying to. I suddenly want to hear what's going on but I don't have the nerve to sit up. My clothes are gathered, the television is shut off, I am walked outside and put in the back seat of their great big yellow car. In the back window, there's a dog with a bobbing head that I usually like to mess around with when I'm riding in the car. I don't even bother to look at it; I just stare out the back window at the night sky.

After about a half hour of driving we pull over and sit at the side of the road. I'm no longer weightless, but unbearably heavy, and tired. My dad pulls up with a crunch of gravel, words are exchanged through open windows, quiet chuckles, I am placed in the front seat between my parents. We pull away, and as we head toward home, the galaxy recedes, the stars move back into position, and the sky stretches out overhead, black and familiar.

They've decided not to hassle me about this. 'What happened, honey?' my mom asks once, gently.

'*Bonanza* made me sad,' I reply.

Cousins

HERE IS A SCENE. Two sisters are fishing together in a flat-bottomed boat on an olive green lake. They sit slumped like men, facing in opposite directions, drinking coffee out of a metal-sided thermos, smoking intently. Without their lipstick they look strangely weary, and passive, like pale replicas of their real selves. They both have a touch of morning sickness but neither is admitting it. Instead, they watch their bobbers and argue about worms versus minnows.

My cousin and I are floating in separate, saline oceans. I'm the size of a cocktail shrimp and she's the size of a man's thumb. My mother is the one on the left, wearing baggy gabardine trousers and a man's shirt. My cousin's mother is wearing blue jeans, cuffed at the bottom, and a cotton blouse printed with wild cowboys roping steers. Their voices carry, as usual, but at this point we can't hear them.

It is five a.m. A duck stands up, shakes out its feathers, and peers above the still grass at the edge of the water. The skin of the lake twitches suddenly and a fish springs loose into the air, drops back down with a flat splash. Ripples move across the surface like radio waves. The sun hoists itself up and gets busy, laying a sparkling rug across the water, burning the beads of dew off the reeds, baking the tops of our mothers' heads. One puts on sunglasses and the other a plaid fishing cap with a wide brim.

In the cold dark underwater, a long fish with a tattered tail discovers something interesting. He circles once and then has his breakfast before becoming theirs. As he breaks from the water to the air he twists hard, sending out a cold spray, sparks of green light. My aunt reels him in, triumphant, and grins at her sister, big teeth in a friendly mouth.

'Why you dirty rotten so-and-so,' my mother says admiringly.

It is nine o'clock on Saturday night, the sky is black and glittering with pinholes, old trees are bent down over the highway. In the dark field behind, the corn gathers its strength, grows an inch in the silence, then stops to rest. Next to the highway, screened in vegetation, a deer with muscular ears and glamorous eyes stands waiting to spring out from the wings into the next moving spotlight. The asphalt sighs in anticipation.

The car is a late-model Firebird, black on black with a T-roof and a tape deck that pelts out anguish, Fleetwood Mac. My cousin looks just like me except she has coarse hair and the jawline of an angel. She's driving and I'm shotgun, talking to her profile.

The story I'm recounting to her is full of what I said back to people when they said things to me. She can sing and listen at the same time, so she does that, nodding and grimacing when necessary.

She interrupts me once. 'What's my hair doing?'

'Laying down. I'll tell you if it tries anything.' Her hair is short but so dense it has a tendency to stay wherever the wind pushes it. When she wakes up in the morning her head is like a landscape, with cliffs and valleys, spectacular pinnacles.

252

'Okay, go ahead,' she says. I finish my story before my favorite song comes on so I can devote myself to it.

We sing along to a tune about a woman who rings like a bell through the night.

Neither of us knows what that means, but we're in favor of it. We want to ring like bells, we want our hair to act right, we want to go out with guys who wear boots with turned- up toes and worn-down heels. We're out in the country, on my cousin's turf. My car is stalled in the city somewhere on four low tires, a blue-and-rust Volkswagen with the door coat-hangered shut. Her car is this streamlined, dark-eyed Firebird with its back end hiked up like a skirt. We are hurtling through the night, as they say, on our way to a bar where the guys own speedboats, snowmobiles, what-ever else is current. I sing full-throttle: *You can take me to paradise, but then again you can be cold as ice; I'm over my head, but it sure feels nice.* I turn the rearview mirror around, check to see what's hap-pening with the face.

Nothing good. But there you have it. It's yours at least, and your hair isn't liable to thrust itself upward into stray pointing fingers. It doesn't sound like corn husks when you brush it.

My cousin, beautiful in the dashboard light, glances over at me. She has a first name but I've always called her Wendell. She pushes it up to eighty and the song ends, a less wonderful one comes on. We're coming to the spot on the highway where the giant trees dangle their wrists over the ground. In the crotch of an elm, during daylight hours, a gnarled car is visible, wedged among the branches.

Up ahead, the cornfields are dark and rustling. The deer shifts nervously behind the curtain of weeds, waiting for its cue. The car in the tree's crotch is a warning to fast drivers, careening kids. Hidden beneath the driver's seat, way up in the branches, is a silver pocketwatch with a broken face. It had been some-one's great-grandfather's, handed down and handed down, until it reached the boy who drove his car into the side of a tree. Below the drifting branches, the ground is black and loamy, moving with bugs. In the silence, stalks of corn stretch their thin, thready feet and gather in the moisture.

The pocket-watch is stopped at precisely 11:47, as was the boy. Fleetwood Mac rolls around the bend and the deer springs full-blown out of the brocade trees. In the white pool of headlights, in front of a swerving audience, it does a short, stark, modern dance, and exits to the right. We recover and slow it down, shaking.

'He could have wrecked my whole front end,' Wendell says. This is the farm-kid mentality. Her idea of a gorgeous deer is one that hangs upside down on the wall of the shed, a rib cage, a pair of antlers, a gamy hunk of dinner. She feels the same way about cows and pigs.

We're in the sticks. Way out here things are measured in shit-loads, and every third guy you meet is named Junior. I've decided I don't even like this bar we're going to, that howling three-man band and the bathroom with no stalls, just stools. Now I'm slumped and surly, an old pose for me. That deer had legs like canes, feet like Dixie cups.

Wendell pats my knee, grinning. 'Settle down,' she says. 'It didn't *hit* us. We're safe.' She likes excitement as long as her car doesn't get hurt. I light a cigarette, begin dirtying up her ashtray, and mess with the tape until our favorite song comes on again. We're back up to eighty on the narrow highway, daring the igno-rant to take a step onto the asphalt. This is Illinois, a land of lumbering raccoons, snake-tailed possums, and flatout running bunnies, all trying to cross the road. The interior of the car smells like leather and evergreen trees, the moon peers through the roof, and Wendell drives with one finger.

'Hey, how's my hair?' she asks suddenly. Her eyes are clear brown, her cheekbones are high and delicate, brushed with pink, her lips aren't too big or too little. She's wearing my shirt. A clump of hair has pushed itself forward in the excitement. It looks like a small, startled hand rising from the back of her head.

I make an okay sign, thumb and forefinger. The music is deafening.

Back in the cluster of trees, the deer moves into position again and the willows run their fingers along the ground. The corn whispers encouragement to itself. In the bar up ahead waitresses slam sloe-gin fizzes down on wet tables and men point pool cues at each other in the early stages of drunkenness. The singer in the three-man band whispers *test* into the microphone and rolls his eyes at the feedback. The sound guy jumps up from a table full of ladies and heads over to turn knobs.

We crunch over the parking lot gravel and wait for our song to finish. *I'm over my head, but it sure feels nice.* The bar is low and windowless, with patched siding and a kicked-in door; the lot is full of muscle cars and pickups. A man and a woman burst through the door and stand negotiating who will drive. He's got the keys but she looks fiercer. In the blinking neon our faces are malarial and buttery. As the song winds down, the drama in front of us ends. He throws the keys at her as hard as he can but she jumps nimbly out of the way and picks them up with a handful of gravel, begins pelting his back as he weaves into the darkness.

Wendell turns to me with a grin, a question on her lips. Before she can ask I reach over and press her excited hair back down.

Their house has a face on it, two windows with the shades half down, a brown slot of a door, and a glaring mouthful of railing with a few pickets missing. Pink geraniums grow like earrings on either side of the porch. It's August and the grass is golden and spiky against our ankles, the geraniums smell like dust. A row of hollyhocks stands out by the road, the flowers are upside-down ladies, red, maroon, and dried-up brown. An exploded raccoon is abuzz over on the far side of the highway and crows are dropping down from time to time to sort among the pieces. On either side of the house, fields fall away, rolling and baking in the heat.

The sisters are sitting on the stoop shelling peas, talking overtop of each other. My mother says mayonnaise goes bad in two hours in the hot sun and my aunt says bullshit. They've just driven out to the fields and left the lunches for the hired men. They argue energetically about this, until the rooster walks up and my aunt carries her bowl in the house to finish the discussion through the screen door. She and the rooster hate each other.

'He thinks you're a chicken,' my mother explains. 'You have to show him you won't put up with it.' She picks up a stick, threatens the rooster with it, and he backs off, pretends to peck the yard. My aunt comes back out.

The front of her head is in curlers, the brush kind that hurt, and she keeps testing her hair to see if it's done. She has on a smock with big pockets and pedal pushers. Her feet are bare, one reason why the rooster is scaring her so much. My mother doesn't wear curlers because her hair is short but she has two clips crisscrossed on either side of her head, making spit curls in front of her ears. Every time a car drives by she reaches up automatically, ready to yank them out. She has on Bermuda shorts and a wide-bottomed plaid blouse with a bow at the neck. They are both pregnant again.

We're going to be in a parade at four o'clock, Wendell and I, riding bikes without training wheels, our dolls in the baskets. We asked to have the training wheels put back on for the parade but they said no. Our older sisters are upstairs somewhere, dumping perfume on one another and trying on bracelets. They'll be in the parade, too, walking behind us and throwing their batons in the air, trying to drop them on our heads.

Wendell jumps at the rooster suddenly and he rushes us, we go off screaming in different directions while he stands there furious, shifting from one scaly foot to another, slim and tall with greasy black feathers and a yellow ruff like a collie. He can make the dirty feathers around his neck stand up and fall back down whenever he gets mad, just like flexing a muscle. Even his wives give him a wide berth, rolling their seedy eyes and murmuring. They get no rest. I haven't yet connected the chickens walking around out here with what we had for lunch, chopped up and mixed with mayonnaise.

The mothers give up and go in the house to smoke cigarettes at the kitchen table and yell at us through the windows. Wendell and I work on decorating our bikes and complaining about no training wheels.

'What about if there's a *corner*?' I say.

'I know,' says Wendell. 'Or if there's *dog* poop?' I don't know exactly how this relates but I shudder anyway. We shake our heads and try twisting the crepe paper into the spokes the way our mothers showed us but it doesn't work. We end up with gnarled messes and flounce into the house to discipline our dolls.

Here is the parade. Boys in cowboy getups with cap guns and rubber spurs, hats that hang from shoestrings around their necks. The girls squint against the sun and press their stiff dresses down. This is the year of the can-can slip so we all have on good underpants without holes. Some kids have their ponies there, ornery things with rolling eyes and bared teeth, all decorated up. Two older boys with painted-on mustaches beat wildly on drums until they are stopped. Mothers spit on Kleenexes and go at the boys' faces while fathers stand around comparing what their watches say to what the sun is doing.

Two little girls wear matching dresses made from a big linen tablecloth, a white background with blue and red fruit clusters. One has a bushy stand of hair and the other a smooth pixie. Both have large bows, one crunched into the mass and the other practically taped on. The scalloped collars on their dresses are made from the border of the tablecloth, bright red with tiny blue grapes, little green stems. There are sashes tied in perfect bows, and pop-bead bracelets. Our shoes don't match.

The dolls rode over to the parade in the trunk of the car so we wouldn't wreck their outfits. They have the ability to drink water and pee it back out but they're dry now, our mothers put a stop to that. They have on dresses to match ours, with tiny scalloped collars and ribbon sashes. We set them carefully in our bike baskets with their skirts in full view. Mine's hair is messed up on one side where I put hairspray on it once.

Wendell's has a chewed-up hand and nobody knows how it got that way. We stand next to our crepe-papered bikes in the sunlight, waiting for them to tell us what to do.

Our sisters have been forbidden to throw their batons until the parade starts and so they twirl them around and pretend to hurl them up in the air, give a little hop, and pretend to catch them again. They are wearing perfume and fingernail polish with their cowboy boots and shorts. They don't like us very much but we don't care.

My mother tells me to stand up straight and Wendell's mother tells her to push her hair back down. The baton twirlers get a last minute talking-to with threats. The parade moves out ragged and wobbly, someone immediately starts crying, a pony wanders out of line and looks for some grass to chew. The main street is crowded with bystanders and parked automobiles. It is never clear what this parade is for, except to dress the children up and show them off, get the men to come in from the fields for a while.

As the parade pulls itself slowly down the street, the mothers stand with wry, proud faces and folded arms while fathers stand smoking, lifting the one-finger farmer's salute as their sons go by. Wendell and I steer carefully and watch our mothers as they move along the sidewalk, following. Tall, lanky frames and watermelon stomachs, the gray eyes and beautiful hands of the Patterson side of the family. Our dolls are behaving perfectly, staring straight ahead, slumped forward in their baskets. My sash has come untied and Wendell's underpants are showing. We don't care, they won't bother fixing us now; we're in the parade and they have to stay on the sidewalk.

The street is brilliant in the sun, and the children move in slow motion, dresses, cowboy hats, tap shoes, the long yellow teeth of the mean ponies. At the count of four, one of our sisters loses control, throws her baton high in the air and stops, one hand out to catch it when it comes back down.

For a long, gleaming moment it hangs there, a silver hyphen against the hot sky.

Over the hectic heads of the children and the smooth blue-and-white blur of crepe-papered spokes and handlebar streamers, above the squinting smiles and upturned eyes, a silver baton rises miraculously, lingers for a moment against the sun, and then drops back down, into the waiting hand.

Back at the bar, someone has hold of me and I'm on the dance floor. Wendell's standing just inside the door. I'm going backward swiftly, in a fast two-step, there's an arm slung across my shoulder. It's good old Ted, trying to make a girl feel welcome. The bar is as dark as a pocket and my eyes haven't adjusted yet. Ted runs me into a couple of people and I tell him his arm weighs a ton. He grins but doesn't move it. He has long legs and a drinking problem. Two ex-wives follow him everywhere, stirring up trouble.

When the song finally ends, I untangle from Ted and look for Wendell. She's got us a table back by the wall, beneath the bored head of a deer. As I pass the bar several guys in turn swivel their stools around and catch me. Blue-jeaned legs are parted, I'm pulled in, pressed against a chest, clamped. Hello, hello. I bum a cigarette from the first one and blow smoke in the face of the second when his hand crawls like a bull snake up the back of my shirt. Even way out here I'm known for being not that easy to get along with.

Wendell takes her feet off my chair and pushes a rum and Pepsi my way. She tries to tell me something over the din.

'What?' I holler back and turn my ear to her.

'I *said*, your *buddy's* here,' she yells into my hair. I pull back and look at her. She jerks a thumb upward, to the passive, suspended face of the deer. Someone has stuck a cigarette butt in one of its nostrils. I show her my middle finger and she sits back again, satisfied. Side by side at the spindly table, we drink our drinks for a while and watch the dancers go around.

Ida's out there, going to town, seventy-five if she's a day, with dyed black hair and tall, permanently arched eyebrows. From nine to midnight, even when it's just the jukebox, she takes herself around the dance floor – fox-trot, swing shuffle, two-step.

She comes here every Saturday night to dance by herself while her grandson drinks Mountain Dew and plays pool in the back room. Her tennis shoes look like they're disconnected from the rest of her body. Every once in a while, she presses one hand against her waist and closes her eyes for an instant, keeping time with her shoulders, all part of some interior dancing-drama, some memory of Pete and her, before they got old, before she up and got widowed. Apparently, they were quite a deal on the dance floor. Nobody ever bumps into her out there, even the drunkest of the drunk make a space for those shoes and that head of hair. She's dancing with a memory, putting all the rest of us to shame.

Here comes our darling Nick. Everyone's in love with him, blond hair in a ponytail and wire-rims, drives a muddy jeep. Too bad he's related to us. He sets us up with two more drinks, takes a joint out of his shirt pocket, puts it in my cigarette pack, and lays a big kiss on Wendell, flat on the lips. Right as he leaves, he zooms in on me unexpectedly. I give him one hand to shake and put the other one over my mouth.

Wendell takes a drink and leans over.

'Gross,' she shouts into my ear. I nod. Cousin cooties.

'I'm telling Aunt Bernie,' I shout back. Aunt Bernie is his mom.

We've been sitting too long. Wendell carries her drink, I light a cigarette, and we move out into the revelers, and lose each other. The rum is a warm, dark curtain in my chest. I suddenly look better than I have in weeks, I can feel geraniums blooming in my cheeks, my mouth is genuinely smiling for once, my hair, fresh from the ironing board, falls like a smooth plank down my back. It's Saturday night and I'm three rum and Pepsis to the wind. I love this bar, the floor is a velvet trampoline, a mirrored ball revolves above the dance floor, stars move across faces and hands, everyone encountered is a close personal friend. I'm in line for the bathroom, chatting with strangers.

'I like your shirt.' This from the woman behind me, she may be trying to negotiate her way up the line.

'Thanks,' I tell her. She's pretty. 'I like yours, too.'

'Your cousin's really drunk,' she says, rolling her eyes. I guess she knows me. She means Nick, not Wendell. Women are always striking up conversations about Nick.

'I know' is what I tell her. I smile when I say it and shrug, trying to indicate that she can come to family dinners with Nick as far as I'm concerned. We lapse back into silence until the door bursts open and three women come out, reeking of reefer and perfume.

I look at the woman who struck up the conversation with me. We raise our eyebrows.

'Nice perfume,' she says, wrinkling her nose.

'Nice reefer,' I say. I let her come in while I go and she checks her makeup and examines her teeth in the mirror. I wait for her, too, bending over at the waist, shaking the hair out, and then flipping it back. It makes it fluffier for a few minutes, before it settles back into the plank again. The bending and flipping sends the room careening for a moment, I'm in a centrifugal tube, then it halts. She wants to know who Nick's going out with.

'His dog, I think,' I tell her. I'm politely not noticing her peeing. 'He's got the nicest golden retriever you ever saw.' I love that dog; it refuses to hunt, just walks along and stirs up ducks and pheasants, watches with surprise when they go flapping off. 'That's one thing about Nick. His dog's nice.' I don't think Nick ever shoots anything anyway, he just looks good in the boots and the vest.

Actually, I think Cousin Nick's going out with everyone, but I don't tell her that. She looks hopeful and sparkly and she's not nearly as drunk as me. I give her a swimmy smile on the way out and we part company forever.

The band rolls into a slow one, with a creaky metallic guitar hook and a lone warbling voice. Someone asks me to dance and we stroll around the floor, amid the stars and the elbows. I close my eyes for a moment and it's night inside my head, there are strange arms moving me around, this way and that, feet bumping into mine. The steel guitar comes overtop of it all, climbing and dropping, locating everyone's sadness and yanking on it. In the shuffling crowd the dark curtain of rum parts for an instant, and reveals nothing. I open my eyes and look up at my partner. He's leading away, a grinning stranger, his hand strolls down and finds my back pocket, warms itself. Christ Almighty.

Ida swims through, and past, eyes blank as nickels, disembodied feet, arms like floating strings. One song ends and a new one starts up, I shake my head at my partner and he backs off with a sullen shrug. Apparently he likes this song because he begins fast-dancing by himself, looking hopefully around at the other dancers, trying to rope a stray.

This is Wendell's favorite song, *She's a good-hearted wo-man, in love with a two-timing man.* Here she is, ready to dance. I move

with her back into the lumbering crowd on the dance floor, and
we carve out a little spot in front of the band. *She loves him in spite
of his wicked ways she don't understand.* The bar has gone friendly
again while I wasn't looking, the faces of the other dancers are
pink with exertion and alcohol, Nick's dancing with the bathroom
girl, Ted's twirling an ex-wife, the singer in the band knocks the
spit out of his harmonica and attaches it to his neck again. Look
at Wendell's face. She's twenty-one and single; her hair has a story
to tell. In the small sticky space in front of the band, we twirl
a few times, knuckles and lifted elbows, under and over, until I
get stomped on. We're singing now, recklessly, it's almost closing
time and us girls are getting prettier by the moment. *Through
teardrops and laughter we pass through this world hand in hand.* Of
course, both Wendell and I would like to be good-hearted women
but we're from the Patterson clan, and just don't have the tem-
perament for it.

The sisters are making deviled eggs. They have on dark blue
dresses with aprons and are walking around in nyloned feet. No
one can find the red stuff that gets sprinkled on top of the eggs.
They're tearing the cupboards apart right now, swearing to each
other and shaking their heads. We all know enough to stay out of
the kitchen.

We're at my grandma's house in our best dresses with towels
pinned to the collars. Our older sisters are walking around with
theatrical, mournful faces, bossing us like crazy, in loud disgusted
whispers. They have their pockets loaded with Kleenex in preparation for making a scene. We're all going to our grandfather's
funeral in fifteen minutes, as soon as the paprika gets found.

Wendell and I get to go only because we promised to act decent.
No more running and sliding on the funeral-home rug. Someone
has *died*, and there's a time and a place for everything. We'll both

get spanked in front of everyone and put in chairs if we're not careful. And if we can't keep our gum in our mouths then we don't need it: both pieces are deposited in a held-out Kleenex on the ride over. Wendell and I are in disgrace from our behavior last night at the visitation.

'It wasn't our fault he moved,' Wendell had explained, right before being swatted in the funeral-home foyer. Our grandfather had looked like a big, dead doll in a satin doll bed. We couldn't stop staring, and then suddenly, simultaneously, got spooked and ran out of the room, squealing and holding on to each other. We stayed in the foyer for the rest of the night, greeting people and taking turns sliding the rug across the glossy floor. We were a mess by the end of the evening.

Our dads have to sit in a special row of men. They're going to carry the casket to the graveyard. We file past them without looking, and the music gets louder. The casket sits like an open suitcase up front. After we sit down in our wooden folding chairs all we can see is a nose and some glasses. That's our grandpa up there, he won't be hollering at us ever again for chewing on the collars of our dresses or for throwing hangers out the upstairs window. He won't be calling us giggleboxes anymore. He doesn't even know we're all sitting here, listening to the music and the whispers. He is in our hearts now, which makes us feel uncomfortable. Wendell and I were separated as a precautionary measure; I can just see the tips of her black shoes. They have bows on them and mine have buckles. She is swinging hers a little bit so I start to swing mine a little bit too. This is how you get into trouble, so I quit after a minute and so does she.

Pretty soon the music stops and my mother starts crying into her Kleenex. My aunt's chin turns into a walnut, and then she's crying too. Their dad is dead. Wendell puts her shoe on the back of the chair in front of her and slides it slowly down until it's resting on the floor again. I do the same thing. We're not being ornery, though. A lady starts singing a song and you can hear her breath. I can see only one inch of her face because she's standing in front of the dads. It's a song from Sunday school but she's singing it slower than we do and she's not making the hand motions. I do the hand motions myself, very small, barely moving, while she sings.

Wendell's mom leans over and tells me something. She wants me to sit on her lap. She has a nickname for me that nobody else calls me. She calls me Jody and everyone else calls me Jo. She's not crying anymore, and her arms are holding me on her lap, against her good blue dress. It's too tight in the armpits but you can't tell from looking.

My mom's got Wendell.

After a while everyone starts crying, except Uncle Evan, my grandma's brother who always spits into a coffee cup and leaves it on the table for someone else to clean up. My aunt rests her chin on my head and rearranges her Kleenex so there's a dry spot. I sit very still while the preacher talks and the mothers cry, not moving an inch, even though my arms don't have anywhere to go. Wendell keeps moving around but I don't. Actually, I don't feel very good, my stomach hurts. I'm too big to sit on a lap, my legs are stiff, and now my heart has a grandpa in it.

The fairgrounds are huge and hot, an expanse of baking bodies and an empty stage. There are guys monkeying around on the lighting scaffold, high in the air. Mostly they're fat, stoned, and intent on their tasks, but Wendell's spied one that might be okay. Ponytailed and lean, he has his T-shirt off and stuck in the waistband of his jeans. I can't look at him because he's too high up, hanging off of things that don't look reliable. Wendell trains her binoculars on him, focuses, and then sets them down. 'Yuck,' she reports.

We will see God this afternoon – this is an Eric Clapton concert. We're sitting on one of our grandmother's worn quilts, spread out on the ground twenty feet from the stage. 'Hey, look.' I show Wendell a scrap of fabric. It's blue-and-red plaid with dark green lines running through. She and I used to have short-sleeved shirts with embroidered pockets made out of that material. On the ride over here we each took a small blue pill, a mild hallucinogen, and now Wendell has to put her face about an inch away from the quilt in order to get a sense of the scrap I'm talking about.

'It used to be seersucker,' she says sadly. 'And now it isn't.' We think that over for a few minutes, how things change, how nothing can be counted on, and then Wendell remembers something. 'My shirt had a pony on the pocket and yours had a *schnauzer*.' She snickers.

For some reason that irritates me no end. I hadn't thought of that schnauzer in years, and she has to bring it up today. Thanks a whole hell of a lot. It did used to be seersucker, too, which is very strange, because now it's not. What could have happened to it? How can something go from being puckered to being unpuckered? You could see if it was the other way around, but this just doesn't make sense. My halter top keeps feeling like it's coming undone.

We put the cooler over the unsucked seersucker so we can quit thinking about it. Wendell stretches out on her back and stares at the sky. I stretch out on my stomach and stare at some grass. We are boiling hot but we don't know it, my hair is stuck to my back and Wendell's is standing straight up in a beautiful manner.

'Your hair is standing straight up in a beautiful manner,' I tell her. She nods peacefully. She holds her arms up in the air and makes a *c* with each hand.

'I'm cupping clouds,' she says. I try to pay closer attention to my grass, which is pretty short and worn down. It looks like it's been grazed. I read somewhere once that hysterical fans used to eat the grass where the Beatles had walked.

'Do you think Eric Clapton walked on this grass?' I ask Wendell. She looks over at me and considers. She thinks for so long that I forget the question and have to remember it again.

'No,' she says finally. I feel relieved.

'Well then, I'm not eating it,' I tell her flatly.

'Okay,' she replies. I wish she had said 'Okey-dokey' but she didn't. She said 'Okay,' which has an entirely different meaning.

I sit up and my halter top sags alarmingly. All I can do is hold it in place. There's nothing else to be done, I wouldn't have any idea how to retie it. Wendell is curled up in a ball next to me with her eyes shut.

'My top is falling off,' I tell her. She doesn't open her eyes. I can feel sweat running down my back like ball bearings. Wendell groans.

'The clouds are cupping *me* now,' she says. 'Get them off.' She's still got her eyes shut, making a whimpering sound. I don't know exactly what to do because I can't see any clouds on her and my shirt is falling off. I have to think for a moment. If I had just taken one bite of grass this wouldn't have happened.

A guy on the blanket next to us tries to hand me a joint. I can't take it because I'm holding my chest. He looks at me, looks at Wendell balled up on the ground, and nods knowingly. 'Bummer,' he proclaims.

I can't stand to have Eric Clapton see me like this. I let go of my shirt for one second and wave my arms over Wendell. My halter top miraculously stays in place. In fact, it suddenly feels too tight. 'I just got the clouds off you,' I inform her. She opens one eye, then the other, and sits up.

'You look cute,' she tells me. She's turning pink from the afternoon sun and her hair is hectic and alive. We open beers from our cooler and start having fun.

By the time old Eric comes out, we've completely forgotten about him, so it's a pleasant surprise. We climb up on our cooler and dance around, waving our arms in the air. We're so close to the stage he is almost life-size. This is amazing. We dance and mouth the words while Eric sings tender love songs about George Harrison's wife and plays his guitar in a godlike manner.

The sky has turned navy blue. Eric stands in a spotlight on the stage. I pick him up once, like a pencil, and write my name in the air, then put him back down so he can play his guitar again. My halter top stays stationary while I dance around inside it naked.

Darling, we sing to Eric, *you look won-der-ful tonight*. The air is full of the gyrations of six thousand people. My cousin is covered with clouds again but she doesn't seem to notice. Although it's still five months until Christmas, tiny lights wink on and off in her hair.

The tablecloth is covered with pie crumbs and empty coffee cups, a space has been cleared for the cribbage board and ashtrays. The sisters are smoking, staring at their cards, and talking about relatives. Neither of them can believe that Bernice is putting indoor-outdoor carpeting in her kitchen.

'You can't tell her a thing,' my mother says. She lays down a card and moves her red peg ahead on the board.

'Shit,' my aunt says softly. She stares at her cards. One of the husbands comes in for more pie. 'What do I do here?' she asks him. He looks at her hand for a moment and then walks around the table to look at my mother's hand. He points to a card, which she removes and lays down. 'Try that on for size,' she tells my mother.

The back door flies open and two daughters enter. There is a hullabaloo. Barbie's little sister, Skipper, was sitting on the fence and accidentally fell off and got stepped on by a pig. 'She's wrecked,' Wendell reports. 'We had to get her out with a stick.' I show them the stick and Wendell shows them Skipper.

'Stay away from the pigs,' my aunt says. She's looking at her cards.

'We *were* staying away from the pigs,' I answer, holding up the muddy stick as evidence. 'Tell them to stay away from *us*, why don't you?' My mother looks up. 'Well,' I say to her.

'You might find out *well*, if you're not careful,' she tells me.

Wendell takes a whiff of Skipper, who is wearing what used to be a pair of pink flowered pajamas. A small bit of satin ribbon is still visible around her neck, but the rest, including her smiling face, is wet brown mud and something else. 'Part of this is *poop*,' Wendell hollers.

My aunt turns around finally. 'Take that goddamn doll outside.' She means business so we go upstairs, put Skipper in a shoe box, and find our Barbies.

'Mine's going to a pizza party,' I say. My Barbie has a bubble haircut, red, and Wendell's has a black ponytail.

'Let's just say they're sitting home and then Ken comes over and makes them go to a nightclub,' Wendell suggests. Hers doesn't have a pizza-party outfit so she never wants mine to get to wear one either.

'Mine's going to sing at the nightclub then,' I warn her.

'Well, mine doesn't care,' Wendell offers generously. She's eye-balling a white fur coat hanging prominently in my carrying case. Her Barbie walks over to mine. 'Can I wear your fur tonight?' she asks in a falsetto.

'If I can wear your bola,' my Barbie replies.

'It's boa, stupid,' Wendell tells me. She digs out a pink feathered scrap, puts it in her Barbie's hand, and makes her Barbie throw it at mine.

'Let's say it's really hot out and they don't know Ken is coming over and they're just sitting around naked for a while,' I suggest.

'Because they can't decide what to wear,' Wendell clarifies. 'All their clothes are in the dryer.' She wads up all the outfits lying around and throws them under the bed.

'Oh God, it's so hot,' my Barbie tells hers. 'I'm going to sit at the kitchen table.' Naked, she sits down in a cardboard chair at a cardboard table. Her hair is a smooth auburn circle, her eyes are covered with small black awnings, her legs are stuck straight out like broomsticks.

Black-haired, ponytailed Barbie stands on tiptoe at the cardboard sink. 'I'm making us some pink squirrels,' she announces. 'But we better not get drunk, because Ken might come over.'

Both Barbies do get drunk, and Ken does come over. He arrives in an ill-fitting suit, and the heat in the Barbie house is so overwhelming that he has to remove it almost immediately.

'Hey baby,' Ken says to no one in particular. The Barbies sit motionless and naked in their cardboard kitchen, waiting for orders. This is where Dirty Barbies gets murky – we aren't sure what's supposed to happen next. Whatever happens, it's Ken's fault, that's all we know.

The Barbies get tired and go lie down on their canopied bed. Ken follows them in and leans at a forty-degree angle against their cardboard dresser. He's trying to tell them he's tired, too.

'You're going to prison, buddy,' Wendell finally says, exasperated. She heaves him under her bed and we get our Barbies up and dress them.

'Ken better not try anything like *that* again,' ponytailed Barbie says. She's wearing a blue brocade evening gown with the white fur coat, and one cracked high-heeled shoe.

'He thinks he's funny but he's not,' my Barbie replies ominously. 'He's in jail and *we're* the only ones who can bail him out.' She's got on a yellow satin-and-net dress with a big rip up the back, and the boa is wrapped tightly around her neck. By the time they get Ken out of jail and into his tuxedo, the whole evening is shot. The judge has to be bribed with a giant nickel that pony-tailed Barbie holds in her outstretched hand.

'Crap,' Wendell says when they holler at us from downstairs. I pack up my carrying case, drag it down the steps and out to the car. I keep sitting down the whole way because I'm tired.

'Get moving,' my mother tells me. My aunt calls me Jody and gives me a little whack on the behind, but she doesn't mean anything by it. I climb in beside my sister and roll down the window.

'Whaaa,' Wendell says to me. This is the sound her Betsy-Wetsy makes when it gets swatted for peeing.

The car pulls out onto the highway and turns toward town. I left my Barbie's pizza-party outfit under Wendell's pillow so she could use it until next time. Too bad, I miss it already. Red tights and a striped corduroy shirt with tassels that hang down. It goes better with a bubble cut than a ponytail, really. I should never have left it.

August, early evening. We're crammed into Uncle Fred's yellow Caddie, driven by Little Freddy, our cousin. I have on a low-backed, peach-colored dress with spaghetti straps and a giant, itching wrist corsage made of greenery and tipped carnations.

Wendell is wearing an ivory wedding gown with a scoop neck and a hundred buttons down the back. It's the dress our grand-mother married our grandfather in and it makes Wendell look like an angel. There are guys present – my boyfriend, a sweet, quiet type named Eric, and Wendell's brand-new husband, Mitch, a mild-mannered, blue-eyed farmer who is gazing at the cornfields streaking by.

Cousin Freddy is in control at this point, possibly a big mistake. One misplaced elbow and all the windows go down at once, causing hot air to whirl around inside the Caddie, stir-ring up everyone's hair and causing a commotion. 'Okay, okay,' Freddy says in a rattled voice. He pushes another button and all

the windows go back up, the commotion stops, the air conditioning comes back into play.

Wendell has a wreath of baby's breath perched on top of her
head like a crown of thorns. A slight crevice has appeared in
the front of her hair, the baby's breath has lifted with the landscape and sits balanced on two distinct formations. The back is
untouched. She wrestles herself over to the rearview mirror and
gets a glimpse.

'Oh my God, it's the Red Sea,' she says. 'You parted my *hair*,
Freddy.'

There is an audible combing noise inside the car for a moment
as she tries to impose some discipline on it. Freddy looks at her
in the rearview mirror. He's got Uncle Fred's five-o'clock shadow
and Aunt Velma's tiny teeth, he's wearing a powder blue short-
sleeved shirt and a flowery necktie, fashionably wide. 'We can
borrow you a rake at one of these farmhouses,' he says, braking.
The Caddie, dumb and obedient as a Clydesdale, slows down,
makes a left and then a right, pulls onto a dirt track leading into
a cornfield. Freddy gets his wedding present from under the seat,
lights it, and passes it back. We pile out into the evening and
stand, smoking, next to the car.

The sky is way up there, a lavender dome. There's a gorgeous
glow of radiation in the spot the sun just vacated, a pale peach
burst of pollution that matches my dress.

The corn is waxy and dark green and goes on forever. We're
standing in a postcard. 'This is my big day,' Wendell mentions.
The crown of thorns is resting peacefully, swifts are swooping
back and forth, drinking bugs out of the sky. We're trying to keep
the hems of our dresses from dragging in the dirt.

'This corn is *ready*,' Mitch says quietly, to no one in particular.
The stalks are taller than us by a foot, a quiet crowd of ten million,
all of them watching us get high and wreck our outfits.

'Don't lean on the car,' I tell Wendell. She stands in her usual slouch, one arm wrapped around her own waist, the other bringing the joint to her lips. She squints and breathes in, breathes out. 'You look like Lauren Bacall only with different hair,' I say.

She considers that. 'You look like Barbara Hershey only with a different face,' she says kindly. We beam at one another. This is Wendell's big day.

'Hey, bats,' Eric says suddenly. He's looking up into the air where the swifts are plunging around. I'm very fond of him for a moment, and then I feel a yawn coming on. A breeze has picked up and the corn is rustling, a low hiss from the crowd. We're making Wendell late to her own party.

The Caddie takes us out of the cornfield, haunch-first. Freddy steers it up to the highway, sets the cruise, and we all lean back, stare out the side windows, and watch the landscape go from corn to soybeans to cows to corn. Next thing you know we're getting out again, this time at Wendell's old house, the farm.

The wedding cake is a tiered affair with peach-colored roses and two very short people standing on top. Our mothers made the mints. This is a big outdoor reception, with a striped awning and a skinned pig. The awning is over a rented dance floor, the pig is over a bed of coals. There are as many relatives as you'd want to see in one place; the men standing around the revolving pig, the women putting serving spoons in bowls of baked beans, potato salad, things made with Jell-O, things made with whipped cream, things made with bacon bits.

Two uncles are tapping the beer keg. They keep drawing up tall glasses of foam and dumping it on the ground.

'I need a beer bad,' Wendell says. She touches her head. 'How's the crown?'

'Firm,' I tell her. We get ourselves two glasses of foam to carry around and wander over to the food tables.

'This has prunes in it, if you can believe that,' an aunt tells us, uncovering a bowl full of something pink that just came from the trunk of her car. Our mothers are standing at a long table where more women are unwrapping gifts and logging them in a book.

Wendell's mother is wearing a long dress, gray silk with big peach-colored roses and green leaves down the front. My mother has on a pantsuit that everyone keeps admiring. They're both wearing corsages. 'Ooh,' my aunt says. A box has just been opened containing an enormous macramé plant hanger, with big red beads and two feet of thick fringe.

'Holy shit,' Wendell says, taking a drink of foam.

The guests eat salads and chips and pig, the sky turns pewter, deep cobalt, then black. The band strikes up; four guys, two of them relatives. They play a fast number and everyone under the age of ten gets out there to dance. The littlest kids concentrate on trying to get it exactly right, swinging their hips and whirling their arms around. After about two songs all of them are out of control and sweating, hair stuck to their head, girls seeing who can slide the farthest on patent-leather shoes, boys taking aim and shooting each other with their index fingers without mercy. The parents have to step in, remove a few examples, and put them in chairs. One gets spanked first for calling his mother a dipshit in front of the whole crowd.

A waltz begins to play and the older couples move out onto the floor, husbands with wives, various uncles with various aunts. My own dad dances me around a few times, tells me my dress is pretty, and delivers me in front of Eric, who looks stupendously bored and not quite stoned enough. 'Hey, lotta fun,' he says insincerely. I make him go dance with my mom.

Wendell takes a break from talking to people and we pull up lawn chairs next to the dance floor. Her ivory dress shines in the darkness. 'I keep losing my drink,' she says. We share a full, warm beer that's sitting on the ground between our chairs, passing it back and forth, watching the fox-trotters.

274

'I wish I could do the fox-trot,' I say wistfully.

She nods. 'We can't do anything good,' she says wearily. 'We can two-step,' I answer, in our defense.

'Yeah,' she says through a yawn. 'But big whoop, the two-step.' Two short great-aunts glide by at a smart clip and wave at us, the bride and the bridesmaid. Wendell waves back like a beauty queen on a float, I smile and twinkle my fingers. 'Yee-haw,' I say quietly. On the other side of the dance floor Mitch stands listening intently to one of our distant, female relatives. He winks at us when she isn't looking and we wink back hugely. 'That's my first husband, Mitch,' Wendell says fondly.

The night air is damp and black against my arms, like mossy sleeves. There are stars by the millions up above our heads. Wendell and I are sitting directly under Gemini, my birth sign, the oddball twins, the split personality. Part of me wants to get up and dance, the other part wants to sit with my head tipped back. All of me wants to take off my wrist corsage.

'Nice ragweed corsage,' I tell Wendell. My arm itches like fire, long red hives are marching up to my elbow. I take it off and put it under my chair.

'Give it a heave,' she suggests, and I do. It lands within twenty feet of our lawn chairs. A giant calico farm cat steps out from nowhere, sniffs it, then picks it up delicately and fades back into the blackness. Under the awning the air is stained yellow, the band is playing a disco song. Our mothers are in the midst of a line dance, doing their own version of the Hustle, out of synch with everyone else. Their work is done, they've mingled, they've been fairly polite. Now they've got about twenty minutes of careening before they collapse in lawn chairs and ask people to wait on them. They're out there trying to kick and clap at the same time, without putting their drinks down. I decide I'd better join them.

My mother's cheeks are in bloom, from sloe gin and exertion, her lipstick has worn off but her corsage is still going strong, a flower the size of a punch bowl. She tries for the relaxed shuffle-kick-pause-clap of all the other line dancers but can't do it. She sets her drink down at the edge of the dance floor where it's sure to get knocked over and comes back to the line, full steam ahead. She starts doing the Bump with Wendell's mom and another aunt. Before they can get me involved, I dance myself over to the edge of the floor and step out into the darkness.

'The moms need to be spanked and put in chairs,' I tell Eric, who hands over his beer without being asked. He looks peaceful and affectionate; his hair is sticking straight up in front and there's something pink and crusty all over the front of his shirt.

'One of those kids threw a piece of cake at me,' he says placidly. He's been smoking pot out in the corn with Freddy, I can tell. The band pauses between numbers and the mothers keep dancing. In the distance, two uncles stand talking, using the blue glow of a bug zapper to compare their mangled thumbnails. Up by the band, the bride is getting ready to throw the bouquet. I'm being summoned to come stand in the group of girl cousins clustered around Wendell. I walk backward until I'm past the first row of corn, Eric following amiably, pink-eyed and slap-happy. He's using a swizzle stick for a toothpick.

Inside the corn it is completely dark, the stalks stand silent, the sounds of the party are indistinct. We can hear each other breathing. There is a muffled cheering as the bouquet gets thrown, and then someone talks loud and long into the microphone, offering a toast. Eric begins nuzzling my ear and talking baby talk.

'Hey,' I whisper to him.

'Mmmm?' he says.

'Have you ever seen a corn snake?'

He refuses to be intimidated. A waltz begins and we absently take up the one-two-three, one-two-three. Around us the dark stalks ripple like water, the waves of the blue Danube wash over us. 'I can show *you* a corn snake,' he says softly, into my hair.

276

*

Here is a scene. Two sisters talk together in low voices, one knits and the other picks lints carefully off a blanket. Their eyes meet infrequently but the conversation is the same as always.

'He's too young to retire,' my mother says. 'He'll be stuck to her like a burr, and then that's all you'll hear. How she can't stand having him underfoot.' One of my uncles wants to retire from selling Motorola televisions and spend the rest of his years doing woodworking.

'How many pig-shaped cutting boards does anybody need?' my aunt says. She holds her knitting up to the window. '*Goddamn* it. I did it again.' She begins unraveling the last few rows, the yarn falling into a snarl around her feet.

'Here,' my mother says, holding out a hand, 'give me that.' She takes the ball of pale yellow yarn and slowly, patiently winds the kinked part back up. While they work, a nurse enters and reads a chart, takes a needle from a cart in the hall, and injects it into the tube leading into my mother's arm. When the door snicks shut behind her, my aunt quits unraveling long enough to get a cigarette from her purse.

'They better not catch me doing this,' she says, lighting up. She's using an old pop can for an ashtray. The cigarette trembles slightly in her long fingers and her eyes find the ceiling, then the floor, then the window. She adjusts the belt on her suit, a soft green knit tunic over pants, with silver buttons and a patterned scarf at the neck. She's sitting in an orange plastic chair.

My mother is wearing a dark blue negligee with a bedjacket and thick cotton socks.

She takes a puff from my aunt's cigarette and exhales slowly, making professional smoke rings. 'Now I'm corrupted,' she says dryly.

'If any of them walked in right now, they'd have a fit,' my aunt replies uneasily. She's worried about stern daughters, crabby nurses.

'Do I give a good goddamn?' my mother asks peacefully. She's staring at the ceiling. 'I don't think I do.' She's drifting now, floating upward, her shot is taking effect. She gets a glimpse of something and then loses it, like a fish swimming in and out of view in the darkness under water. She struggles to the surface. 'I hope you get a girl,' she says.

My aunt is knitting again, the long needles moving against each other, tying knots, casting off, creating small rosettes. Wendell is ready to have a baby any day now. 'Well, she's carrying it low,' my aunt answers skeptically. The room is dimming, she turns her chair more toward the window. There is a long pause, with only the needles and the tedious breath, the sterile landscape of cancer country.

'That doesn't mean anything,' my mother finally replies. Her father bends over the bed to kiss her, as substantial as air; he's a ghost, they won't leave her alone. She moves slowly through the fluid and brings a thought to the surface. 'We carried all of ours low, and look what we got.' They swim through her lake, gray-eyed sisters, thin- legged and mouthy. They fight and hold hands, trade shoes and dresses, marry beautiful tall men, and have daughters together, two dark-eyed cousins, thin-legged and mouthy. A fish splashes, a silver arc against the blue sky, its scales like sequins. She startles awake.

'I hope you get a girl,' she says again. This is all she can think to say. Her sister, in the dimness, sets down her work and comes to the bed. She bends over and pulls the blanket up, straightens it out. She can't think of what to say either. The face on the pillow is foreign to her suddenly, distant, and the weight of the long afternoon bends her in half. She leans forward wearily, and lets herself grimace.

'We got our girls we wanted so bad, didn't we?' my mother whispers to her, eyes still shut. My aunt straightens and fingers a silver button at her throat.

'Those damn brats,' she comments. She presses both hands against the small of her back and shuts her eyes briefly. For an instant she sees the two original brats – wearing their droopy calico dresses, sassing their mother, carrying water up from the pump at the home place, knocking into each other. 'You were always my sister,' she says softly.

My mother is completely without pain now, the lake is dark, the fish move easily out of her way. Her sister swims by and makes a statement. 'I know it,' she answers. She tries to think of a way to express something. Sequins fall through the water, fish scales, and a baby floats past, turned upside-down with a thumb corked in its mouth. The morphine is a thin vapor in her veins. She rouses herself.

'He did do a nice job on those Christmas trees,' she says. My aunt nods. She's talking about the woodworking uncle now, who made Christmas trees for all the sisters to put in the middle of their dining-room tables.

'I told him to make me a couple more for next year,' my aunt says. 'My card club went nuts over it.' She lights another cigarette, hating herself for it. My mother is silent, her hands cut the water smoothly, like two long knives. The little gray-eyed girls paddle and laugh. She pushes a spray of water into her sister's face and her sister pushes one back. Their hair is shining against their heads.

In the dimness of the hospital room, my aunt smokes and thinks. She doesn't see their father next to the bed, or old Aunt Grace piddling around with the flower arrangements. She sees only the still form on the bed, the half-open mouth, the coppery wig. She yawns. Wendell's stomach is out to here, she remembers, any day now. That's one piece of good news.

My mother sleeps silently while my aunt thinks. As the invisible hands tend to her, she dives and comes up, breaks free of the water. A few feet over a fish leaps again, high in the air. Her arms move lazily back and forth, holding her up, and as she watches, the fish is transformed. High above the water, it rises like a silver baton, presses itself against the blue August sky, and refuses to drop back down.

Behind the Screen

I'M LOOKING AT THE BACKS of all their heads. They're sitting on lawn chairs in the dusk and so am I, only their lawn chairs are on the lawn while mine is on the enclosed back porch. I have to look at the backs of their heads through the screen. We're waiting for the fireworks to begin.

My sister is wearing shorts, a midriff top, and all manner of jewelry – a pop-bead necklace, a Timex wristwatch, a mood ring, and a charm bracelet that makes a busy metallic rustle every time she moves her arm, which she does frequently. On the charm bracelet, between a high-stepping majorette and a sewing machine with movable parts, is a little silver book that opens like a locket to display The Teen Commandments.

Engraved in infinitesimal letters: *Don't let your parents down, they brought you up; Choose a date who would make a good mate;* and the famous *At the first moment turn away from unclean thinking – at the first moment.* It has such an urgent tone it forces you to think uncleanly. Right now my sister is sitting in a lawn chair waiting for it to get dark. Every few minutes she raises and lowers her right arm so the charm bracelet, which I covet, clanks up to her elbow and then slides slowly and sensuously back down to her wrist. She doesn't bother turning around to see how I take this. She knows it's killing me.

They won't let me off the porch because I'm having an allergy attack. A low whistling sound emanates from my chest whenever I breathe. I can put a little or a lot of force behind it, depending on my mood. I'm allergic to ragweed and thistles and marigolds and dandelions and daisies, so we're all used to me being stuck on the porch while everyone else is having fun. Also grass; I'm allergic to grass. Right now one nostril is completely plugged up while the other runs in a steady drip.

My four-year-old brother is wearing cowboy boots and shorty pajamas, a gunbelt minus the guns, and a hat with earflaps. He's shooting each member of my family in turn with his crayon-size index fingers. He smiles at me, his little teeth glinting in the dusk. 'You dead,' he says.

I press my face up against the screen. It smells like dirt. I put my tongue out tentatively. It tastes like dirt. 'Go to H,' I say.

My mother turns her head halfway around and looks into my father's ear. 'You're gonna get a whole lot sicker, miss,' she tells me. Stars are beginning to be visible through the cloudy beehive of her teased hair. It's the Fourth of July 1962, and our city is having a fireworks display in the park. I have my own bowl of popcorn on the porch, and a glass of pop. The fireworks will be visible over the top of the dying elm tree in our backyard. It's impossible for me to eat the popcorn because I'm wearing a nose tourniquet, an invention I came up with myself: half of a twisted Kleenex, one end stuffed into one nostril, the other end in the other nostril. It has a wicking effect, and saves the effort of swabbing all the time.

'I can't even taste this pop,' I say to the screen, after taking a sip. They all ignore me. The family dog, Yimmer, is sitting on my father's lap, growling quietly each time my brother shoots her.

My sister takes a loud swig out of a bottle of Pepsi, wipes her mouth elaborately, and says, 'Man, was that good.'

I examine a series of interesting scabs on my right knee. None of them are ready to be removed, although a couple are close. 'You should see these scabs,' I say to the backs of their heads.

My brother marches in place, talking to himself in a stern whisper.

My mother lights another Salem and positions a beanbag ashtray on the metal arm of her chair.

My father leans down and gives Yimmer's head a kiss.

Suddenly the scruffy edges of the elm tree are illuminated. The night sky turns pale above the garage, staccato gunfire, and a torpedo of light wiggles upward, stops, and fizzles. There is a beat of silence and then a burst of cascading pink and green worms. A long sigh is heard, from my family and the family next door.

I have my forehead against the screen, breathing in the night air and the heavy, funereal scent of roses, the only flower I'm not allergic to. A noodle skids across the sky, releasing a shower of blue spangles, jewels on a black velvet bodice. Way up there is outer space. I lean back and touch my forehead; an indented grid from the screen has been pressed into it. All these fireworks are somehow scaring me. 'You should see my forehead,' I say to my mother's hair.

'What's wrong with it?' she asks patiently. She doesn't turn around.

'I keep pressing it on the screen,' I say.

'Don't push on that screen,' my father says.

'I'm not,' I say.

The sky is full of missiles. All different colors come out this time, falling in slow motion, red and blue turning to orange and green. It's so beautiful, I have to close my eyes. My family joins the neighbors in oohing. Suddenly, as the delayed booms are heard, I have to lean forward and put my head on my knees, inhaling the scent of Bactine and dirt. Everything is falling away from me. I open my eyes.

Black sky, dissipating puffs of gray smoke, the barely visible edges of the elm tree.

My father's hand is dark against the white of the dog's fur. My brother is aiming both forefingers at the sky. A match flares suddenly; my mother touches it to her cigarette and inhales.

I am stuck somewhere between the Fourth of July and the rest of time, the usual chaos inside my head distilled down into nothing. I put my cheek against the screen, feeling the grid. There is an uproar, gunfire, sounds from the crowd.

Shooting stars in the cold of outer space; one after another the missiles are launched until the sky is brilliant with activity and smoke. Huge arcs of pink and yellow. Orange things that fizzle for an instant and then send out sonic booms. Long terrible waterfalls of yellow and blue. In the brightness, the backs of all their heads look rapt. My brother has his hands over his ears. My sister's mouth is open. The dog has her head in my father's armpit. It goes on for minutes, the booming sounds and the brilliant light.

Closing my eyes doesn't work, it makes me feel like I'm falling backward. Instead I watch their hair, all the different styles right in my own back yard, and say The Teen Commandments quietly to myself: *Avoid following the crowd; be an engine, not a caboose. Stop and think before you drink.* Gunfire, one last wild spiraling of colors, and it's over.

'I'm not going to bed,' my brother says resolutely.

The dog jumps down and stretches.

I remain in my lawn chair as they all troop into their house. One of my sister's better personalities comes out and she stops to comb her fingers through my hair and carries my full popcorn bowl into the house.

'She can't eat a thing,' she tells my mother piously.

'Bath,' my mother says to her. I hear my sister stomp up the stairs and then I hear my brother stomp up behind her, two feet on each stair.

'I saw a goddamned mosquito in here,' my mother says. There's some flailing around, the whap of the flyswatter, and then my dad says, 'Ick.' The freezer opens, a bowl is clattered out of the cupboard. Ice cream. There's the unscrewing sound of a jar opening. Marshmallow stuff. My head hurts. I remove my spent nose tourniquet and start twisting a new one. Before I can get it in place there is a damp trickle on my lip.

'You guys?' I say. Any minute now they're going to send me upstairs.

There's an expectant pause in the kitchen.

'This lawn chair is stuck to my legs,' I tell them.

A bottle is opened and an audible swig is taken. The lighter snaps and there's silence while she exhales.

Uh-oh.

'Bath,' she says.

Coyotes

A SMALL GESTURE OF MOVEMENT, a hiss of grass, and he is frozen stone for an instant, yellow eyes pinned on the spot, ears cocked forward. A quick lunge of muscles and paws, a darting switchback, and suddenly a rabbit is beating itself to death inside his mouth, against his tongue. This is lunch, unexpected.

In the tall papery weeds he pants and heaves and eventually, regretfully, begins licking the red off his paws. This will lead, as always, to the licking of his whole body, the coarse mangy fur like sawgrass against his tongue. He spreads the toes of one back paw and gnaws something hard and spiny away from the pad. He shakes his head fiercely to dislodge it from his teeth and then groans, rolls over flat on his side. He is in a trance now, one lobe of the brain completely at rest, in a smooth white fog that settles completely, like bedcovers, and doesn't lift until dark. The other lobe is on edge, senses opened so wide they collect amazing things: the screaming of unseeable insects hopping from one hair follicle to another; the droning currents emanating from power lines a quarter mile away; the throbbing of water deep beneath the ground. In the fog each paw twitches in preparation for the leap, the bite, the flat-out escaping run.

Through the mist creeps a glowing, dull-witted bunny, eyes stupid, tail erect. Yellow paws pulse against the dirt as the coyote closes over its belly and suddenly the bunny is a chicken and the prized feel of it – white feathers beating softly against his muzzle – causes him, like a dog being petted, to wag heavily against the grass and bark lightly in sleeping pleasure.

In my dreams the ground murmurs over and over, until I'm ready to wake up swinging. *I am Kansas*, it says, *I am Kansas I am Kansas I am Kansas.* This is a train headed for Arizona and those are other passengers. The guy across from me has on house slippers and a hat because it's freezing in here. He's reading a book with a sprawled dead woman on the cover. Beside me, Eric is sleeping with his neck exposed and both hands lying open and empty. God. I put my own hands back into my armpits, bring my knees up, bend my head down, and try to sink back into some kind of blankness. Inside my mind a green and brown landscape appears, a mountain hillside with white-tailed deer arranged here and there, a stump, a path, a clump of rocks. Old slides from past vacations click into place and then disappear, one after another. The wheels drone. A burned forest, the sharp gaze of a fox, a pair of ponies standing at a fence, wildflowers, and broken barns; they each snap into position, linger while I look, and then make way for the next. Beneath me the gravelly ground goes on and on, explaining itself in dull tones: *I am Kansas I am Kansas I am Kansas.*

Small- to medium-size creatures creep and coil themselves over the desert floor, making their separate ways toward their separate destinies. Big creatures drive their cars along its roads and mostly don't get out, except to take leaks at the edge of the blacktop.

Or point their cameras, hesitate, and give up. It looks different through the lens than through the windshield. Empty and blank and pointless.

I'm in a green tent that turned luminous a few minutes ago when the sun hit it. Eric is cooking breakfast and I'm lying in a sleeping bag not wanting to get up. It is freezing, that much is definitely true. And my shoulders hurt from too much sun and the ground is hard as a city street.

'Come on and get up,' Eric calls. 'It's warm out here.' I peel up a corner of the green door and see him turning omelets with one gloved hand. The other is inside his coat pocket. He's got binoculars around his neck and a purple wool baseball cap on his head. He looks like a maniac.

I'm getting up.

He roams in the blistering sunlight. The sand beneath his paws feels like fire. Every two or three miles he finds a spot of shade and stretches out, squinting into the distance, panting fast and loud. A quick movement, an interruption in the blankness of the sand, and he rises and runs, ears cocked, feet springing off the sandy ground. Mice and snakes. It takes several to make a meal. If the head of the snake rises in the air, he backs off, whining and growling; if not, he pursues it, sometimes winning, sometimes not. In his dreams at night the long limber bodies of the serpents move unexpectedly at him. Awake, he bites the heels of the beasts in the pastures, on the long empty range, dodging the hooves, tasting the dirt and dung and the coarse fringe of fur. The coyote hates horses and mules, the lowing cows, rich men and poor men. He likes mice and rats, the birds that burst forth in a glorious fan of wings, a squawk.

He roams in the blistering sunlight. His stomach gnaws and his eyes become more alert. The scent of water rises in his consciousness, he presses his nose upward and springs into his lilting trot. Around water is food. The desert gives way to the dappled green of sparse bushes, billowing grass. The coyote tilts his head sideways and uses the round dish of his upright ear to bring in any sounds along the bank. He drinks, listens again, and settles himself to wait. He scratches the area right where his heart beats. Small sounds come forward tentatively from the buzzing emptiness. The grass begins to sway as the breeze picks up. The sun is receding; it is long past dinnertime.

The current carries small sticks and leaves, twirling, past his face as the coyote watches the bank, still as stone, waiting for a creature to come forth. From the cover of the wavering rushes, the rabbits press low against the ground, against the urge to run-run-run. The riverbank breathes quietly and patiently; the coyote pins his eyes on a moving reed, turns his ear, lifts his muzzle slightly. A chipmunk leaves the shelter of the grass to step forward. A cluster of oblong seeds on the moist bank has called to him and he must obey.

Inside its green skin a frog blinks, a rectangular insect with a tender belly is claimed by a sticky tongue. The chipmunk squeaks once, the coyote wags and growls as he chews, the dying sun pinkens the air.

We are under a giant balanced rock. There are trees here with bark like alligator hide. Suitcases with leaves. Their roots pop up out of the shallow soil like bent knees poking out of bathwater. We have canteens, just like cowboys, but the water tastes old and filthy after it's been sitting in there. My shoes are covered with dust and a mile ago a small, thick rattlesnake buzzed at us from the edge of the trail. From above, this place appears as rugged badlands, big craggy pinnacles sticking up like blunt bayonets. The snake made me jumpy as all get-out but I've already filed the image of it away – recoiling on itself, the head a pulled-back wedge, its pattern subtle, smudged and blended like a charcoal drawing on the rock's surface – to be remembered later when I'm back in my own habitat, standing on a linoleum floor somewhere. What I really want to see is a javelina, but of course I won't. They're piglike things with tusks and they run in small herds, snorting and huffling over the pine needles and fallen logs at the bottom of this place. This is a bowl of mountains and greens with tender pieces of meat roaming here and there.

My thighs are on fire, from the burn of the sun and the exertion. From the lip of the bowl, up top, it looked more treacherous and lively than it turned out to be. The cleared overlook at the tip of the trail, Massai Point, is named for a Chiricahua Apache man who stole a horse out from under the droopy mustache of a settler. The startled, righteous white man gathered up some of his buddies and they stood at the point and watched for the Apache to show the top of his head. Rifles poised and scanning, they kept their eyes peeled. From the overlook there are a hundred thousand gaps and crevices between the balanced monoliths and stacked boulders. Breathing into the granite walls, hands flat and calming against the heaving sides of his new horse, he waited them out, watching the sky darken and the moon lift its face. They got tired of waiting and rode back to their settlement, miffed at the giant sheltering landscape, the defiant stone thumbs that hid wild Indians in their shadows.

This is daytime. My soap opera is on right now, somewhere. Back in Iowa. My people are roaming back and forth on the television screen, all prepared for any kind of upheaval; there are a lot of chiffon dresses and dyed-to-match shoes. I mention to Eric that my show is on. He turns with a grin and watches me ski down a dissolving patch of trail. Loose rocks roll beneath my feet as I'm carried along. This is elementary physics, ancient Egyptians used it to take house-size rocks here and there, up and down various hills. I skid one foot halfway under an overhanging rock and a curled ribbon of skin peels up my leg. Rattlers hang out under rocks, waiting for a shin to come along. Yee-ikes. I pull my lower leg back out where it belongs and start making an enormous deal out of my injury. Eric sprinkles water on it and yawns. He remembers that we're an hour off down here, the soap is already over.

The air turns tangy and alive, the sun is gone, the sky is black. Glimmers of light bristle forward in the dome above the coyote's head. He moves out. The night has a seething quality, a crisp silence that hides the tunneling of small, cowering mammals, the slumped somnolence of the wandering cattle, the wide-eyed jitters of the stick-leg deer. The moon, from the bitter cold of outer space, croons to the griddle of the desert. The coyote listens and turns to the west. An image has moved forward in his head: Out of the murk a picture comes to the forefront, melting into view. The thick, spongy edges of lightness, the dark legs and face, the palpable panic of the herd. The sheep are waiting. The moon pushes him forward from behind and snakes slide under bushes until he passes. Out of nowhere a skunk appears, startled, hunkering low with wide mirrored eyes. The coyote darts, bites, and opens the belly with one efficient fang. He drags it around in a gleeful circle, then thrusts one shoulder at a time into the cooling wetness. It is night and feelings are rising up, like blood to a scrape.

The desert is lunar. Every so often a night bird courses low over the sand and the mice shudder, the lizards peer lidlessly around, unroll their tongues and reel them in again. The moon lowers itself, sitting for a few moments on the shoulders of a western butte, considering the lake of shadows. In its distant, porous memory, the moon can conjure up how it pulled the ice back like a bedsheet, exposing the tender ground beneath. The face on the butte is ice blue and furious, slumping beneath its shoulders infinitesimally, down and down, until it is gone and the stars are livid and blinking. The insects teem, the rodents scrabble, the night-blooming flowers push themselves open and await their guests.

We have two things going for us: a spectacular white rental car and a bag of red-hot cinnamon Fireranchers. We discuss for a fair amount of time while sucking on the Fireranchers whether it is right to 'beat' a rental car more than you would beat your own car. We decide it isn't right, although we immediately follow that up by seeing how fast it can go on a stretch of gummy blacktop. It goes to one hundred and thirty miles an hour before it starts shivering.

The rental car has air conditioning but we're not using it. Instead we're keeping a spray bottle full of water in the cooler and spritzing ourselves with it every few miles.

Now there is a contest to see who can put a new Firerancher in his or her mouth and not bite it for however long it takes it to disintegrate. I will lose this game and we both know it. We're playing it because we're stupendously bored but still in high spirits. Every so often I put my foot on the dashboard for a leg inspection. My shinbone is a gentle, peeled blue. This is from when I fell down the mountain into the den of rattlesnakes.

'It wasn't a mountain, it was a path,' Eric says. 'And there weren't any rattlesnakes.'

I spray cold water on my shin and then put my leg back down where it belongs. My whole body feels swampy. The air is a blast furnace and the windshield is a magnifying glass trained on our forearms. We are one moment from ignition. I turn the water bottle around and squirt myself flat in the face and then offer to do Eric.

'I'll do myself,' he says threateningly. I hand the bottle over. It's not my style to squirt him with ice water while he's driving but predictably he falls apart for an instant and turns the bottle on me. It dries in one second from the hot breath coming through the window. We roll along in silence for awhile, sweating and thinking, working on our Fireranchers. Mine is so thin I try just resting my teeth on it to see how it feels. I bite it in half.

We are taking the low road from Tucson to a national monument on the border of Mexico. The map says we are now passing through the Comobabi Mountains, but outside the windows of our car the desert is as flat as a sheet of parchment. The saguaros have given way to brush and patches of gravelly dirt; along the highway from time to time are homemade altars. We keep passing them, eighty miles an hour. The next one we'll stop at so I can see who it's an altar to. There aren't even any jet trails out here, the sky is a long, blue yawn. Neil Young comes on the radio.

We see a hawk up ahead, standing on the hood of a broken-down car. We slow down to gaze and it stares at us. Its black-trousered legs are sturdy and long, its beak is curved. We peel off, back up to warp speed, and the landscape turns into a melting blur out the windshield.

'Look, sweetie,' Eric says, turned toward me in the driver's seat.

On the very tip of his tongue is his Firerancher. Thin as tissue paper, it looks like the moon in the daytime sky. Suddenly love is looming over the car, as big and invisible as the ghost mountains of the Comobabi range. I smile at him and turn up the radio with my toes.

*

293

He snaps peevishly at his haunch, bending stiffly backward to chew the peppery trail of a flea. The walls of the den are pungent with the smell of safety and his own fur. He gives up and flops back over, closes his eyes in the dimness and begins panting. No good, he's awake now, it's time to step back out into the day. In the sunlight he blinks and stretches, fore and aft, like a collie. He shakes so hard he almost knocks himself off his feet. The sky is as blue as blue and the coyote is in a good mood.

He lifts his muzzle and takes in a long snort of air, pulling with it the invisible happenings in the vicinity. There's something big and dead looming just over the rise. The coyote yawns and his tail swings down between his back legs in its traveling position. He puts his nose to the ground and begins his afternoon expedition.

Somewhere, right on the edge of what his nose is capable of, a rabbity perfume is lingering. He breaks into a lope just for the fun of it but drops back down to a trot after a hundred yards or so. The sun is pressing burning fingers into his spine. The black-top dips into view, and as the coyote moves toward it he prepares himself for the highway's big medicine. The sandy dirt beneath his paws gives way just a bit as each foot lands and springs off, the small stones and irregularities in his path add juice to his travels but rarely pain. Under his paws it is *sand ... sand ... rock ... sand ... stick ... sand ... stick* and then the highway's medicine: *hard ... scalding ... scalding ... scalding* and then *gravel ... sand ... rock ... sand ... sand ... rock ... sand* again.

As he passes once more safely through the hard pond of highway fire the coyote is startled by something in the air, something dangerous bearing down on him. Alert and agile, he jumps to the side, cringing and whining, but it is too late. An empty bread wrapper hits him smack in the side of the head.

*

The landscape has changed from the invisible Comobabi Mountains of love to the barren flats of boredom and annoyance. The sun is a yellow baseball hanging over right field, the driver's side is in the shade and the passenger's side is sizzling. I decide it's my turn to drive.

Eric glances over. 'Uh, doubt it,' he says.

I've just noticed how his hairline has taken a daring swoop down his forehead and back up again, just like his father's. I mention this to him while inspecting my fingernails.

He smiles and addresses me by my mother's name. 'I mean, honey,' he corrects himself, 'the kid's got the wheel and the kid's keeping it.' He's leaning back in his seat, steering with one finger, brow arched. We are very bored.

The kid is a shithook, I remark.

A shithook with the *wheel*, though, he clarifies. He points out that I'm sweating a lot, more than he's ever seen me do. 'Pretty hot over there, eh?'

I begin calling him Lovey, and suggest that we change drivers without stopping. He gives in reluctantly, only because he knows eventually he'll lose. If I don't get to drive pretty soon I will open my car door while we're moving and he can't stand that. He's afraid I'll get sucked out by accident and it'll be his fault for being a control freak.

You have to be going really fast for this trick, over seventy miles an hour. Both of us recline our seats all the way down, I do the gas pedal with my left foot and hold the steering wheel steady with my left hand while Eric climbs into the back seat. I move over the gear shift and slide into his seat while he climbs over my reclined seat back into the passenger side. It's not exactly that smooth, of course, there is a lot of swerving and hollering that goes along with it. We settle in and bring our seat backs into position and open a can of malt liquor.

'Yee-haw,' I say, now that I'm in the driver's seat. Eric tries to rig up a shade for his window using a white T-shirt. He can't get it to stay draped over while he rolls up the glass. I enjoy watching him do this a few times and then look sympathetic when he gives up. 'Pretty hot over there, isn't it?' I ask him.

'Not really,' he answers.

Twenty miles later we enter the Valley of the Ajo and head for the monument, right above the border of Mexico. The road is endless, with wavering lines of heat rising up and a mirage that looks like a silver pool always about half a mile ahead of the car.

Suddenly Eric points and I press on the brake. Along the edge of the blacktop on the opposite side of the highway is a coyote, pushing a bread wrapper along with his nose. He ignores us completely, stops and puts one paw on the plastic wrapper, takes it in his teeth, and begins pulling it apart. He shakes his head like a dog. I pull off into the gravel and try to sit quietly, like I'm not a human. He's staring at me now, still nosing into the bag, gold eyes looking up from the dirty plastic.

The car is a boiling caldron. The coyote stands scruffy and skittish, like a wild dingo dog I met once, who bit everything in sight, wagging his tail like a maniac. Eric slides the camera to me and puts a hand on my arm. He whispers in my ear. I nod. I love dogs better than anything else on earth, next to cigarettes and a couple of people.

I find him in the lens, framed in a square. As I click the shutter he jumps sideways and takes off, running a few yards and then skidding to a halt, looking back over his shoulder. He's not afraid of us, he's just horsing around. In the rearview mirror he canters over the rocks, low to the ground, tail tucked. In the slide, projected on my living room wall, he will be a gray, moving blur, a running pelt. The gracious arms of an organ pipe cactus direct him up the hill, over the rise, out of the frame, and into memory.

*

The saguaros send out long lavender fingers into the afternoon. Grains of sand cool and then warm again as the slow sweep of the shadows moves past. Something looped and coiled unravels gradually, in no hurry, to follow the pool of purple, the spot where the shadow meets its source. It feeds a tongue out, testing the temperature of the air, and begins to wind back into the debris of the cactus again, until there is only a barely visible presence on the ground, a tangled rope with scales and eyes.

Nearly fifty feet in the air a scar, made with a pocketknife and dirty fingers, is visible on the skin of the cactus. A flicker lands on the green pinnacle and peers around, pokes the needle of its beak into the flesh, and peers again. A ridge ten miles west stands fluted and browning, like the crust of a pie, a hawk slides down a current of air and floats above it. The flicker thrusts again and shrugs the moisture down its throat.

The cactus receives the bird, tiny claws like pins, with the same indifference as it had the man with the pocketknife on the shuddering horse. Weak and boiling, he dug and dug into the spiny hide with his pocketknife. The horse died within the reach of the saguaro's shadow, descending into a dull bag that collapsed on itself, bones moving out across the desert floor in the mouths of jackals.

The man either made it or didn't. The words he spoke and the voice he spoke them in linger high above the ground nearly two hundred years later, buffeted by the hot wind, nourished by desperation and the terrible solitude. The flicker turns his head into the wind, finds the moisture again, drinks, and lifts off. The currents of air move around the top of the cactus, over the thorny scar.

Now, as then, the saguaro stands beneath the sun as the desert clock sweeps over the ground in circles, and begins the slow, tedious task of sealing its wound.

*

This is the campground: acres and acres of barren plots, bent and scraggy trees, stand-up grills, picnic tables, no people. One big vehicle is parked about a hundred yards away, on the other side of the bathrooms, tethered to an electrical hookup. The people won't come outside until the sun leaves, but a small apricot poodle ventures out a few times and barks at itself wildly. The door opens to let it back in, sending out a big waft of refrigerated air for the bugs and birds to enjoy.

Our tent is all set up, with a minimum of arguing. We stretch out inside it to see how long we can stand to lie there. First it gets very stuffy, then the air leaves completely. We climb out and sit in the front seat of the car, listening to the radio and eating potato chips, waiting for the sun to back off. I'm reading a book about vampires that is so graphic in various parts that I have to breathe through my mouth and stop eating chips. Eric is thumbing through an astronomy magazine. Every once in a while I'll tell him a detail from the vampire book and he'll show me his magazine, explain something about one of the pictures, a black background with white dots. We read and thumb until the landscape is a hazy 3-D postcard and the sky is a turquoise tent. Our legs decide to walk.

The Official Map and Guide stresses not once but twice that rattlesnakes are protected here. It has a curt, no-nonsense tone that indicates we'd better act right. Small quail run across the path, back and forth, stopping and starting, murmuring and pecking. In the distance one cactus stands apart, reaching at least two feet taller than any of the others, a surly foreman, the dad of the landscape. I want to go see it, see how tall it is compared to me.

Eric has a forked stick that he's using for a divining rod. 'It'll come in handy for snakes,' he tells me, '*and* show us where there's water.' The stick suddenly lifts in the air and starts shaking, he manages to hold on and push it back down. 'I accidentally pointed it towards the bathrooms,' he says.

The camper people are out with their little dog. The guy has a garden hose that he's spraying the path with because he doesn't want dust from cars to get on his Astroturf rug. I feel like talking to him but he just nods without smiling and we have to keep walking. He points the hose politely in another direction until we're past, and the poodle barks and barks.

I tell Eric I wish I had a little dog like that one.

'Of course you do,' he answers, 'that's the one thing you're short on.' Three dogs mingle and mill somewhere in the vast universe, in Iowa, wondering why we're not there petting them. I muse on this for a while. A big dog, a medium-size dog, and a charming lapdog with a mean streak.

'They don't even know we're gone,' I tell Eric, 'they think we went in the other room and just haven't come back yet.' The minds of dogs interest me, the way they never bother to anticipate problems.

By the time we get to the tall cactus the light has softened to a benign burn, a warm pat on the head. We both look great all of a sudden, stained brown with pink auras. Eric sets down his stick and moves back to get the whole cactus in the frame, with me standing at the base for comparison. At the very top of the saguaro a crista has formed over some kind of damage. The scar blooms out, hard and dark green, like the tiny head on a giant. I step over the debris at the base and arrange myself with arms out, bent at the elbow. The cactus is very old and very tall; up close it is hard and weathered and looks important; a cactus emeritus.

I stand in the soft, end-of-day shadow and have my picture taken. It feels like being on Mars here, the light is strange, these green men stand all over the terrain.

Ninety-three million miles due west, the sun continues to shoot off its bottle rockets. The desert has edged away now, out of range. At the foot of the saguaro, a snake, without moving anything but the thread of tongue, gently touches shoe leather, considers it, and decides no.

The nervous birds are gone from the ground now, it is night. The coyote runs in a mile-wide circle, at a lope, thirty miles an hour. There is nothing else moving. The moon bounces in the sky, over his right shoulder, now behind. A rock rises, a cholla extends soft elbows in his path, a dry husk stares up from the ground. There is nothing. The moon is a wide, mottled face, the countenance of an enraged idiot. The coyote runs and runs, not gasping, until there is something.

Three mule deer spring and run in various directions, bounding, flinging their hooves in the air. He picks one and chases halfheartedly for a distance, hearing his own feet, feeling the moon. They reassemble farther out, staring at him through the dimness, long ears moving back and forth like wings, each face small and wary. The one he chased turns first and takes up its occupation again: finding forage and trying not to die. He holds the moment until he can stay still no longer and begins running again, away from the sky. The ground is silver, the rocks are gleaming. There is nothing.

We play euchre and hearts, drink beer, rearrange the lantern thirty times. Finally we put it under the picnic table and it illuminates our legs and shorts, blows the whistle on a large furred spider.

'It's got knees,' I marvel. Actually, it has sort of a face, too, attached to a slender neck. I decide to sit on top of the table for a while.

'Let me get my spider stick,' Eric says. He holds the tines of the divining rod and gently points the way for the spider. It scuttles a few feet and then pauses, goes back into a trance. 'Get along, buddy,' he urges, giving it a prod. It does several push-ups, puts a leg in the air, and then moves of its own volition out from under the table and into the darkness.

We play a few more hands of hearts, until I realize that we both want me to win and I still can't manage it. The whole desert is disappointed. We fold our hands and practice being bored for a while. Our dogs are sleeping at home, two of them nose to nose and snoring, one off by herself, flat on her side, dreaming of me. The stars are no match for the wash of the moon, the night air is navy blue and coolish against our skin.

The camper people are out of it. Their colored lanterns are dark now and the TV is on inside, the glow of Letterman and his guests reflected in the window. I can see a head framed in the light, surrounded by a frizz of hair. It's the poodle, looking at stars.

We clear the table and spread out a sleeping bag on it, flannel side up. This is the best way to watch the sky. Eric has his red flashlight and charts, I have my sweatshirt zipped and a Walkman with two pairs of headphones. It's his turn to choose a tape so I'm waiting for something discordant and spooky but when he pushes the button it's one of my favorites. *Thank you*, I mouth to him. He smiles, closes his eyes, and takes my hand. Side by side. He moves into the solitude of headphones and constellations. I am perched on planet Earth, Milky Way galaxy, who knows what universe. Way up there, satellites are parked with their motors running, and vivid rings of plasma do laps around Saturn. Way down here, there is only the terrible arch of the sky, the sagging moon, and nothing else.

The earphones make my head feel like a hollow tube, full of horns and drums and a voice that echoes like green glass. I am alone inside my own skin and the edges of everything have begun to darken slightly, curling and browning, the beginnings of disintegration. Inside my chest a heart begins knocking to get out. I am alone down here, and up there, clinging to the spoke of a satellite, looking upward at the dark velvet, and downward at the dark velvet.

There is nothing.

Pockmarked and surly, the moon steps back and drops the curtain, darkens the theater for the stars. The clock is halted, the desert gives up its heat. A finger-size lizard with infrared spots and oval eyes finds itself, one second too late, in the damp cotton of a mouth. Power lines gleam and bounce their signals on the ground, startling the brain waves of small mammals, putting thoughts in their heads. Something swims through the medium of sand and surfaces, pinches hard and holds on.

In the endless black of deep space a small comet hurtles along, tossing iceballs and dirt behind it, on a perpetual path, around and around and around, pointless and energetic. Propelled by the force of its combustion, the comet passes within a light year of Sirius, burning out of control. Under the press of gravity and air, inside the earth's atmosphere, the coyote reads the signals in the ground, whirls, stops, and sprays a bush. He begins loping again, without awareness, the desire widening, a dark basin, until he cries as he runs, low and controlled. They are somewhere.

The moon is gone and Eric has fallen asleep beside me. Planets and stars. I know only the ones that everyone knows: the sun, the moon, the dippers, Gemini and Cancer. They move into formation, still and distant as dead relatives, outlining the shape of my mother's mouth. Nothing moves. Inside my head images emerge and retreat, emerge and retreat. I have to open my eyes. In the vivid blackness overhead a diamond falls through the sky, trailing its image, a split-instant of activity. By the time I realize I've seen it, the sky has recovered. I can't breathe in this emptiness. I turn on my side on the hard picnic table and look at Eric.

He is awake, watching me. He knows the desert is making me sad, that I have these moments; he smiles and moves up close. I can feel the sky on my face, the warm flannel of the desert floor below. I can feel the face of the man beside me. In the silence of the monument he begins whispering the names of the constellations while I listen: Cygnus the Swan, Pegasus the Horse, Canis Major the Great Dog, Cassiopeia, Arcturus.

I am on planet Earth.

They are near. He pulls in the scent with loud snorts, running from bush to rock to bush again. This is a clearing, a high naked spot. On the distant rise, just ahead, waiting, they are still invisible, but the scent rises in the air around him, palpable as mist. He opens his mouth wide and stands frozen, ears back, eyes pressed shut. The dirt beneath his pads is hard and dry, devoid, the moon is gone.

As the mist rises around him, the sound comes forth, pulled from tendon and muscle. It pushes itself through his lungs and into the night, a long trembling wail, dying slowly, drifting finally, without his help, dissipating. Still frozen, he listens for a moment to the roaring silence, waiting, and slowly the sound moves back toward him, fainter, broken into parts like music. Many voices.

They are ahead of him, in the high clearing where the deer sometimes sleep, pausing to listen, ready to bring him in with the radar of their voices. He begins running again and gravity relinquishes its hold. The terrain becomes buoyant and he soars low over the ground, like a night bird, a skipped stone.

The tent is completely dark. I am floating on the ocean in a canoe, each dip of the oar pours out a panful of light, beneath the surface small silver minnows hover like aircraft. My big collie roams along the shore, following the boat, whining low in her throat, stamping her white paws against the sand. I row toward the beach, casting light behind me, and she begins to bark.

I am awake suddenly in the darkness. Outside the tent is the padding of feet, around and around, a swift turning, a pause. There is something in our campsite, trying to get our food. Eric startles and wakes, I touch his hair, breathe into his ear. The paws turn again, there is loud panting, the low whine, and then a series of barks and yelps, a prolonged terrible howl. It is deafening and wild, I can feel him out there, conjuring hysteria out of the dark. A long, plaintive keening, and suddenly it ends, drifting off, carried away from us. We are breathing low and shallow, resting on our elbows.

When the reply comes he joins in, barking first and then crying, pitched high then low, the howl of loneliness and communion. It is lunar and eerie, the pleading of the cold, dead moon to the blue and green revolving earth, the call of sister stars across years of space, the cry of a child who has lost her mother. Now it is coming from every side, the beautiful wailing; they are swarming over us, gray and brown ghosts, distant relatives.

In our green cocoon, we move closer to each other, hands, faces, knees. The walls of the tent press down like skin, the ground presses up like bone. The coyote is gone, suddenly, the air thins out and becomes ours again. Inside the narrow landscape of the tent, hills and valleys realign, adjust themselves, realign again with whispers.

The coyote runs, straining to reach the others, a quarter mile away, over the crest of the ridge. They are waiting for him in the darkness, in the burning desert with its lifted arms of cactus. In the dark tent, on my smooth ocean, inside my mind, he is there already, gray and golden like the desert, like the moon, moving among them in the clearing, feeling the thrust of snouts, the padding of many paws, the push of love.

Against the Grain

IT'S OKAY TO BE MARRIED to a perfectionist, at least for a while. Just don't try to remodel a house with one, is all I can say. This is what he'll do: set you up with practice boards and nails to make sure you have the technique completely down before you attend to the task at hand, which he has suggested would be the best task for you at this particular time in your training. You sigh and jokingly threaten him with the hammer but because you aren't adept at pulling nails from ceiling trim you grudgingly work on the practice boards until you can almost remove a nail without splitting the wood all to hell. It makes your knees hurt to crouch that way so you take a doughnut break, staring out the dirty window at the neighbor's house across the way. The perfectionist comes in on his way from a completed task to a waiting, un-begun one. He notices you standing there and grins.

'It doesn't get done that way, does it?' he kids you.

You feel revitalized from the jelly filling and pour a tepid cup of coffee from the thermos, head back in, crouch some more. The pieces of trim are in pretty good shape, long stately things that will nestle up against the ceiling, hopefully hiding the uneven line between wallpaper and paint. The perfectionist is feeling very sensitive about that particular uneven line, since he tried and tried to make it straight. You assured him over lunch the previous day and again over dinner that the line would be covered up by the lovely trim. You, in fact, feel encouraged knowing that an uneven, almost jaggedy, edge will be hiding in the house. You tell the perfectionist this in a joking way and he stares at you for a long moment and then smiles uncertainly.

In the other room you can hear him giving explicit directions to his brother-in-law, who owes you guys a big favor for helping him put an oak floor in his den last summer. The perfectionist convinced him to go ahead and sand and refinish all the floors in the house while he was at it. After all, he explained, you might as well do it right. Then it's done and you can feel good about it. You know? His own sister didn't speak to the perfectionist for about three weeks after that, until the job was done and her furniture was back in place. He kept advising her to try another way whenever she got frustrated and started sanding wildly against the grain. Unfortunately, she knew that 'try another way' is what they used to say to the retarded citizens at the sheltered workshop where he worked after college.

'I'm not retarded, pal,' she told him.

No matter how hard you try, the long, lovely pieces of trim start out fine and end up with these odd-looking splits and splinters. He's whistling in the other room. You try a different technique than he showed you and suddenly the longest piece has become divorced from itself. Oh dear.

'Well,' says the perfectionist, standing in the doorway. 'We're having trouble, I see.' He sets down his chisel and shows you once again how to tease the nail from the wood. 'You can't just go nuts on it,' he explains. 'You can't *wrestle* it.'

Carefully and efficiently, he sets himself to the task. Within fifteen minutes the wood is free of the nails, which are stacked, mostly unbent and ready to be used again, on a windowsill. You open the can of spackle with a screwdriver and begin the tedious job of filling all the little holes left behind. He's behind you before you know it.

His hair is tufted up in back from the hat he's been wearing and his pants have plaster dust on the knees. He has the sweetest face of any man you've ever seen. He smiles. 'Just be sure not to glob it on,' he says gently, and then retreats again, into the rest of the house, which is structurally unsound but possibly fixable, just like you.

The Fourth State of Matter

THE COLLIE WAKES ME UP about three times a night, summoning me from a great distance as I row my boat through a dim, complicated dream. She's on the shoreline, barking. Wake up. She's staring at me with her head slightly tipped to the side, long nose, gazing eyes, toenails clenched to get a purchase on the wood floor. We used to call her the face of love.

She totters on her broomstick legs into the hallway and over the doorsill into the kitchen, makes a sharp left at the refrigerator – careful, almost went down – then a straightaway to the door. I sleep on my feet, in the cold of the doorway, waiting. Here she comes. Lift her down the two steps. She pees and then stands, Lassie in a ratty coat, gazing out at the yard.

In the porchlight the trees shiver, the squirrels turn over in their sleep. The Milky Way is a long smear on the sky, like something erased on a chalkboard. Over the neighbor's house, Mars flashes white, then red, then white again. Jupiter is hidden among the anonymous blinks and glitterings. It has a moon with sulfur-spewing volcanoes and a beautiful name: Io. I learned it at work, from the group of men who surround me there. Space physicists, guys who spend days on end with their heads poked through the fabric of the sky, listening to the sounds of the universe. Guys whose own lives are ticking like alarm clocks getting ready to go off, although none of us is aware of it yet.

The collie turns and looks, waits to be carried up the two steps. Inside the house, she drops like a shoe onto her blanket, a thud, an adjustment. I've climbed back under my covers already but her leg's stuck underneath her, we can't get comfortable. I fix the leg, she rolls over and sleeps. Two hours later I wake up again and she's gazing at me in the darkness. The face of love. She wants to go out again. I give her a boost, balance her on her legs. Right on time: 3:40 a.m.

There are squirrels living in the spare bedroom upstairs. Three dogs also live in this house, but they were invited. I keep the door of the spare bedroom shut at all times, because of the squirrels and because that's where the vanished husband's belongings are stored. Two of the dogs – the smart little brown mutt and the Labrador – spend hours sitting patiently outside the door, waiting for it to be opened so they can dismantle the squirrels. The collie can no longer make it up the stairs, so she lies at the bottom and snores or stares in an interested manner at the furniture around her.

I can take almost anything at this point. For instance, that my vanished husband is neither here nor there; he's reduced himself to a troubled voice on the telephone three or four times a day.

Or that the dog at the bottom of the stairs keeps having mild strokes which cause her to tilt her head inquisitively and also to fall over. She drinks prodigious amounts of water and pees great volumes onto the folded blankets where she sleeps. Each time this happens I stand her up, dry her off, put fresh blankets underneath her, carry the peed-on blankets down to the basement, stuff them into the washer and then into the dryer. By the time I bring them back upstairs they are needed again. The first few times this happened I found the dog trying to stand up, gazing with frantic concern at her own rear. I praised her and patted her head and gave her treats until she settled down. Now I know whenever it happens because I hear her tail thumping against the floor in anticipation of reward. In retraining her I've somehow retrained myself, bustling cheerfully down to the basement, arms drenched in urine, the task of doing load after load of laundry strangely satisfying. She is Pavlov and I am her dog.

I'm fine about the vanished husband's boxes stored in the spare bedroom. For now the boxes and the phone calls persuade me that things could turn around at any moment. The boxes are filled with thirteen years of his pack-rattedness: statistics textbooks that still harbor an air of desperation, smarmy suitcoats from the Goodwill, various old Halloween masks and one giant black papier-mâché thing that was supposed to be Elvis's hair but didn't turn out. A collection of ancient Rolling Stones T-shirts. You know he's turning over a new leaf when he leaves the Rolling Stones behind.

What I can't take are the squirrels. They come alive at night, throwing terrible parties in the spare bedroom, making thumps and crashes. Occasionally a high-pitched squeal is heard amid bumps and the sound of scrabbling toenails. taken to sleeping downstairs, on the blue vinyl dog couch, the sheets slipping off, my skin stuck to the cushions. This is an affront to two of the dogs, who know the couch belongs to them; as soon as I settle in they creep up and find their places between my knees and elbows.

I'm on the couch because the dog on the blanket gets worried at night. During the day she sleeps the catnappy sleep of the elderly, but when it gets dark her eyes open and she is agitated, trying to stand whenever I leave the room, settling down only when I'm next to her. We are in this together, the dying game, and I read for hours in the evening, one foot on her back, getting up only to open a new can of beer or take peed-on blankets to the basement. At some point I stretch out on the vinyl couch and close my eyes, one hand hanging down, touching her side. By morning the dog-arm has become a nerveless club that doesn't come around until noon. My friends think I'm nuts.

One night, for hours, the dog won't lie down, stands braced on her rickety legs in the middle of the living room, looking at me and slowly wagging her tail. Each time I get her situated on her blankets and try to stretch out on the couch she stands up, looks at me, wags her tail. I call my office pal, Mary, and wake her up. '*I'm weary*,' I say, in italics.

Mary listens, sympathetic, on the other end. 'Oh my God,' she finally says, '*what* are you going to do?'

I calm down immediately. 'Exactly what I'm doing,' I tell her. The dog finally parks herself with a thump on the stack of damp blankets. She sets her nose down and tips her eyes up to watch me. We all sleep then, for a bit, while the squirrels sort through the boxes overhead and the dog on the blanket keeps nervous watch.

I've called in tired to work. It's midmorning and I'm shuffling around in my long underwear, smoking cigarettes and drinking coffee. The whole house is bathed in sunlight and the faint odor of used diapers. The collie is on her blanket, taking one of her vampirish daytime naps. The other two dogs are being mild-mannered and charming. I nudge the collie with my foot.

'Wake up and smell zee bacons,' I say. She startles awake, lifts her nose groggily, and falls back asleep. I get ready for the office.

'I'm leaving and I'm never coming back,' I say while putting on my coat. I use my mother's aggrieved, underappreciated tone. The little brown dog wags her tail, transferring her gaze from me to the table, which is the last place she remembers seeing toast.

The collie continues her ghoulish sleep, eyes partially open, teeth exposed, while the Labrador, who understands English, begins howling miserably. She wins the toast sweepstakes and is chewing loudly when I leave, the little dog barking ferociously at her.

Work is its usual comforting green-corridored self. There are three blinks on the answering machine, the first from an author who speaks very slowly, like a kindergarten teacher, asking about reprints. 'What am I, the village idiot?' I ask the room, taking down his number in large backward characters. The second and third blinks are from my husband, the across-town apartment dweller.

The first makes my heart lurch in a hopeful way. 'I have to talk to you right *now*,' he says grimly. 'Where *are* you? I can never find you.'

'Try calling your own house,' I say to the machine. In the second message he has composed himself.

'I'm *fine* now,' he says firmly. 'Disregard previous message and don't call me back, please; I have meetings.' Click, dial tone, rewind.

I feel crestfallen, the leaping heart settles back into its hole in my chest. I say damn it out loud, just as Chris strides into the office.

'What?' he asks defensively. He tries to think if he's done anything wrong recently.

He checks the table for work; none there. He's on top of it. We have a genial relationship these days, reading the paper together in the mornings, congratulating ourselves on each issue of the journal. It's a space physics quarterly and he's the editor and I'm the managing editor. I know nothing about the science part; my job is to shepherd the manuscripts through the review process and create a journal out of the acceptable ones.

Christoph Goertz. He's hip in a professorial kind of way, tall and lanky and white-haired, forty-seven years old, with an elegant trace of accent from his native Germany. He has a great dog, a giant black outlaw named Mica who runs through the streets of Iowa City at night, inspecting garbage. She's big and friendly but a bad judge of character and frequently runs right into the arms of the dog catcher. Chris is always bailing her out.

'They don't understand dogs,' he says.

I spend more time with Chris than I ever did with my husband. The morning I told him I was being dumped he was genuinely perplexed.

'He's leaving *you*?' he asked.

Chris was drinking coffee, sitting at his table in front of the chalkboard. Behind his head was a chalk drawing of a hip, professorial man holding a coffee cup. It was a collaborative effort; I drew the man and Chris framed him, using brown chalk and a straightedge. The two-dimensional man and the three-dimensional man stared at me intently.

'He's leaving *you*?' And for an instant I saw myself from their vantage point across the room – Jo Ann – and a small bubble of self-esteem percolated up from the depths. Chris shrugged. 'You'll do fine,' he said.

During my current turmoils, I've come to think of work as my own kind of zen practice, the constant barrage of paper hypnotic and soothing. Chris lets me work an erratic, eccentric schedule, which gives me time to pursue my nonexistent writing career. In return I update his publications list for him and listen to stories about outer space.

Besides being an editor and a teacher, he's the head of a theoretical plasma physics team made up of graduate students and research scientists. During the summers he travels all over the world telling people about the magnetospheres of various planets, and when he comes back he brings me presents – a small bronze box from Africa with an alligator embossed on the top, a big piece of amber from Poland with the wings of flies preserved inside it, and, once, a set of delicate, horrifying bracelets made from the hide of an elephant.

Currently he is obsessed with the dust in the plasma of Saturn's rings. Plasma is the fourth state of matter. You've got your solid, your liquid, your gas, and then your plasma. In outer space there's the plasmasphere and the plasmapause. I like to avoid the math when I can and put a layperson's spin on these things.

'Plasma is blood,' I told him.

'Exactly,' he agreed, removing the comics page and handing it to me.

Mostly we have those kinds of conversations around the office, but today he's caught me at a weak moment, tucking my heart back inside my chest. I decide to be cavalier.

'I wish my *dog* was out tearing up the town and my *husband* was home peeing on a blanket,' I say.

Chris thinks the dog thing has gone far enough. 'Why are you letting this go on?' he asks solemnly.

'I'm not *letting* it, that's why,' I tell him. There are stacks of manuscripts everywhere and he has all the pens over on his side of the room. 'It just *is*, is all. Throw me a pen.' He does, I miss it, stoop to pick it up, and when I straighten up again I might be crying.

You have control over this, he explains in his professor voice. You can decide how long she suffers.

This makes my heart pound. Absolutely not, I cannot do it. And then I weaken and say what I really want. For her to go to sleep and not wake up, just slip out of her skin and into the other world.

'Exactly,' he says.

I have an ex-beauty queen coming over to get rid of the squirrels for me. She has long red hair and a smile that can stop trucks. I've seen her wrestle goats, scare off a giant snake, and express a dog's anal glands, all in one afternoon. I told her on the phone that a family of squirrels is living in the upstairs of my house and there's nothing I can do about it.

'They're making a monkey out of me,' I said.

So Caroline climbs in her car and drives across half the state, pulls up in front of my house, and gets out carrying zucchinis, cigarettes, and a pair of big leather gloves. I'm sitting outside with my sweet old dog, who lurches to her feet, staggers three steps, sits down, and falls over. Caroline starts crying.

'Don't try to give me zucchini,' I tell her.

We sit companionably on the front stoop for a while, staring at the dog and smoking cigarettes. One time I went to Caroline's house and she was nursing a dead cat that was still breathing. At some point that afternoon I saw her spoon baby food into its mouth and as soon as she turned away the whole pureed mess plopped back out. A day later she took it to the vet and had it euthanized. I remind her of this.

'You'll do it when you do it,' she says firmly.

I pick the collie up like a fifty-pound bag of sticks and feathers, stagger inside, place her on the damp blankets, and put the other two nutcases in the backyard. From upstairs comes a crash and a shriek. Caroline stares up at the ceiling.

'It's like having the Wallendas stay at your house,' I say cheerfully. All of a sudden I feel fond of the squirrels and fond of Caroline and fond of myself for heroically calling her to help me. The phone rings four times. It's the husband, and his voice over the answering machine sounds frantic. He pleads with whoever Jo Ann is to pick up the phone.

'Please? I think I might be freaking out,' he says. 'Am I ruining my life here, or what? Am I making a *mistake*? Jo?' He breathes raggedly and sniffs into the receiver for a moment, then hangs up with a muffled clatter.

Caroline stares at the machine like it's a copperhead.

'Holy fuckoly,' she says, shaking her head. 'You're *living* with this crap?'

'He wants me to reassure him that he's strong enough to leave me,' I tell her. 'Else he won't have fun on his bike ride. And guess what; I'm too tired to.' Except that now I can see him in his dank little apartment, wringing his hands and staring out the windows. He's wearing his Sunday hairdo with a baseball cap trying to scrunch it down. In his rickety dresser is the new package of condoms he accidentally showed me last week.

Caroline lights another cigarette. The dog pees and thumps her tail.

I need to call him back because he's suffering.

'You call him back and I'm forced to kill you,' Caroline says. She exhales smoke and points to the phone. 'That is evil shit,' she says.

I tend to agree. It's blanket time. I roll the collie off onto the floor and put the fresh ones down, roll her back. She stares at me with the face of love. I get her a treat, which she chews with gusto and then goes back to sleep. I carry the blankets down to the basement and stuff them into the machine, trudge back up the stairs. Caroline has finished smoking her medicine and is wearing the leather gloves which go all the way to her elbows. She's staring at the ceiling with determination.

The plan is that I'm supposed to separate one from the herd and get it in a corner. Caroline will take it from there. Unfortunately, my nerves are shot, and when I'm in the room with her and the squirrels are running around all I can do is scream. I'm not even afraid of them, but my screaming button is stuck on and the only way to turn it off is to leave the room.

'How are you doing?' I ask from the other side of the door. All I can hear is Caroline crashing around and swearing. Suddenly there is a high-pitched screech that doesn't end. The door opens and Caroline falls out into the hall, with a gray squirrel stuck to her glove. Brief pandemonium and then she clatters down the stairs and out the front door and returns looking triumphant.

The collie appears at the foot of the stairs with her head cocked and her ears up.

She looks like a puppy for an instant, and then her feet start to slide. I run down and catch her and carry her upstairs so she can watch the show. They careen around the room, tearing the ancient wallpaper off the walls. The last one is a baby, so we keep it for a few minutes, looking at its little feet and its little tail. We show it to the collie, who stands up immediately and tries to get it.

Caroline patches the hole where they got in, cutting wood with a power saw down in the basement. She comes up wearing a toolbelt and lugging a ladder. I've seen a scrapbook of photos of her wearing evening gowns with a banner across her chest and a crown on her head. Curled hair, lipstick. She climbs down and puts the tools away.

We eat nachos.

'I only make food that's boiled or melted these days,' I tell her.

'I know,' she replies.

We smoke cigarettes and think. The phone rings again but whoever it is hangs up.

'Is it him?' she asks.

'Nope.'

The collie sleeps on her blankets while the other two dogs sit next to Caroline on the couch. She's looking through their ears for mites. At some point she gestures to the sleeping dog on the blanket and remarks that it seems like just two days ago she was a puppy.

'She was never a puppy,' I say. 'She's always been older than me.'

When they say good-bye, she holds the collie's long nose in one hand and kisses her on the forehead; the collie stares back at her gravely. Caroline is crying when she leaves, a combination of squirrel adrenaline, and sadness. I cry, too, although I don't feel particularly bad about anything. I hand her the zucchini through the window and she pulls away from the curb.

The house is starting to get dark in that terrible early-evening twilit way. I turn on lights, get a cigarette, and go upstairs to the former squirrel room. The black dog comes with me and circles the room, snorting loudly, nose to floor. There is a spot of turmoil in an open box – they made a nest in some old disco shirts from the seventies. I suspect that's where the baby one slept. The mean landlady has evicted them.

Downstairs, I turn the lights back off and let evening have its way with me. Waves of pre-nighttime nervousness are coming from the collie's blanket. I sit next to her in the dimness, touching her ears, and listen for feet at the top of the stairs.

They're speaking in physics so I'm left out of the conversation. Chris apologetically erases one of the pictures I've drawn on the blackboard and replaces it with a curving blue arrow surrounded by radiating chalk waves of green.

'If it's plasma, make it in red,' I suggest helpfully. We're all smoking illegally in the journal office with the door closed and the window open. We're having a plasma party.

'We aren't discussing *plasma*,' Bob says condescendingly. He's smoking a horrendously smelly pipe. The longer he stays in here the more it feels like I'm breathing small daggers in through my nose. He and I don't get along; each of us thinks the other needs to be taken down a peg. Once we had a hissing match in the hallway which ended with him suggesting that I could be fired, which drove me to tell him he was *already* fired, and both of us stomped into our offices and slammed our doors.

'I had to fire Bob,' I tell Chris later.

'I heard,' he says noncommittally. Bob is his best friend. They spend at least half of each day standing in front of chalkboards, writing equations and arguing about outer space. Then they write theoretical papers about what they come up with. They're actually quite a big deal in the space physics community, but around here they're just two guys who keep erasing my pictures.

Someone knocks on the door and we put our cigarettes out. Bob hides his pipe in the palm of his hand and opens the door.

It's Gang Lu, one of their students. Everyone lights up again. Gang Lu stands stiffly talking to Chris while Bob holds a match to his pipe and puffs fiercely; nose daggers waft up and out, right in my direction. I give him a sugary smile and he gives me one back. Unimaginable, really, that less than two months from now one of his colleagues from abroad, a woman with delicate, birdlike features, will appear at the door to my office and identify herself as a friend of Bob's. When she asks, I take her down the hall to the room with the long table and then to his empty office. I do this without saying anything because there's nothing to say, and she takes it all in with small, serious nods until the moment she sees his blackboard covered with scribbles and arrows and equations. At that point her face loosens and she starts to cry in long ragged sobs. An hour later I go back and the office is empty. When I erase the blackboard finally, I can see where she laid her hands carefully, where the numbers are ghostly and blurred.

Bob blows his smoke discreetly in my direction and waits for Chris to finish talking to Gang Lu, who is answering questions in a monotone – yes or no, or I don't know.

Another Chinese student named Shan lets himself in after knocking lightly. He nods and smiles at me and then stands at a respectful distance, waiting to ask Chris a question.

It's like a physics conference in here. I wish they'd all leave so I could make my usual midafternoon spate of personal calls. I begin thumbing through papers in a businesslike way.

Bob pokes at his pipe with a bent paper clip. Shan yawns hugely and then looks embarrassed. Chris erases what he put on the blackboard and tries unsuccessfully to redraw my pecking parakeet. 'I don't know how it goes,' he says to me.

Gang Lu looks around the room idly with expressionless eyes. He's sick of physics and sick of the buffoons who practice it. The tall glacial German, Chris, who tells him what to do; the crass idiot Bob who talks to him like he is a dog; the student Shan whose ideas about plasma physics are treated with reverence and praised at every meeting. The woman who puts her feet on the desk and dismisses him with her eyes. Gang Lu no longer spends his evenings in the computer lab, running simulations and thinking about magnetic forces and invisible particles; he now spends them at the firing range, learning to hit a moving target with the gun he purchased last spring. He pictures himself holding the gun with both hands, arms straight out and steady; Clint Eastwood, only smarter. Clint Eastwood as a rocket scientist.

He stares at each person in turn, trying to gauge how much respect each of them has for him. One by one. Behind black-rimmed glasses, he counts with his eyes. In each case the verdict is clear: not enough.

The collie fell down the basement stairs. I don't know if she was disoriented and looking for me or what. But when I was at work she used her long nose like a lever and got the door to the basement open and tried to go down there except her legs wouldn't do it and she fell. I found her sleeping on the concrete floor in an unnatural position, one leg still awkwardly resting on the last step. I repositioned the leg and sat down next to her and petted her. We used to play a game called Maserati, where I'd grab her nose like a gearshift and put her through all the gears, first second third fourth, until we were going a hundred miles an hour through town. She thought it was funny.

Now I'm at work but this morning there's nothing to do, and every time I turn around I see her sprawled, eyes mute, leg bent upward. We're breaking each other's hearts. I draw a picture of her on the blackboard using brown chalk. I make Xs where her eyes should be. Chris walks in with the morning paper and a cup of coffee. He looks around the clean office.

'Why are you here when there's no work to do?' he asks.

'I'm hiding from my life, what else,' I tell him. This sounds perfectly reasonable to him. He gives me part of the paper.

His mother is visiting from Germany, a robust woman of eighty who is depressed and hoping to be cheered up. In the last year she has lost her one-hundred-year-old mother and her husband of sixty years. She mostly can't be cheered up, but she likes going to art galleries so Chris has been driving her around the Midwest, to our best cities, showing her what kind of art Americans like to look at.

'How's your mom?' I ask him.

He shrugs and makes a flat-handed so-so motion.

We read, smoke, drink coffee, and yawn. I decide to go home.

'Good idea,' he says encouragingly.

It's November 1, 1991, the last day of the first part of my life. Before I leave I pick up the eraser and stand in front of the collie's picture on the blackboard, thinking. I can feel him watching me, drinking his coffee. He's wearing a gold shirt and blue jeans and a gray cardigan sweater. He is tall and lanky and white-haired, forty-seven years old. He has a wife named Ulrike, a daughter named Karein, and a son named Goran. A dog named Mica. A mother named Ursula. A friend named me.

I erase the Xs.

Down the hall, Linhua Shan feeds numbers into a computer and watches as a graph is formed. The computer screen is brilliant blue, and the lines appear in red and yellow and green. Four keystrokes and the green becomes purple. More keystrokes and the blue background fades to the azure of a summer sky. The wave lines arc over it, crossing against one another. He asks the computer to print, and while it chugs along he pulls up a golf game on the screen and tees off.

One room over, at a desk, Gang Lu works on a letter to his sister in China. *The study of physics is more and more disappointing*, he tells her. *Modern physics is self- delusion* and *all my life I have been honest and straightforward, and I have most of all detested cunning, fawning sycophants and dishonest bureaucrats who think they are always right in everything.* Delicate Chinese characters all over a page. She was a kind and gentle sister, and he thanks her for that. He's going to kill himself. *You yourself should not be too sad about it, for at least I have found a few traveling companions to accompany me to the grave.* Inside the coat on the back of his chair are a .38-caliber handgun and a .22-caliber revolver. They're heavier than they look and weigh the pockets down. *My beloved elder sister, I take my eternal leave of you.*

The collie's eyes are almond-shaped; I draw them in with brown chalk and put a white bone next to her feet.

'That's better,' Chris says kindly.

Before I leave the building I pass Gang Lu in the hallway and say hello. He has a letter in his hand and he's wearing his coat. He doesn't answer and I don't expect him to. At the end of the hallway are the double doors leading to the rest of my life. I push them open and walk through.

Friday afternoon seminar, everyone is glazed over, listening as someone explains something unexplainable at the head of the long table. Gang Lu stands up and leaves the room abruptly; goes down one floor to see if the chairman, Dwight, is sitting in his office. He is. The door is open. Gang Lu turns and walks back up the stairs and enters the meeting room again. Chris Goertz is sitting near the door and takes the first bullet in the back of the head. There is a loud popping sound and then blue smoke. Shan gets the second bullet in the forehead, the lenses of his glasses shatter. More smoke and the room rings with the popping. Bob Smith tries to crawl beneath the table. Gang Lu takes two steps, holds his arms straight out, and levels the gun with both hands. Bob looks up. The third bullet in the right hand, the fourth in the chest. Smoke. Elbows and legs, people trying to get out of the way and then out of the room.

Gang Lu walks quickly down the stairs, dispelling spent cartridges and loading new ones. From the doorway of Dwight's office: the fifth bullet in the head, the sixth strays, the seventh also in the head. A slumping. More smoke and ringing. Through the cloud an image comes forward – Bob Smith, hit in the chest, hit in the hand, still alive. Back up the stairs. Two scientists, young men, crouched over Bob, loosening his clothes, talking to him. From where he lies, Bob can see his best friend still sitting upright in a chair, head thrown back at an unnatural angle. Everything is broken and red. The two young scientists leave the room at gunpoint. Bob closes his eyes. The eighth and ninth bullets in his head. As Bob dies, Chris Goertz's body settles in his chair, a long sigh escapes his throat. Reload. Two more for Chris, one for Shan. Exit the building, cross two streets, run across the green, into building number two and upstairs.

The administrator, Anne Cleary, is summoned from her office by the receptionist. She speaks to him for a few seconds, he produces the gun and shoots her in the face. The receptionist, a young student working as a temp, is just beginning to stand when he shoots her in the mouth. He dispels the spent cartridges in the stairwell, loads new ones. Reaches the top of the steps, looks around. Is disoriented suddenly. The ringing and the smoke and the dissatisfaction of not checking all the names off the list. A slamming and a running sound, the shout of police. He walks into an empty classroom, takes off his coat, folds it carefully and puts it over the back of the chair. Checks his watch; twelve minutes since it began. Places the barrel against his right temple. Fires.

The first call comes at four o'clock. I'm reading on the bench in the kitchen, one foot on a sleeping dog's back. It's Mary, calling from work. There's been some kind of disturbance in the building, a rumor that Dwight was shot; cops are running through the halls carrying rifles. They're evacuating the building and she's coming over.

Dwight, a tall likable oddball who cut off his ponytail when they made him chair of the department. Greets everyone with a famous booming hello in the morning, studies plasma, just like Chris and Bob. Chris lives two and half blocks from the physics building; he'll be home by now if they've evacuated. I dial his house and his mother answers. She tells me that Chris won't be home until five o'clock, and then they're going to a play. Ulrike, her daughter-in-law, is coming back from a trip to Chicago and will join them. She wants to know why I'm looking for Chris; isn't he where I am?

No, I'm at home and I just had to ask him something. Could he please call me when he comes in.

She tells me that Chris showed her a drawing I made of him sitting at his desk behind a stack of manuscripts. She's so pleased to meet Chris's friends, and the Midwest is lovely, really, except it's very brown, isn't it?

It *is* very brown. We hang up.

The Midwest is very brown. The phone rings. It's a physicist. His wife, a friend of mine, is on the extension. Well, he's not sure, but it's possible that I should brace myself for bad news. I've already heard, I tell him, something happened to Dwight. There's a long pause and then his wife says, Jo Ann. It's possible that Chris was involved.

324

I think she means Chris shot Dwight. No, she says gently, killed too.

Mary is here. I tell them not to worry and hang up. I have two cigarettes going.

Mary takes one and smokes it. She's not looking at me. I tell her about the phone call.

'They're out of it,' I say. 'They thought Chris was involved.'

She repeats what they said: I think you should brace yourself for bad news. Pours whiskey in a coffee cup.

For a few minutes I can't sit down, I can't stand up. I can only smoke. The phone rings. Another physicist tells me there's some bad news. He mentions Chris and Bob and I tell him I don't want to talk right now. He says okay but to be prepared because it's going to be on the news any minute. It's 4:45.

'Now they're trying to stir Bob into the stew,' I tell Mary. She nods; she's heard this, too. I have the distinct feeling there is something going on that I can either understand or not understand. There's a choice to be made.

'I don't understand,' I tell Mary.

We sit in the darkening living room, smoking and sipping our cups of whiskey.

Inside my head I keep thinking *Uh-oh*, over and over. I'm in a rattled condition; I can't calm down and figure this out.

'I think we should brace ourselves in case something bad has happened,' I say to Mary. She nods. 'Just in case. It won't hurt to be braced.' She nods again. I realize that I don't know what *braced* means. You hear it all the time but that doesn't mean it makes sense. Whiskey is supposed to be bracing but what it is is awful. I want either tea or beer, no whiskey. Mary nods and heads into the kitchen.

Within an hour there are seven women in the dim living room, sitting. Switching back and forth between CNN and the special reports by the local news. There is something terrifying about the quality of the light and the way voices are echoing in the room. The phone never stops ringing, ever since the story hit the national news.

Physics, University of Iowa, dead people. Names not yet released. Everyone I've ever known is checking in to see if I'm still alive. California calls, New York calls, Florida calls, Ohio calls twice. All the guests at a party my husband is having call, one after the other, to ask how I'm doing. Each time, fifty times, I think it might be Chris and then it isn't.

It occurs to me once that I could call his house and talk to him directly, find out exactly what happened. Fear that his mother would answer prevents me from doing it. By this time I am getting reconciled to the fact that Shan, Gang Lu, and Dwight were killed. Also an administrator and her office assistant. The Channel 9 newslady keeps saying there are six dead and two in critical condition. They're not saying who did the shooting. The names will be released at nine o'clock. Eventually I sacrifice all of them except Chris and Bob; they are the ones in critical condition, which is certainly not hopeless. At some point I go into the study to get away from the terrible dimness in the living room, all those eyes, all that calmness in the face of chaos. The collie tries to stand up but someone stops her with a handful of Fritos.

The study is small and cold after I shut the door, but more brightly lit than the living room. I can't remember what anything means. The phone rings and I pick up the extension and listen. My friend Michael is calling from Illinois for the second time. He asks Shirley if I'm holding up okay. Shirley says it's hard to tell. I go back into the living room.

The newslady breaks in at nine o'clock, and of course they drag it out as long as they can. I've already figured out that if they go in alphabetical order Chris will come first. Goertz, Lu, Nicholson, Shan, Smith. His name will come on first. She drones on, dead University of Iowa professors, lone gunman named Gang Lu.

Gang Lu. Lone gunman. Before I have a chance to absorb that she says, The dead are—

Chris's picture.

Oh no, oh God. I lean against Mary's chair and then leave the room abruptly. I have to stand in the bathroom for a while and look at myself in the mirror. I'm still Jo Ann, white face and dark hair. I have earrings on, tiny wrenches that hang from wires. In the living room she's pronouncing all the other names. The two critically wounded are the administrator and her assistant, Miya Sioson. The administrator is already dead for all practical purposes, although they won't disconnect the machines until the following afternoon. The student receptionist will survive but will never again be able to move more than her head. She was in Gang Lu's path and he shot her in the mouth and the bullet lodged in the top of her spine and not only will she never dance again, she'll never walk or write or spend a day alone. She got to keep her head but lost her body. The final victim is Chris's mother, who will weather it all with a dignified face and an erect spine, then return to Germany and kill herself without further words or fanfare.

I tell the white face in the mirror that Gang Lu did this, wrecked everything and killed all those people. It seems as ludicrous as everything else. I can't get my mind to work right, I'm still operating on yesterday's facts; today hasn't jelled yet. 'It's a good thing none of this happened,' I say to my face. A knock on the door and I open it.

The collie is swaying on her feet, toenails clenched to keep from sliding on the wood floor. Julene's hesitant face. 'She wanted to come visit you,' she tells me. I bring her in and close the door. We sit by the tub. She lifts her long nose to my face and I take her muzzle and we move through the gears slowly, first second third fourth, all the way through town, until what happened has happened and we know it has happened. We return to the living room. The second wave of calls is starting to come in, from those who just saw the faces on the news. Shirley screens. A knock comes on the door.

Julene settles the dog down again on her blanket. It's the husband at the door, looking frantic. He hugs me hard but I'm made of cement, arms stuck in a down position.

The women immediately clear out, taking their leave, looking at the floor. Suddenly it's only me and him, sitting in our living room on a Friday night, just like always. I realize it took quite a bit of courage for him to come to the house when he did, facing all those women who think he's the Antichrist. The dogs are crowded against him on the couch and he's wearing a shirt I've never seen before. He's here to help me get through this.

Me. He knows how awful this must be. Awful. He knows how I felt about Chris. Past tense. I have to put my hands over my face for a minute.

We sit silently in our living room. He watches the mute television screen and I watch him. The planes and ridges of his face are more familiar to me than my own. I understand that he wishes even more than I do that he still loved me. When he looks over at me, it's with an expression I've seen before. It's the way he looks at the dog on the blanket.

I get his coat and follow him out into the cold November night. There are stars and stars and stars. The sky is full of dead men, drifting in the blackness like helium balloons. My mother floats past in a hospital gown, trailing tubes. I go back inside where the heat is.

The house is empty and dim, full of dogs and cigarette butts. The collie has peed again. The television is flickering *Special Report* across the screen and I turn it off before the pictures appear. I bring blankets up, fresh and warm from the dryer.

*

After all the commotion the living room feels cavernous and dead. A branch scrapes against the house and for a brief instant I feel a surge of hope. They might have come back. And I stand at the foot of the stairs staring up into the darkness, listening for the sounds of their little squirrel feet. Silence. No matter how much you miss them. They never come back once they're gone.

I wake her up three times between midnight and dawn. She doesn't usually sleep this soundly but all the chaos and company in the house tonight have made her more tired than usual. The Lab wakes and drowsily begins licking her lower region. She stops and stares at me, trying to make out my face in the dark, then gives up and sleeps. The brown dog is flat on her back with her paws limp, wedged between me and the back of the couch.

I've propped myself so I'll be able to see when dawn starts to arrive. For now there are still planets and stars. Above the black branches of a maple is the dog star, Sirius, my personal favorite. The dusty rings of Saturn. Io, Jupiter's moon.

When I think I can't bear it for one more minute I reach down and nudge her gently with my dog-arm. She rises slowly, faltering, and stands over me in the darkness. My peer, my colleague. In a few hours the world will resume itself, but for now we're in a pocket of silence. We're in the plasmapause, a place of equilibrium, where the forces of the Earth meet the forces of the sun. I imagine it as a place of silence, where the particles of dust stop spinning and hang motionless in deep space.

Around my neck is the stone he brought me from Poland. I hold it out. *Like this?* I ask. Shards of fly wings, suspended in amber.

Exactly, he says.

Bulldozing the Baby

AT AGE THREE, MY MOST SUCCESSFUL RELATIONSHIP was with Hal, a boy doll. He had molded brown hair, a smiling vinyl face, and two outfits. One was actually his birthday suit, a stuffed body made of pink cloth with vinyl hands and feet attached. Clothes encumbered me; I liked the feeling of air on skin, and when left alone for more than five minutes, I'd routinely strip us down to our most basic outfits and we'd go outside to sit on the front stoop. Hal's other outfit was a plaid flannel shirt with pearl buttons and yellow pants with flannel cuffs. He had black feet molded in the shape of shoes.

The gorgeous thing about Hal was that not only was he my friend, he was also my slave. I made the majority of our decisions, including the bathtub one, which in retrospect was the beginning of the end. Our bath routine was like this: My mother would pick me up and stand me in the tub – I had fat, willful legs, and I wouldn't bend them while she was touching me – then while I was settling into the water and coordinating the bathtub toys, she'd undress Hal and sit him down on the toilet tank to watch me.

'Tell Jo-Jo she is *not* to stand up in the tub,' she'd say to Hal, before leaving us to our own devices. I found it unnerving to have

330

her speak directly to him; didn't she know he was a doll? Plus, Hal couldn't stop me from doing anything. The moment she left I'd stand up and sit back down whenever I felt like it. Hal's job was to watch.

The bathtub toys were dull in an indestructible kind of way. You could drown them or bounce them off the ceiling and they were still unbreakable plastic in primary colors. Hal, however, was both filthy and destructible; my mother had proved it by trying to scour his head with an S.O.S. pad – he now had a small bald patch on the crown of his head, just like a real guy.

I decided on impulse to bring Hal into the tub with me, just to see what would happen. First he floated, then when I pressed on his stomach he submerged, smiling placidly. It was at that exact moment that the spark went out of him – he became waterlogged in an unflattering way and all I could do was put him back up, dripping, on the toilet tank. He sat more slumpedly, and the pink cloth of his stuffed body had a gray cast to it. Something had gone wrong with my experiment.

My mother came in and tried to wash my hair. She'd given up reasoning with me long ago, had adopted a style that married brute force with loud comforting comments. 'You're such a good girl,' she lied, struggling to hold my head in the water. Soap was lapping onto my face. I shrieked and tried to shake my head; a wave washed over my mouth. 'One more time and then we're done,' she said resolutely, sitting me back up with one viselike hand and squirting soap on my head with the other. I looked her in the eye and shrieked again. My father came and stood in the door of the bathroom, watching.

'What're you doing to her?' he asked my mother.

'She's doing it to *me*,' my mother replied grimly. She gestured with her head. 'Look at Hal.'

Crap. Now I'd have to listen to that. I stepped up my end of the struggle.

'Oh dear,' my father said. Hal was collapsed on himself, dripping slightly. My father rolled him in a towel and wrung him a couple of times. I screamed; they were trying to kill us.

'*Shut up*,' my mother said. She stood me up and began brassknuckling my head with a towel. When she was done she swatted my wet rear. It made a loud insulting noise without exactly hurting. I collapsed on the bath mat, wailing, while she strode off to find my jammies.

The bathroom ceiling had sparkles on it. The dog-in-the-boat stain was still there.

Hal was wadded up inside a towel on the floor. I unrolled him and we lay on the bath mat together, panting quietly. They had manhandled us.

My mother has hung Hal upside down on the clothesline. I'm spending the morning in the sandbox to be near him, using an old comb to make furrows and lines which I then plant blades of grass in. I'm making a farm. Every once in a while I use the comb on my own hair, and warm sand falls down the back of my shirt. Hal is watching from upside down, clothespins pinched into his calves, vinyl hands dangling near his ears.

'I *am not hurting him*,' my mother said dangerously as she pinned him up there. I better not pull a trick like that again or somebody's in trouble. I try to reach the measuring cup and my leg makes the grass fall over. I have to stand up and stomp on it carefully and then sit back down and start over, combing in the rows. Once I find a caterpillar and hold it up to show Hal. He can't see too good upside down. The caterpillar won't get off my finger so I scrape it onto the sand and use my scoop to throw it out on the ground, along with a considerable amount of sand.

I have on blue sunglasses with wiener dogs on the frames. I can pull up my shirt and fill my belly button with sand except if

I do she'll dig it out with the washcloth tonight. I'm starting to learn cause and effect. Hal in the bathtub means Hal up in the air. He still doesn't have his clothes on. I climb out of the sandbox and sit down on the ground to take my sandals off. I put my sunglasses on top of them and stand back up. After I push my shorts and underwear down I have to sit again in order to pull them off my feet. The shirt gets stuck on my head and I can't see. After a frantic second I get it off but it yanks my nose. The barrettes slid out of my hair while the shirt was going past; I put one inside each sandal. I get up and sit on the edge of the sandbox to rest.

A bee is on the hollyhock by the fence. It steps into the flower and walks around, then steps out again, flies to the sandbox, and hangs in the air in front of my face, buzzing. I shake my head at it and it hovers for another instant and then takes off again, flies to Hal, and lights on his hanging hand.

Injury laid right over top of insult. I start screaming.

When she comes out we look at each other for a long moment, then she sighs, reaches up, releases the clothespins, lets him drop, then catches him before he hits the ground. She hands him over and stoops to collect my clothes while I put my sunglasses back on. I follow her to the back door, carrying Hal by the feet. His shoes are warm from the sun and he smiles as I drag his face along through the grass and then – bump, bump – up the two steps and into the house.

Hal's body has become lumpy, with protrusions of wadded stuffing in some spots and absolutely nothing in others. My mother tries to fix him each morning by squeezing him like a tube of toothpaste, forcing the stuffing from his lower body into his upper body. A gritty, sandlike substance is coming through his pores. He's still smiling. Hal and I are the only ones who don't care about personal appearances.

333

'She tried to give him a bath,' my mother tells my aunt, who is holding Hal and looking at him through the bottoms of her bifocals. They're trying to figure out if he can be given a torso transplant. My aunt runs her thumb over his bald spot.

'The paint's wearing off his head,' she says definitively. 'Throw him out and get her a new one.' Thus spake Bernice.

'No,' I say, shaking my head vigorously. I get right up in Aunt Bernie's face. I shake my head again, harder. She holds Hal out of my reach. I do one short bloodcurdling scream and she hands him over.

My mother, the one who is not taking credit for the bald spot on his head, lights a cigarette nervously and exhales. Bernie is the oldest of five brothers and sisters. My own big sister Linda is playing jacks on the kitchen floor and every time I move she calls out *She's getting my jacks*. My mother believes her. One more time and I'm going to be sat right down in a chair. Aunt Bernie is still waiting for a reply. Her eyebrows are in the middle of her forehead.

'Listen,' my mother tells her. 'She will scream until we're *all* in the asylum, you included.' Bernie snorts, takes a cigarette and lights it. Smoke pours out her nose.

'She may run *you*,' Bernie says dryly, 'but she doesn't run me.' Her own daughters are in the living room standing in separate corners. The crime was cursing. It's time for Hal's thumb to be sucked.

'She's got that thing in her *mouth*,' Bernie says.

'Don't put that in your mouth,' my mother tells me in a stagey, I'm-the-mother voice. I stare at her until she reaches over and gives his hand a yank. It doesn't move.

'She's *biting* on it,' Bernie says.

'I don't know what's got into her today,' my mother says nervously. She lights another cigarette and gives me a desperate glare. Linda's rubber ball bounces one, two, three, four times. Hal's hand drops back down to his side. 'Okay then,' my mother says.

When they put me down for my nap Bernie looks around the bedroom and says she doesn't know why they've got me in a crib. 'It's either a crib or a leash,' my mother says shortly. When they leave I cry the minimum amount and then put my feet through the bars. Hal is lying with his head on the pillow and the blanket up to his chin. I put him down at the bottom where he belongs and then I go down there with him. The ceiling is white and has sparkles just like in the bathroom. If I pee in this bed it doesn't matter but I don't have to pee right now. I put my face next to Hal's and close my eyes. The ceiling sparkles appear against my eyelids, like stars. Hal's got his arm under me.

In my sleep I show my girl cousins how to tie shoes, just like my dad showed me. Make a bunny, cross over, push one ear through, and pull. It's supposed to be a bow but it unravels, just like always. *I can't do it.* My girl cousins disappear and in their place is Bernice, who points to the corner. I shake my head. She takes the manual, grasp-and-steer approach. *This is not a good idea,* my mother whispers. I'm in the corner all alone and I can't feel Hal's arm in my back. Wherever I am, that's where Hal's supposed to be. I turn around and around, but the corner is completely empty. All that's in it is me.

Under the sofa: quite a bit of dirt, several jacks, a book called *The Wait for Me Kitten,* a ballpoint pen, and the crust off a peanut butter sandwich. No Hal. To look behind the refrigerator you have to put your cheek against the kitchen wall. All that's back there is dirt. The broom closet doesn't even have a broom in it, just the vacuum cleaner. Under Linda's bed are about ten sandwich crusts, a clear plastic coin purse with an empty lipstick tube inside, the usual dirt, and a strange piece of red felt that looks like the tongue of a stuffed animal. The bedroom closets yield nothing but shoes. Hal wouldn't be able to go out to the sandbox by himself because he can't walk.

Nevertheless, I open the back screen door and call to him.

Nothing from Hal, but in the kitchen my mother drops what she's doing and moves directly to the telephone. She dials with a pencil, puts a cigarette in her mouth, fishes around in her pocket for a lighter, finds it, snaps it open, lights the cigarette, and says into the receiver Let me talk to your mom.

The kitchen counter can be gotten to by way of a red step stool; you can climb up there while your mother is in the other room and eat chocolate chips out of the cupboard. You can also stand in the sink and look at the whole backyard through the window. She stops me before I make it up to the counter. She's carrying the phone, the receiver pinned to her shoulder. The other arm picks me off the stool and sets me on the floor. I point to the cupboards.

'He's not up there,' she says shortly.

She knows something.

Back in the living room I watch her as she finishes the call and hangs up. She leans back in her chair, lights another cigarette, and blows large ragged smoke rings up to the ceiling. Even when I lie down on the floor right at her feet she won't look at me.

From upside down she doesn't resemble herself; she could be a lady from anywhere.

I gently kick the rungs of her chair, once, twice. Her eyes flicker downward for an instant, and then back up. She checks her watch, and then a second later checks it again.

Any minute now our menfolk should be coming home.

From the kitchen come the sounds of sizzling and whispering. Fried chicken and a mother and father. From outside, the rhythmic thump and scrape of a game of jacks being played on the front stoop. Linda and her best friend, Pattyann. In the living room is the sound of a thumb being sucked. My mother has brought out

Petie, a stuffed dog with a missing tongue, to sit with me. We're on the sofa, being quiet and waiting. My mother peeks her head out of the kitchen and then summons my father.

'She's back to sucking her t-h-u-m,' she says.

'B,' my father tells her.

'What?' she says.

'There's a *b* on it,' he explains.

'What did I say?' she asks.

'"T-h-u-m,"' he says.

'Either way,' she answers.

She's wiping her hands on a dish towel and he's holding a spatula. They're looking at me. Two thumps, a scrape, and Linda tells Pattyann she's a cheater. I use my foot to move Petie down to the floor where he belongs. They consider me and I consider them. My mother is the first to fold.

'Jesus H.,' she says, disappearing into the kitchen.

My father brings a pencil and a piece of paper over to the coffee table. We're going to draw pictures. I climb down off the couch and stand watching.

'You don't want to step on Petie, do you?' he asks me. Petie is underneath my feet.

I take the thumb out of my mouth and nod, then put it back in.

He draws a triangle with a beak. 'That's a bird,' he says, and offers me the pencil.

I can draw pretty hard as long as the pencil doesn't break. When I'm done the whole paper is covered with a picture, and the bird is nowhere in sight. My father licks one finger and rubs the extra pencil marks off the coffee table.

'Jo-Jo made a gorgeous picture,' he calls to my mother. He considers it carefully, turning the paper sideways and then back.

'Is it a house?' he asks me. 'Is it a dog? Is it Mommy?'

No, no, and no.

My mother comes in and stands over us. She looks at the picture and then at me.

'Hal?' she asks.

I take my thumb out just long enough to nod.

'This is truly unbelievable,' my mother says. She's sitting in the rocking chair with her shoes off, smoking. My father is walking back and forth across the living room, singing. Each time he gets to the fringe on the rug he turns around and walks to the other fringe. The song is one he made up, called 'Bye Oh Baby,' and usually I hum along but not tonight. I can't actually cry anymore but I can still make the crying noise. He's patting me on the back and I'm patting him on the back. We're walking the floor with each other.

'She's a sandbag,' he tells my mother as we go past.

'Tell me about it,' she answers.

Linda appears suddenly, squinting in the light. She has her nightgown on backward and her hair is messed up from being asleep. She shields her eyes with one hand and stares at us all. 'Can we have pancakes in the morning?' she asks the room.

'I'm going to pancake somebody right now,' my mother says, preparing to stand up. Linda stomps back the way she came.

'I'd like to pancake *Bernice*,' my father says darkly. He moves me to the other shoulder, turns, and walks. My hand is tired of patting, I'm just watching the rug go by. Three more times and he walks me over to the rocking chair and points me at my mother.

'She asleep?' he whispers.

My mother and I are looking at each other. 'You asleep?' she asks.

I shake my head.

She sighs, stands up, goes to the telephone table, dials, and scratches her head with a pencil while she waits. 'Wake up and

338

smell the hysteria,' she says into the receiver, and then carries the phone out to the kitchen. My father switches shoulders again and we sit down to rock.

When my mother comes back in she's carrying a bottle of beer. She's glad we're sitting down. Bernie and the monsters stopped at the Dairy Queen out on Route 50 to get ice cream cones on their way home.

'You *bet* they did,' my father says, rocking. His shirt smells good.

There was no reason to cart the d-o-l-l in question all the way home, so he was placed in a t-r-a-s-h b-i-n at said Dairy Queen. Under the awning, next to the counter. That would have been approximately three o'clock, and it would be now, oh, twelve-thirty.

My father groans. 'Shit,' he says.

The chair is rocking and rocking.

My mother lifts her beer bottle by the neck and takes a sip. The chances are slim to none but maybe Roy Rogers should get on Trigger and ride out there. Dale Evans will stay here with her beer.

Rocking and rocking.

My eyes won't open, but I'm still wide-awake. I go back up in the air with my eyes closed and then down the hallway and to the right. My arms flop when he puts me down, but I'm not asleep. He leaves and comes back with Petie and I try to make the crying noise but nothing comes out.

After he closes the door, I struggle up just long enough to force Petie through the bars and onto the floor where he belongs.

'My pancakes have bonanas in them,' Linda tells me. She's wearing shorts, a midriff top, and an Easter hat, pointing her fork at me. I'm sitting in the big-girl chair with a dish towel tied around me so I don't climb down. My pancakes are clean.

'Jo-Jo can have all the bananas she likes,' my mother says.

339

'But they don't interest her.' She's drinking coffee and yawning, tapping a cigarette against her wrist. She can't find her lighter this morning.

'That's because her doll is gone and she misses him,' Linda recites sadly. 'Even though our dad went to find him he wasn't there because he probably went to the dump which we're all sad about but there's nothing we can do.' She forks in a mouthful of pancake, chews thoughtfully, and swallows. 'And now she keeps thinking, "Where is my *doll*? Where is my *poor doll*? What will I *do* without my *doll*?"' She takes a long drink of milk and looks at my mother. 'Right?'

'Right,' my mother says dryly. She gets up and lights her cigarette using a burner on the stove. Linda starts to speak again, fork in the air, but she's halted with a look and a pointed finger.

I can't eat pancakes that don't taste good. I push the plate away and lean over as far as the dish towel will allow, put my cheek on the tablecloth, and close my eyes. Now they're gone and it's pure dark. My thumb tastes like syrup.

She's talking to her girlfriend on the phone and polishing the spoons at the same time. I'm sitting on the footstool which I've pushed in front of the picture window. Linda walks by on her way outside, carrying a plastic bowl which she holds way up in the air as she passes.

'I've got a norange,' she tells me.

And I have a pop bead that rolled out from under the footstool. It fits perfectly in my nose but we're not doing that. I'm just holding it.

'You didn't ruin it,' my mother says. 'Fill it with water, put in a tablespoon cream of tartar, and then boil the hell out of it. You'll take all that black off there.' She listens for a minute, polishing. 'Well, you can be the bad housewife and I'll be the bad mother.'

She listens again. 'Sitting at the window, staring out,' she says in a low voice. 'I don't know what to do next.' More listening and then she laughs. I put my forehead and both my hands against the glass. Behind me is the sound of snapping fingers. She can snap her fingers so loud it scares you. I climb down off the foot-stool to get my bead and then climb back up again. She snaps again, twice, and I have to carry the bead over and deposit it in her hand. She puts it in the pocket of her pants and we stare at each other. 'Maybe he ought to be cooking for *you*, since he's the big expert,' she says. She feels my forehead, runs one hand quickly down the back of my shorts, turns me around, and points me at the stool. 'I sprinkle potato chips over the top before I put it in,' she says.

The front sidewalk has a hopscotch picture on it but Linda and Pattyann aren't out there. I don't know where a dump is, and I don't know how long it takes to get back from one. A car pulls up to the curb, stops, and one of my girl cousins gets out holding a sack. Aunt Bernie and my other cousin stay in the car.

My mother hangs up the phone and goes to the door while Bernice and I watch each other through the glass. 'We went to the store and this is for Jo-Jo,' my cousin says when she hands the sack over. She's been crying. '*We* didn't get anything!' she bursts out.

My mother sends her into the kitchen for cookies. 'One for you, one for your sister, and none for your mom,' she tells her. She holds up the sack and calls, 'You didn't have to do this!' to Bernie, who rolls down her window.

'You're raising a brat!' she hollers.

My mother laughs and shakes her fist in the air. The girl cousin goes back down the sidewalk and triumphantly shows her mother the cookies before getting in. They pull away from the curb and my mother waves as they head down the street, then says, 'I'd like to slap that mouth right off her face.'

Linda and Pattyann come into view on the other side of the

street. They look both ways and then hop across the street on one foot.

'I can't *wait* to see what's in here,' my mother says brightly, setting the sack on the coffee table. She checks all her pockets, looking for her lighter, then puts a cigarette in her mouth and heads to the kitchen to light it on the stove.

They got that sack at the store. Outside, a lady is walking by with a dog, and Linda and Pattyann pet the dog so fervently the lady has to pull him away and keep going.

The sack is folded over at the top and it's pretty big but not that big. Linda and Pattyann start playing hopscotch on the front sidewalk, using soda crackers for markers.

My mother is all excited about the sack. She sits down with her ashtray and pats the couch next to her. I climb up and then lie down with my eyes closed. She can't figure out why we aren't more curious about our new present. It must be something very special or they wouldn't have brought it all the way over here. You know, there just might be something inside that will make Jo-Jo forget her troubles. So. Is somebody ready to go down for her nap, or is she ready to *sit up here right now* and see what's in the sack?

It's a box with a picture of a girl on it. She's wearing an apron over her dress and a pearl necklace. Her hair is curled and she has lipstick on. Inside the box are a broom, a dustpan, and a vacuum cleaner.

'Christ,' my mother snorts. She puts her cigarette out, pulls me onto her lap, and rests her chin on my head. 'Poor Jo-Jo,' she says quietly.

They are miniature, and the vacuum cleaner has a pretend cord and a pretend knob to turn it on and off. The broom is yellow, the dustpan is pink, and the vacuum cleaner is orange with a pink-and-yellow-striped handle.

They're so glamorous I can barely look at them.

*

'She spent the whole afternoon cleaning under the beds,' my mother tells my father. They're sharing a beer in the living room. My hair is wet from the bath and I have my cowgirl jammies on. Linda is in the bathtub now, singing a loud, monotonous song about not getting a new toy.

My mother is sewing a button on my father's shirt while he's still wearing it. 'I was having this terrible feeling,' she says, 'that she'd be this forty-year-old woman, going around telling people that we took her d-o-l-l away from her.' She leans down to bite off the thread.

My father tests his new button and it works perfectly. 'In three days she won't remember she even *knew* that d-o-l-l,' he predicts.

They stop talking and, in unison, lift their feet so I can vacuum under them.

The Family Hour

IF SHE HAS TO COME UP HERE we're both going to regret it. It's ten o'clock at night and there has been a territorial dispute over where the line down the middle of the bed really is. After a short skirmish we have yelled downstairs to the mediator. From the top of the stairs all we can see is my father's bare feet crossed on the white divan and a corner of my mother's newspaper. They're drinking beer and eating popcorn. Linda pins my arms behind my back and I bite her. There are screaming noises.

She's had it. Once more and it's going to be the belt.

This surprises us and we tiptoe back into the bedroom. My mother's spanking abilities scare her and so she has a ratio of about one spank per forty threats. We always know where we happen to be along the spanking continuum. That's why we can't believe she's going straight for the belt. We're more afraid of her hand than the belt, because the belt is a cloth one from a house-dress, while her hand is made of granite. But still, this is erratic behavior on her part, and we don't care for it.

Once we're back in the bedroom with the door closed, I say, 'I'll give *her* the belt.' Linda opens the door again and points her face down the hall toward the stairs.

'Mother?' she calls. 'Jo Ann just said something you might want to hear.'

There's a thud from downstairs and the sound of feet stomping. Linda slams the door shut and leaps for the bed; we hide under the covers, breathing into our nightgowns, but nothing happens. She faked us out.

The border dispute has to be settled with what is known as a foot-feet fight. This is where you lie on your back and put the soles of your feet against the soles of your sister's feet and then push with all your weak might until she gets tired of it and shoves you off the bed. There are rules to foot-feet fighting, but they are frequently defied, and then someone gets hurt, usually from being rocketed off the bed backward and onto the floor (me). On this occasion what goes wrong is that my own right foot slips from its station on her left foot and propels itself forward until it is stopped by her eye socket.

She rolls herself up into a ball.

'That didn't hurt,' I say immediately. She's got her head under a pillow, crying furiously and trying to kick me. I carefully get out of the way of her legs until she has me wadded up at the foot of the bed. Her sobs now have an alarming, forlorn quality, and it isn't like her to muffle them. I try a different approach: I start crying, too.

Eventually we fall asleep and roll as we always do into the demilitarized zone down the center of the bed. When I wake in the morning she's sitting in the rocking chair with her ankles crossed, virtuously reading her science book. I go back under the covers immediately. She has the most pronounced black eye I've ever seen, even on TV. I'm a dead man.

We dress ourselves slowly, not looking at one another; her underwear says Friday, mine says Wednesday, but today it doesn't matter who is right. White knee socks, navy blue knee socks, a gray skirt, a plaid one. Blouses. Teeth, faces, hair.

On the third step from the bottom we stop and look at ourselves in the hallway mirror. I've got my barrette in wrong. Linda has her mohair sweater buttoned over her shoulders like a cape, the way the girls in her class do it. Her face is thin on one side and fat on the other. The fat side is purple. I move slightly so that my own reflection goes into the bevel of the mirror, distorting my nose and one eye until I look like the monster that I am. It's time to sit down.

'Oh no you don't,' she says firmly, lifting me by the collar of my shirt, steering me into the kitchen ahead of her. My mother is at the table, looking into a magnifying mirror, putting on makeup. A cigarette is going in the ashtray. My father is cracking our morning eggs into a bowl, dish towel tied around his waist, a spatula in his back pocket. He's singing the 'I'm a Bum' song that drives my mother nuts. She's turning the radio up right at the moment we step into her line of view. The announcer makes a staticky squawk and then disappears into silence. My father sets his spoon down. My mother puts her glasses on.

Linda steps forward, Jo Ann steps backward.

I am immediately dispatched to the living room, where I can hear every word but not defend myself by looking stricken. In the kitchen my father whistles long and appreciatively until my mother tells him to shut up. 'Look at this,' she cries. I know just what she's doing: turning Linda's face back and forth, back and forth. I pick up some knitting from its basket and before I realize it I've unraveled a row and a half. My heart starts pounding. I'm a maniac, kicking people in the head and unraveling knitting.

'We *want* the truth,' my mother says, in a voice that ensures she will never get it. A pause, an inhalation, an exhalation, and then the story unfolds. It has a complicated plot that is difficult but not impossible to follow, and several very dramatic things occur, but the gist is this: the bathroom doorknob poked her in the eye. It's a play with several acts but only one actress; my name is never mentioned. I hope he puts the eggs on pretty soon because I'm suddenly hungry. I begin fiddling with my barrette, trying to fix it.

'The doorknob would come up to about *here*,' my mother says. I imagine she's pointing to my sister's stomach.

'Well, it didn't,' Linda responds flatly. 'It came up to *here*, as a matter of fact.'

There is a long, stand-off silence in which all you can hear is Linda thinking.

'I had to pee so bad I was bending *over*,' she says firmly. Brilliant. This is why she's the older sister and I'm the younger one.

Snap. Crack. My mother's lighter and my father's eggs. I don't see why I'm quarantined in the living room when I didn't do anything.

'Can someone please fix my *barrette*?' I call out.

Right before we file out the door for school, my mother calls me over. She takes off her glasses to get a better bead on me. 'Do *you* have any idea why your sister has a black eye?' she asks.

I hesitate. You hate to say it, but when it's the truth, it's the truth. She *never* looks where she's going.

In addition to Linda and me, there's a brother, a strange little guy named Bradley, obsessed with his own cowboy boots. He paces around and around the house, staring at his feet and humming the G.I. Joe song from the television commercial. He is the ringleader of a neighborhood gang of tiny boys, four-year-olds, who throw dirt and beat each other with sticks all day long. In the evenings he comes to dinner with an imaginary friend named Charcoal.

'Charcoal really needs a bath,' my mother says, spooning SpaghcttiOs onto his plate. His hands are perfectly clean right up to the wrists and the center of his face is cleared so we can see what he looks like. The rest of him is dirt.

'Charcoal was locked in the garage all day,' he replies. My mother made fried chicken for dinner, but Brad will only eat food prepared by Chef Boyardee.

Across the table from me, Linda pushes a mouthful of potatoes past her teeth and lips until it's hanging there, making me sick. I will only eat potatoes in the form of french fries, and that's because I don't know that french fries *are* potatoes. I have a weak stomach. The second I open my mouth to complain, she sucks it back in and swallows, touches a napkin to her lips, and goes for a preemptive strike.

'Jo Ann is making me sick,' she tells my mother. Everyone stops eating and looks at me. I'm searching my chicken leg for the big rubbery string. If I get that string in my mouth, dinner is over.

'I can't find it,' I say. The fork won't do what I want it to, and chicken juice is getting on my hands. *Quit looking at me.* My mother reaches over and takes the chicken leg, drops it on my father's plate.

'Find the string for her,' she tells him shortly. He looks at her, looks at the leg, and finally picks it up. He begins hacking at it amiably, gazing around the table in benign spirits. He's not paying attention to what he's supposed to be doing; the leg slips suddenly out of his grasp and, in the ensuing clatter, milk is dumped over and my father's plate is flooded.

'Well, I'll be,' he says slowly, watching with surprise as his beans and potatoes become islands. A full minute passes while we wait for my mother to do something about it. Eventually she gets up from the table, takes his plate, scrapes it into the dog's bowl, gets another plate from the cupboard and hurls some food onto it. While she's doing all this, my father is sitting with his elbows on the table and his face in his hands.

By the time she puts the new plate of food down in front of him, he's asleep. She shoves him and he comes to with a snort. He no longer has the amiable slap-happy look that offends her; now he looks belligerent. She tells him he's a sorry excuse for a man, which causes him to shrug.

'Who do you think you are?' she asks him. She has her face right up in his. 'Dean Martin? Because he's nothing but a lush, too.'

My father not only drinks like Dean Martin, but he actually looks like him. They sing alike, too, Dean on TV, and my father when he's shaving. He can't help but like Dean Martin, because they have so much in common. Somehow, though, the word lush hits him the wrong way and he guffaws instead of fighting back. My mother quickly corrects herself.

'He's a *drunk*,' she says.

My father doesn't like that one bit. He tries to counter it by insulting Carol Burnett but my mother cuts him off. You don't see Carol Burnett standing there with a drink in her hand; she actually puts on a *show*. Usually I try to think of other things when they fight like this at the dinner table, like how to swallow. But by using television personalities, they're holding my interest. My favorite show is *That Girl*, but I'm one hundred percent sure they aren't going to mention her.

Linda ignores them completely, staring instead at me, willing me to look. I can see out of the corner of my eye what appears to be a Ping-Pong ball coming out of her mouth. Next to me, Brad is a country unto himself, quietly stirring his SpaghettiOs and taking occasional peeks under the table at his cowboy boots. His mouth is orange.

Dinner ends when my father gets indignant and tries to stand up. He falls backward into the wall and the big ceramic salad fork drops from its hook and shatters. My mother can't have anything nice; the minute she gets something decent, it's ruined. She works all day and then comes home and makes a beautiful meal like this, and the dog is the only one who will eat it.

Soon there are distant unrestful snores coming from upstairs; from the sewing room the furious, intermittent buzz of the

Singer 9000. In the living room, Brad and Charcoal play a friendly game of cards. 'When I go like this, it means you lose,' the visible one tells the invisible one.

This is our house in Moline, Illinois, a big white clapboard that needs new gutters.

There's a little garage out back, and in the corner of the garage is an old cupboard. Inside it are cans of paint, folded rags, tools for cleaning fish, an old dog brush, and a bottle of vodka in a brown paper sack.

Here in the kitchen, African violets bloom wildly on the windowsill, hopped-up with fertilizer. The radio on the counter plays a new Beatles song and the girls take a break from clearing the table to clutch their hearts and listen. Tuesday night at the Beard household, and it's business as usual: Linda washes, Jo Ann dries.

Yimmer the dog is missing. She spends most of her time shedding on the furniture, or balanced on her back legs at the end of her chain, barking at the house. Right now, the last time any of us can remember seeing her was hours ago, at lunch, when she coughed up part of a garter snake on the living room rug. My father is also missing, which has led the authorities – my mother and her girlfriend – to believe they are together.

'It isn't enough that he goes to the tavern in broad daylight,' my mother says to Helen. Her mouth is full of pins. 'He's got to advertise it to the neighbors.' Popular thinking places Yimmer at the crime scene, a white dog against a brown brick establishment, fodder for local dinner table discussion tonight.

'If there's a garter snake in this neighborhood, then I'm moving,' Helen tells her. They're making sheers for Helen's dining room, so she can open her drapes without the whole world looking in. They keep taking the pins out of their mouths in order to smoke, and then putting them back in. As soon as they get the hard part done they plan to switch from iced tea to beer.

All three kids have been dispatched to find the dog on our own block, but I have come back early, due to the bogus nature of the mission. We all know where she is. I'm trying to get my parakeet to look at me. No matter where I stand, next to his cage, he turns around in a single hopping motion and looks the other way.

'I think this bird is mad at me,' I say. He wants me to put my finger in there so he can peck it. The back door slams and the refrigerator opens.

'Get out of there,' my mother says through her pins.

Linda flops down on the sofa and opens her book, taking small bites off a radish. 'She's putting her fingers in the birdcage,' she tells my mother.

'I forgot,' I say quickly.

'Well, he'll be happy to remind you,' my mother says.

'Linda's eating a radish without washing it,' I report.

'I wish I had about eight more just like them,' my mother tells Helen. She goes to the back door and calls for Brad, very, very loudly, in a voice designed to scare all neighborhood children, then stops at the refrigerator and gets two cans of beer.

It takes Brad a full ten minutes to report in, and when he does, it turns out he forgot his mission altogether and was making a campfire in the middle of the alley.

'We're rubbing the sticks together and then we're going to cook things over it,' he tells my mother. His mouth is still vivid from lunch and he has his T-shirt on inside out. Helen is charmed by him and exclaims over the idea of a campfire in the alley. He glances at her. 'Don't worry,' he explains, 'it's all pretend.'

What about the dog?

'Huh?' he says.

The tavern is several long blocks away. The girls are to get their shoes on and go over there with the leash and see if the dog is waiting outside. If she is, they are to put the leash on her and bring her home. If it turns out they can do that without fighting, then they won't get beat to a pulp when they get back.

Helen thinks this is funny and so does my mother.

Two things we are never, under any circumstances, to do. Ride double on a bike and ride a bike on Nineteenth Avenue. Riding double means the person in control isn't, and if she ever catches one of her kids doing it, that's it for the bike; sold. Nineteenth Avenue is at the end of our street, a double-laned thoroughfare with no stoplights, lined with parked cars and carpeted with the pelts of squirrels and stray cats. We aren't even allowed to cross it on foot.

Linda's bike is new and almost too tall for her. We wheel it behind the garage and I climb on the back fender. I've got the dog leash wrapped conveniently around my neck. She gets on and we wobble for a distance, recover momentarily, and then fall over.

This time I sit on the handlebars, which is more comfortable, except Linda can't see around my head and if I shift my weight we swerve harshly. We veer past the campfire crew, who are sitting on the ground holding long sticks over a pile of short sticks; Brad's face is a blur of startlement, but he can be counted on to forget it as soon as we've crossed his line of vision. I'm balancing us by using my legs as rudders and keeping my head to the side so Linda can see where she's going.

Directly to Nineteenth Avenue and a right-hand swerve, out into the stream of Saturday afternoon cars. I bank my legs going around the turn and then am forced to retract them altogether, due to the close nature of the parked cars to my right and the whiz-zing cars to my left. Once my feet are settled on the front fender, I have to sit straight in order not to fall off, and once I sit straight, Linda can't see. Wobbling begins to occur almost immediately, along with shouting. I'm trying to tell her where to steer and she's trying to tell me she can't. Somebody's mother gets into the act by yelling at us out the window of a car going the other direction. Cars are honking and careening out around us, causing mayhem.

Up ahead there's a gap in the parked cars. A little street. I can't tell if she plans to take it or not, but I'm going for it. I bank my legs again and the traffic arcs out around us; Linda tries to compensate by leaning in the other direction. She uses her forehead to butt me between the shoulder blades.

No.

Yes.

Around the corner, clipping a parked car.

Sewer grate. *Here comes a sewer grate.*

Hard to describe how skinny my legs are, except to say that one of them fit perfectly down the sewer grate. I'm wearing the bike like a cape on my head and shoulders; Linda is in a heap with the wind knocked out of her. Her lips are moving but the sound is missing.

My leg is in the sewer.

One end of the handlebars is jammed into the grate and the front wheel, now curved like a potato chip, is pinning my head down. Six feet away, Nineteenth Avenue roars dynamically. Below the street, the air is cool and damp, like air-conditioning.

MY LEG IS IN THE SEWER.

Linda is up, making a bleating sound and circling her bike. Okay, she can't believe this. This is a practically *new* bike. This bike is now *ruined*. If it isn't ruined, you could've fooled *her.*

MY LEG IS IN THE SEWER.

She grabs the handlebar and tries to twist it out of the grate. When she lets go, my chin is pressed to the ground. I can now see the undercarriages of cars whizzing past, six feet away. The first one that decides to turn the corner will smash me like a garbage can lid. The direness of the situation dawns on both of us at the same moment. Linda steps discreetly onto the curb and starts walking backward.

DON'T LEAVE ME HERE.

'I'm not,' she says, and then turns and starts running. She stops at the end of the block and begins limping, holding her elbows, until she's out of view.

This is more of an alley than an actual street, and the houses look like nobody's home. I try hollering as loud as I can, but Nineteenth Avenue drowns me out. Now my throat hurts. I'm going to be killed, and the only people I know in heaven are my grandfather and an old dog named Mike, who *got hit by a car.*

Help! Help! Help!

Nobody helps you when you need help. When your sister left you trapped in the sewer and your dad is at the tavern, drinking with the dog. Screaming doesn't work but I can't stop doing it. Nobody is helping me!

Oh, wait. Here they come. My mother and Helen, walking briskly, Linda hanging back a few paces, nursing herself. Helen points and suddenly my mother breaks into a run. I've never seen her run before! She gets larger and larger, her mouth a stark gash across her face, until she's just a pair of feet, the bike is wrenched out of the grate and thrown on the curb, I'm lifted, turned, and pulled. Up and out.

Well. That was easier than it looked.

Helen unwinds the leash from my neck, picks the gravel out of my shinbone, and tugs my shorts back around where they belong. She brushes the seat harder than she needs to, but I'm not in a position to say anything. My mother is sitting on the curb with her head on her knees, panting quietly and weeping.

Linda is just arriving on the scene. 'Well, *that* was a close one,' she says. 'Just the kind of situation you read about, where a kid is riding her sister's bike and gets too close to Nineteenth Avenue.' She's talking directly to Helen. My mother looks up.

'Get home,' she says.

Linda is in for it.

'The both of you,' she tells me.

We try to wheel the bike but it won't. Linda picks up the front end and I pick up the back end. At the end of the street we have to set it down for a second. My mother and Helen are still back there, sitting on the curb. My mother is talking and Helen is shaking her head.

My sewer leg is still cool to the touch. We pick up the bike and carry it another half block before resting. My mother and Helen are a ways behind, walking slowly.

'I think she's laughing,' I tell Linda.

She sets down her end, fiddles with her shoelace, looks backward under her armpit, and then picks up the bike again. We resume walking. 'I think she's crying.'

She may be right. Either thing is possible.

We stow the bike in the garage for our dad to look at once he sobers up.

Tomorrow, or a week from tomorrow, hard to say. In the house, we divide up. I take a can of Pledge into the living room and start polishing the furniture; Linda runs dishwater and briskly begins dumping glasses and spoons into it. This place is a mess. My parakeet is asleep on his perch. I stick my finger through the bars and he's on it in an instant, biting into my knuckle with his beak. The door slams and I race back to my Pledge and spray it dramatically on the coffee table, all around the plastic flower arrangement.

Yimmer trots into the living room, leash trailing. She inspects the spot where she threw up earlier and then goes back into the kitchen for a long drink. My mother and Helen must have swung by the tavern on their way back. Well, that's a relief; one of the boozehounds is home.

The other one, lacking a leash, is always harder to retrieve.

*

355

I'm reading a book called *I Was Murdered*, a mysterious ghost story about a lady who can't rest until her killer is found. The cover has a picture of a typewriter, with two bloody hands typing the title on a piece of paper. I got it out of the neighbor's trash, along with some comic books that I already read. I'm partial to ghost stories, but this is nothing like the ones at the school library, where the ghosts invariably turn out to be real people guarding buried treasure. This book has a severed head in a refrigerator and other goings-on that I'm way too young to read about. That's the main reason I can't stop.

My sister is watching *The Man from U.N.C.L.E.* and putting on clear fingernail polish. She's quote babysitting unquote while my parents are over at the tavern. She made Brad go to bed a half hour ago but we can still hear him up there, punching his inflatable clown, which hits the floor and bobs back up again repeatedly. Sometimes he steps on the clown's head for a while to keep him down, and then there's silence. We don't care what he does, as long as he does it up there.

My book has me terrified. I want a bottle of pop really bad but it's in the refrigerator. I can picture it in there keeping a severed head company, blood dripping, pooling up on the Tupperware containers, seeping into the vegetable bin. My mother should watch me better and not let me read books like this, but if I do, my sister should go out to the refrigerator during a commercial and get my pop for me.

'Are you *kidding*?' she says, insulted.

This is grounds for a fight but before I can formulate my opening arguments, the sound of a key in the back door startles us both. *Man from U.N.C.L.E.* is followed by *Mission Impossible* is followed by *Creature Feature*. We're supposed to be able to watch all of them before our parents come home. It's getting so you can't count on anything around here.

My mother comes in and peruses the situation briefly, then listens at the stairs.

Brad has fallen suddenly silent up there. I can tell by her face there won't be any *Creature Feature*, and popcorn is out of the question. Linda is watching her show intently, looking neither left nor right. I put my book down and watch it, too.

'This is a *great* show,' I say to the room.

Out in the kitchen, my father is opening cupboards and getting spoons. When he opens the refrigerator there's a long moment of silence and then he shuts it again. I guess there was no head in there. A minute later he appears with ice cream, a bowl for Linda, a bowl for me, and a giant mixing bowl of it for himself. He joins us for the last fifteen minutes of *The Man from U.N.C.L.E.*, acting very impressed when Illya Kuryakin shoots a guy using his ballpoint pen for a gun. Yimmer is sitting on his lap.

'Is this the one where he has a telephone in his shoe?' he asks me.

'*Get Smart*,' I tell him. This confuses him for a moment and then he understands, and nods. It's been about two months since he's had a drink. Every night he sits in here while we watch TV, reading his bird books and talking to us. At first we didn't like it, but now we do.

My mother is in the kitchen alone, chipping the polish off her nails and smoking. I put the ice cream dishes in the sink and drift toward the refrigerator, where my bottle of pop is waiting.

'No you don't,' she says curtly.

Nothing is fair around here. I can't decide whether to argue or not. The only light is coming from the living room, and she has her glasses off. Her eyes look weak and vulnerable, but her lips look like blades.

'He embarrassed me to death tonight,' she says.

Uh-oh. Why did I come out here; what was I thinking?

'In front of everyone,' she continues. 'Embarrassed. To *death*.'

She looks pretty alive to me, but if the truth be known, I've been embarrassed by him myself. Slumped and staggering, or

357

sleeping all night in the passenger seat of the car, parked in the driveway, because he can't manage the back steps. Disappearing into the garage at odd times during the day, sipping from a sack and staring at the back of the house through the dark doorway, thinking no one can see him. We see him.

'There we all are,' she says in a low voice. 'Playing cards, trying to have *fun*, drinking a few cocktails, and he sits there for two hours drinking *orange juice*. Holier than thou; won't even have a drink on a Saturday night when we're at a *tavern*.'

I think about this, standing on one foot. The dark kitchen, her cigarette going, the bitten-off words. It's hard to know what expression to put on my face. From the living room comes the sound of a fuse burning and then a theme song starts up.

'*Mission Impossible* is on,' I tell her. She turns back to her ashtray and I return to the sofa. Linda is explaining the gist of the show to my dad.

'They all have different identities, and they have impossible missions,' she tells him.

'I see,' he says agreeably. 'All different identities and missions.'

'Impossible ones,' she stresses.

'They aren't *impossible*, the people just think they are,' I explain.

'They *seem* impossible, until the different-identity guys take over,' he clarifies. 'Is that it?'

We nod. He's drinking a glass of milk.

'Want me to get you a bottle of beer?' I ask him. Linda swivels her head around to stare at me but my dad keeps watching the television. After a minute he shakes his head no.

I want to go back to my book and leave them to their show, my mother to her dark kitchen, but I can't. My words are still hanging in the air of the living room, drowning out the TV. My dad is staring at *Mission Impossible* but he's no longer watching it.

Eventually, he shifts his weight and Yimmer stands up on his lap. She turns around and stares him in the face with her ears

358

folded back and her tail going. He kisses her on the forehead, sets her on the floor, and stands up. Out to the kitchen. The refrigerator door opens, closes.

Yimmer's ears go up as she listens. Linda looks at me and I look at my book. Then the familiar, inevitable sound of a bottle being opened.

There's going to be a style show at school, something the PTA dreamed up. My mother is sewing three matching outfits and we have to be in it. Every time I think about it I feel sick; the dress she's making for me has the wrong kind of sleeves and she's threatening to give me a permanent. The last time she gave me a permanent only one side of it took, and I looked like I had a bush stuck to my head.

'You're not going to be in a style show with stringy hair,' she tells me. She's working on a little shirt for Brad made of the same material as my dress and Linda's.

'Why don't you put puffy sleeves on *him* for a change?' I ask her. He's in the kitchen, eating a post-dinner bowl of cornflakes.

'No!' he calls out, alarmed.

'If I hear another word about sleeves, you won't *be* in a style show,' she says to me.

'Sleeves,' I reply.

Brad's in the doorway with a dripping spoon. She shows him his shirt with its long sleeves attached. It's getting cowboy fringe on the yoke. He goes back in the kitchen.

Linda is doing her homework at the same big table where my mother is sewing.

Neither of them is interested in talking to me. The pattern for our dresses shows a picture of two girls, a younger one with short curly hair and puffy sleeves, an older one with long swingy hair and a little cape.

'You should make Linda wear this cape,' I say to my mother. Linda looks up.

'You'll both have the cape,' my mother says firmly.

A cape! Oh my God.

Linda starts poking herself in the head with the eraser on her pencil. She can't do her math and she's starting to get hysterical. My dad is the only one who can do math around here and we have no idea where he is. He didn't show up for dinner again, and it's a sore subject with my mother.

'Let me see,' she tells Linda. This won't work. My mother can always get the answers but she figures it out in her head instead of on the paper. They make us figure it out on the paper to keep our parents from doing it for us at night when we're having hysterics.

'That's *old math*, Mother,' Linda says desperately. 'Do it in *new math*.'

'Oh, *new math*,' my mother says. 'What a load of bullshit.' She goes back to her sewing.

One time when Linda was three she shoved a tiny toy train up her nose to see how far it would go. It went quite a ways and she had to have it removed at the hospital. My mother has never gotten over this, and in our house, Life Savers and dry cleaning bags are treated like loaded handguns. So when Brad makes a choking noise out in the kitchen all hell breaks loose here in the dining room. My mother leaps up, throwing the shirt one way and the fringe the other, Linda drops her pencil, Yimmer barks.

Brad appears in the doorway, enormous-eyed. He points back to the kitchen with his spoon and then pushes past my mother into the living room where he turns and points again, then buries his shocked face in a sofa pillow. There's something in the kitchen! The rest of us crowd through the doorway to see.

Nothing.

My mother screams. I look around wildly and then I see it. Through the glass of the back door, framed by my grandmother's

360

lace curtains, a face wearing a creature-feature mask. Black hair, forehead, two stunned eyes, and then the rest is blood. It looks like my dad. He fumbles for the doorknob but can't see through the mask, his hand slips and he cries out, something slides from his mouth and lands on his shirtfront; a wad of blood. My mother springs forward, opens the door, and we get the full picture. His clothes are frozen to his body and over it all, shirt, sport coat, trousers, is dark blood, coming from his mouth. Some of it is frozen and some of it is fresh. He can't move at all and when Linda and my mother try to pull him inside he groans and resists.

We get him up over the threshold, my mother on one side, Linda and me on the other, and then try to sit him in a chair in the middle of the kitchen. His legs won't bend. He groans again and then, with a noise like cracking ice, sits. My mother opens the oven door and turns it up to five hundred. She wants to look inside his mouth but he won't let her, so she gets a clean dish towel, wets it under the faucet, and starts wiping the blood from his face while Linda and I try to remove his shoes. The laces are stiff but the shoes come off okay. When we peel the socks away, his feet look like long yellow boats. My mother gasps when she sees them, then hands each of us a towel and tells us to rub. When we do, he makes the groaning noise again so we stop. She resituates him so he's closer to the oven, and then fills a dishpan with tepid water. When she sets his feet in it he makes a moaning sound.

Still working on his face, she tells me to go to the phone. I do. She tells me the number to dial and what to say. My aunt answers.

'It's Jo,' I say.

'Well, hi Jo,' she answers cheerfully.

'My mom needs you right now,' I recite.

There is no pause. She's on her way. Twenty minutes.

The oven is blasting heat out into the kitchen. As my father thaws, the story comes out. It's hard to understand what he's saying, his words are slurred and when he talks blood dribbles out, over his chin and onto his soaked shirt. He wrecked the car.

Oh! my mother cries. The beautiful new Impala! Gold with gold interior!

He was drinking with Charlie at Silver's.

Silver's! Down in the west *end*? Silver's!

Left and started driving back, was coming around the viaduct, something happened.

The *viaduct*! At the slough? Clear down *there*? Oh my God!

She's walking in circles, frantic, stopping to clear the blood from his mouth. *The slough!* Linda is gone, somehow, it's only me in here with them.

Lost control and the car went down over the embankment into the water.

Into the *water*? Oh my dear goddamned *God*!

When he opened his eyes he was underwater and the window wouldn't roll down.

My mother is moaning and twisting the bloody dish towel.

He got it down finally and swam to shore, started walking, and came home.

You *walked*? From the *viaduct*? Five *miles*?

The kitchen is baking hot, but it's November outside. When I traipsed the four blocks to school this morning I had on my winter coat, a scarf, a hat, and mittens. And I was still cold. Suddenly my mother stops.

'Where's Charlie?' she asks him. Charlie is his drinking buddy.

He doesn't know.

Where is Charlie? Was he in the car?

He can't remember. My mother's face is stark white. Linda appears in the doorway. With her eyes on my father, she reaches out for me and we hold on to each other while my mother fumbles the phone book out of the drawer and begins clawing through it. She finds the number and dials. Someone answers.

'You S.O.B.,' she says into the receiver and hangs up.

I guess he was home. The back door opens and my aunt comes in. When she sees my father she starts weeping with her hand over her mouth. Like everyone else, she's fond of my dad, she just wishes he would behave better. My mother tells her the story in terse words while my father dozes off, his head falling forward on his chest. He jerks awake and groans. Linda takes his feet out of the water and dries them.

'We love you, Dad,' she whispers. He groans again as she tries to put dry socks on his poor feet. She stops and looks at me.

'We love you, Dad,' I whisper. I help get the socks on and then we step back and wait until my aunt sends us into the living room. They're going to take him to the hospital.

From the sofa, arms around each other, we listen to the sounds from the kitchen, grunts and cries as they get him to his feet. My aunt appears in the doorway with her purse over her arm.

'Where's Brad?' she asks us.

Linda is mute. 'Upstairs,' I say.

'Jody, you go check on him,' she tells me. 'And I'll be back here as soon as we get your dad taken care of.' She disappears again and there's a series of muffled cries as they ease him through the door and down the back steps. Linda and I each take our arms back and sit quietly, side by side on the sofa. Finally I have to speak.

'What was in his mouth?' I ask her.

'Everything but teeth,' she replies.

His teeth are gone! His beautiful teeth that he smiles with.

The kitchen has to be cleaned up. There are bloody towels all over the floor and the oven is still blasting out heat. Linda will do that while I go upstairs to find Brad. She stands up wearily and doesn't move until I give her a push from behind. The steps go on and on forever until I'm finally at the top. The only light on upstairs is in the bathroom.

Brad is in there, throwing up. I listen for a moment, until it's silent, and then push the door open. He's sitting on the floor next to the toilet, a dripping washcloth in his hand. I take it from him and wring it out. All around the toilet are chewed cornflakes and old SpaghettiOs.

'I can't find Charcoal!' he tells me. 'He saw Dad and runned away!' I give the washcloth back and tell him to stay there, I'll go look for Charcoal.

I close the door behind me and stand for a moment in the dark upstairs hallway. I can hear Linda in the kitchen, moving things around, running water in the sink. In the morning, down at the slough, we'll watch them lift our gold Impala, dripping, from the icy water. By then we'll know that four of his ribs were broken on impact, and my mother will show us the terrible gouges on the steering wheel where his front teeth hit and were driven up into his head, behind his nose, perilously close to his brain. She'll tell us how the surgeon had to go in with a scalpel and remove them, one by one, while he thrashed, too drunk to be put under. His anesthesiologists were named Jack and Bud, she'll say grimly, drawing on her cigarette. Jack Daniel's and Budweiser.

I wait in the dark hall, counting to twenty, and then to fifty. I push the door open and go back in the bathroom.

'I found good old Charcoal,' I say.

Brad looks up at me from his spot on the floor. He's been rubbing the washcloth across his brow and his hair is standing up in front. He stares at the air next to my shoulder for a moment, searching. Suddenly relief floods across his face.

'Hi,' he says.

Waiting

HE PLACES HIMSELF IN THE GENTLE CURVE of the kidney-shaped desk. It is reddish mahogany, gleaming with Pledge and elbow grease. My sister can't take her eyes off the desk, because she's been looking for one like that at yard sales and estate sales and Saturday morning auctions for months. I, on the other hand, am captivated by the little guy sitting at the desk. He's in a somber profession, a low-voiced talker, a sympathizer, a crooning gentleman, here to make it all less of a hassle. He shuffles papers, twists the top of his thin gold pen and the ballpoint moves gently into place. He looks like he's been carefully dusted with talc – his head is bald and pink but it is not gleaming or garish in any way. Instead it has a matte surface, and the white hair around the bottom half of his head is straight and coarse. His shirt is white and the tips of the collar are crisp as notebook paper. Beneath his chin and above the snowy embankment of his shirtfront rides a bowtie, black with a pattern of small golden shields. It manages to be both pert and dignified, cheerful if you feel like being cheerful, or old-fashioned and somber if you're bummed.

Linda suddenly gets the hiccups and doesn't try to hide it. Each time she hiccups he touches his ear or clicks his gold pen. His earlobes are amazingly long and thick for such a little old man. Linda hiccups loudly and begins weeping. I give her the usual sympathetic glance and pat her hand, he gently leans forward and indicates with a gesture the box of tissues on the corner of the desk. She takes one and hiccups into her hand, subdued. She is over it already, I can tell. I try to catch her eye to point out the combed tufts emerging from his ears. He smiles a dim and sincere smile, finds the floor with his tiny feet, rises. He comes out from around the kidney-shaped desk and prepares his face for the task at hand. We move in behind him and trail down the carpeted hallway of the mansion, Linda noticing the wainscoting and chandeliers, me watching the back of his neck. He opens the door with a miniature flourish and moves back demurely. We step past him and into the room full of coffins.

The best ones are wood, rubbed to the sheen of the mahogany desk, lined with soft padding, intricate tucks and pleats and folds. All that effort. Linda runs her hand along the surface of one, pokes the satin pillow delicately with one finger. It has the kind of brass handles you find on an old-fashioned sideboard. 'This one looks like a yacht,' she remarks.

I glance at Mr. Larson but he's looking studiously at the tips of his shoes, rocking himself gently forward and backward, waiting. Somewhere deep within the house something flushes, long tubes feed fluids into and out of stiffening lumps.

'I can't do this,' I tell them. He reaches behind the door for a folding chair and as he pulls it out the seat falls smoothly into place with a satisfying click. I sit down while Mr. Larson pads down the hall to get me a glass of water. He is accommodating and resourceful but clearly unimpressed, like a plumber in the presence of a medium clog.

*

While he's gone Linda takes my hair in her hands and winds it softly, lets it drop. She points to the hull of a metal-sided casket.

'I like that one,' she says. She wanders over and peers inside, touches the lid. She turns after a moment. 'Can you keep doing this or do you need to leave?'

I shrug. Better now than later, which could end up being Christmas morning. The casket she's touching looks like the *Titanic*, gunmetal gray, waiting to be launched.

'What a waste, don't you think? All those gorgeous trees being chopped down just to get planted all over again,' she said. 'Here comes your guy.'

He crouches to hand me the cup of water, hands on knees, wrinkled-up brow. It tastes like water from a bathroom sink.

'We think we might get her a metal one,' I tell him, rising. 'We like the wooden ones but they're too nice to put in the ground.' I look to Linda and she nods in support.

'Plus,' she says, 'you know.' She thinks for a second while we wait and then it comes back to her. 'They go in a *vault*,' she finishes. 'So who cares.' She looks at him probingly. Her eyes have soft blue pouches underneath and she's getting a dangerous air about her.

'We have to get going anyway,' I tell him. 'We have to get back before she wonders where we are.'

In her hospital bed, bent like a branch against the pain, she watches the clock, anticipates the arrival of a daughter. *Where have you been?* Her voice vanished three days ago, leaving eyes and hands for communicating. *I've been here all alone, no one would stay in the room with me, you're the only one and you left.* This is my shift alone with her. The afternoon pulls itself along.

On the rolling lunch tray is a plate of Christmas cookies decorated with glaring Santas and crooked reindeer shapes. One kind has maroon jelly poured into a reservoir in the center and I take a small bite. I have a thing about red jelly but creaky old Velma

Edwards made it so I'm willing to give it a shot. Ready, aim, it lands with a crumbling thud in the wastebasket. My mother rolls her gray, diminishing eyes and gives an invisible smirk. Linda has eaten almost all the good ones, left the jelly and green sugar for me. *Where did you girls go?* She has a clear tube poked up her nose nowadays, connected to an oxygen tank like an astronaut prepared to leave the ship. There is absolute silence, the clank and squeak of the hospital giving way for a moment as an angel passes over, wings beating. The instant passes and the hospital resumes itself, a cart bumps, a nurse calls out loudly, rudely, somewhere down the hall. In the room Coke seethes as I pour it into a glass. *Where did you girls go? Why did both of you need to go at once, leaving me here by myself?* I get a picture of her long ago, shopping, eating lunch in the mezzanine at McCabe's, picking out school clothes. Tall and thin in a beautiful suit; lemon meringue pie and coffee. The slide changes and the tufted ears of tiny Mr. Larson click into view. *Why did both of you have to go at once?* I rise to the occasion. Now-now, I point out, it's awful close to Christmas to be asking those kinds of questions.

Her eyes move past me, over my head, and I feel suddenly the tepid breath of Barnelle. He's a swashbuckler today, actually wearing one of those head things, like a doctor in the movies. It is a flat metallic disk connected to a band and he lifts it off and shoves it into the pocket of his suitcoat. The hair over the top of his head is a delicate auburn doily. He pats it down, using the palm of his hand, pushing the tattered strands back in place, willing them to stay there. He's wearing a plastic Santa Claus face on his lapel. He smiles at her, he has always acted as though he loves her and regrets this. He acknowledges me with a tilt of the head, some kind of invisible language that works, lifts her wrist and counts the pulse, corpuscles stepping through from her hand to her arm, one by one, like soldiers heading back to camp. He finishes and says Hello, girls in a sweet, cheerful voice and then pulls the string on his Santa Claus. The nose lights up and beams across the bed-covers. Barnelle is sending us a signal, Santa's nose twinkling like Mars. It's four o'clock and I'm ready to do something else for a while. My legs want to walk, my eyes keep finding the window.

'I saw Barn-door,' Linda announces. She is back, ready for her shift, standing in the doorway with snow melting on her coat collar. 'He was climbing into his gold-plated Cadillac, hightailing it home.' Linda hates Barnelle with a rare enthusiasm, able to tick off his crimes on the fingers of both hands. She passes the plate where the rejected Christmas cookies used to be. 'God, you'll eat anything,' she remarks cheerfully. She's leaving tracks all over the clean floor, in meandering circles. She's been wrapping Christmas presents for her kids, I know, and her eyes look better. She crinkles them at me sympathetically. 'Was Barn-door open?' she asks. This is rhetorical. Over on the bed the gray eyes are closed. Linda wants to know how it's going, how she's doing, but the eyes might open again unexpectedly. We tiptoe out.

'I stopped at home and went through her closet,' Linda tells me. Nowadays she and I speak of the house where we grew up as home, we forget for long hours the places we live now, which have cupboards with our spices and canned peas, dressers with our clothes. When an aunt or our brother relieves us at the hospital we drive over there for some empty time, some quiet, and sit at her kitchen table with the carvings of childhood forks in its surface, stand drinking coffee right on the worn spot where she stood to stuff chickens, weave the crusts on pies. Home, we say to each other, drawing those dented walls around us like a wool blanket, two little girls in matching nightgowns, pinching and elbowing, acting hateful, getting yelled at. She was browsing, trying to find something to bury her in.

I stretch and yawn, shake it off, tell her about Barnelle's Santa.

'Gawd,' she drawls. 'Did he let on when or anything?' She squints when she asks this, afraid to know, afraid not to. Barnelle has predicted two days, which will land us right smack on Christmas. We have told each other ironically, Why not? and marvel at how the universe is dribbling us like a basketball and then shooting us into the air.

'He couldn't,' I tell her, 'because she was alert. And I couldn't follow him out because she already got on me about leaving with you this morning. She wanted to know where we went.' We both shiver at that and then in turn begin crying, the ugly kind, where you turn your clenched face to the wall until it passes. A nurse comes forward, silent, and touches our shoulders. This nurse told me yesterday she hadn't finished her shopping, still had crowds and the hectic traffic at the mall to contend with. Last week, when she could sit upright and talk a little, my mother had given me her wedding ring for Christmas.

There is slush and cold air all up and down the hall. When I go back in to get my coat her eyes are open, talking even though no one can hear. *You girls left me again.* Linda is behind me, getting her needlepoint out, untangling skeins of bright yarn. I pull on my gloves slowly, pushing each finger down meticulously, getting my keys ready for the cold, avoiding her eyes. Behind me Linda says, Hey, remembering something. She digs around in her coat pocket.

'Look, Ma,' she says softly, moving toward the bed. I step backward into the doorway, halfway gone. Linda holds a sprig of plastic mistletoe in the air above my mother's head. She whispers something I can't hear and bends down. I'm gone.

Suddenly I have this notion that she needs to wear flannel against her skin. I stop at a department store and join the current of tinkling people, Christmas shoppers. Music rains down and a clerk comes forward to ask if she can help. She has lost the heel to one pump and is trying to compensate by walking on tiptoe with that foot. She leads me to lingerie and begins thumbing patiently through nightgowns on a rack, showing me things. I tell her that it needs to be worn beneath a blouse. This confuses her and she thinks wearily for a second, one finger to her lip, one heel up in thin air. She produces an expensive long-underwear shirt made of raw silk, a tiny pink satin flower on the scooped neckline. I buy it even though I'm not sure anymore why I'm here, what I'm doing. I decide I might as well go back, only two days left.

I run into Barnelle in the main lobby, he's got his small son with him. I feel bad that he can't get any rest, can't be left alone for five minutes. He speaks frankly to me while his son attempts to tie his shoes together. He says quite honestly that he has gotten very attached to her and I say I have too, actually. He hugs me then, hard, his arms like a big pair of forceps. He lets go and one hand scans his head, searching out the wandering hairs, laying them flat. I've seen him on a bench before, reading X-rays and shaking his head, biting his nails. He bends down now and unties the laces before he takes a step, his son disappointed but philosophical. There are Christmas presents waiting at home.

The room is darkening, Linda is asleep in the chair, knees drawn up like a shield, hands circling her stockinged feet. I can't tell what's happening on the bed until I turn on the light. Her eyes are opened wide, frightened, helpless. *You left me, you girls, and here I am in the dark!* Darkness has a personality now, a power. I understand this very well, quilted satin pressing down in the velvet blackness, brushing the nose, the face. I turn on all the lights but Linda continues to sleep soundly until I bump her chair with my foot. She stretches her legs out and groans, gives me a dirty look, and I give her one back. I hold two fingers up to remind her of how much longer she needs to keep this up, to pay attention. She holds up one finger, guess which one, to remind me of who's the oldest, who's the boss. I would love more than anything to slap her.

I go to the cafeteria for a strawberry shake instead, which I can eat in front of her. On the way back up I land in an elevator with ten Christmas carolers. They seem like churchy types, the men are all shaved within an inch of their lives and the women look good-natured and opinionated. Two of them are quietly trying to harmonize on something I've never heard before, something Latin-sounding and mournful. A couple others practice scales and end up sounding out of tune. They get out on my floor and consult a list, everyone trying to get his or her head in there and direct the way. They end up following me, trying to stay a few paces behind. They are going where I'm going.

I close the door behind me and motion my sister over, whisper to her while the eyes on the bed try to make out what I'm saying. Quietly behind me, behind the oak of the door, their voices join together, hesitantly at first and then, gaining momentum, confidently. They are taking care to remember they are in a hospital, there are sick people here, but they love these songs, I can tell. One of the guys has a lilting baritone and one of the women a high vibrato. Linda hesitates and then opens the door, gestures for them to step in. We move to the head of the bed and stand like cops with our arms folded, trying to smile. They finish one song and all look expectantly at the lady with the vibrato. She says, Three, and they begin to sing 'White Christmas.' This is our mother's favorite, she used to put Bing Crosby on the turntable when we all sat down for Christmas Eve dinner. It was part of the feast, like the white candles, the clean linen tablecloth, the gleaming china. As she passed the first bowl and our father stood to carve they would sing it together, one at each end of the table, softly serenading their children. Our father, in fact, had a wonderful strong baritone just like someone in the crowd of carolers. Suddenly regret is swelling in the room like the voices of the choir. As she lies in the bed she weeps, for Bing, for the melting, shimmering candles, the filigree on the holiday tablecloth. She is an unwilling astronaut, bumping against the thick glass of the ship, her line tangling lazily in zero gravity, face mask fogged with fear.

My sister reaches across, over the bed, and we both embrace the mother, holding her on earth, pulling her onto the ship, breathing our oxygen into her line. Ten hours later she is dead.

Oh God, it is bitterly cold. The snow is crusted over into shocked mounds, hard as Styrofoam. My fingers are burning twigs inside my gloves, my toes ache like amputations. The heater fan in Linda's car screamed until we had to turn it off and give ourselves over to the freezing-freezing cold. Old man Larson is offering something warm in delicate cups. My poor fingers. It is morning now and he is drinking his own cup of something hot. I guess it's coffee, although I can almost see through to the bottom of the cup. He tips the cup to his little-guy lips but refrains from raising a pinky – he couldn't care less about cheering me up. He's in the morning-after mode right now; he's not looking directly at either of us and he has cleared his throat several hollow times.

Linda sits up straighter and visibly tries to pay better attention. She shakes her head and clears her own throat one, two, three times in a row. Now Larson is glaring at her, his eyes vivid blue on a yellow background.

I look away. I can feel her gazing at my ear. I look back. Then she winks and he sees and now it's even more tense.

We have selected the *Titanic* with ivory satin and the vault with the million-year guarantee of no seepage. He has accepted with grace both the outfit we've brought on a wire hanger and the pre-scription bottle full of safety pins, all sizes, that we think he'll need to make her clothes fit her now. Linda thought he probably had special clamps for that sort of thing but we decided it would be better if he used the safety pins from her junk drawer. He looked at them for a long second and then set them on the corner of the kidney-shaped desk. I've given up on the long-underwear idea. Actually, I'm wearing it myself because of how cold it is outside.

In a brown paper sack sitting next to my chair, between Linda and me, is her wig. We hate to give it over, both of us have held it in our laps at different times during the last few hours. It is too morbid, though, even for us. She takes it out of the bag quickly and shows it to Larson, puts it back in. She told me in the car she was going to try and scare him with it, but I guess she changed her mind.

He informs us that the flowers have started to arrive, invites us to come back and see how they have begun to arrange them on stands and in clusters. We rise and leave the pale gray suit on its hanger, the wig crouching in its sack, the bottle of pins from the top left kitchen drawer. My sister touches the mahogany desk like it's a tree in the forest. As we match his tiny steps down the wainscoted hall we have no idea, at this minute, that he is an artist, a gentleman. We have no idea as we move toward the scent of the flowers and the Christmas greens that he will continue on through his beautiful house, leaving us behind to read cards and talk. He will go through two more rooms, down a set of stairs to a place where she lies. While we linger, rubbing our hands and whispering to each other, the grandson who is minding us watches the wall and chews gum. At this moment we don't know that downstairs he is working magic, that he will present to us a woman who looks rested.

That's how I will get to see her last, in her pale gray wool suit and pink blouse, her glasses resting on her nose as though she's just dropped off for a minute; her cheeks will be okay again. The clothes will fit perfectly, as though she hadn't lost a pound.

Before the crowd arrives, when it's just me and my sister and an aunt, he will reach in his pocket and bring forth the bottle of pins, half gone.

Her hands are the only wrong thing. They look strange to me and I can't figure out why until Linda picks up my hand and shows me: Her wedding ring is on my finger; I forgot she gave it to me.

The hands begin to look more normal to me now, and the silence of the room gives way to the breathing of the sisters, the coldness of the kissed hands, and the empty air that says *You girls, you girls.*

Out There

IT ISN'T EVEN EIGHT A.M. and I'm hot. My rear end is welded to the seat just like it was yesterday. I'm fifty miles from the motel and about a thousand and a half from home, in a little white Mazda with 140,000 miles on it and no rust. I'm all alone in Alabama, with only a cooler and a tape deck for company. It's already in the high 80s. Yesterday, coming up from the keys through Florida, I had a day-long anxiety attack that I decided last night was really heat prostration. I was a cinder with a brain; I was actually whimpering. I kept thinking I saw alligators at the edge of the highway.

There were about four hundred exploded armadillos, too, but I got used to them. They were real, and real dead. The alligators weren't real or dead, but they may have been after me. I'm running away from running away from home.

I bolted four weeks ago, leaving my husband to tend the dogs and tool around town on his bicycle. He doesn't love me anymore, it's both trite and true. He does love himself, though. He's begun wearing cologne and staring into the mirror for long minutes, trying out smiles. He's become a politician. After thirteen years he came to realize that the more successful he got, the less he loved me. That's how he put it, late one night. He won that screaming match. He said, gently and sadly, 'I feel sort of embarrassed of you.'

I said, 'Of what? The way I look? The way I act?'

And he said, softly, 'Everything, sort of.'

And it was true. Well, I decided to take a trip to Florida. I sat on my haunches in Key West for four weeks, writing and seething and striking up conversations with strangers. I had my thirty-fifth birthday there, weeping into a basket of shrimp. I drank beer and had long involved dreams about cigarettes, I wrote nearly fifty pages on my novel. It's in my trunk at this very moment, dead and decomposing. Boy, do I need a cup of coffee.

There's not much happening this early in the morning. The highway looks interminable again. So far, no alligators. I have a box of seashells in my back seat and I reach back and get a fluted one, pale gray with a pearly interior, to put on the dashboard. I can do everything while I'm driving. At the end of this trip I will have driven 3,999 miles all alone, me and the windshield, me and the radio, me and the creepy alligators. Don't ask me why I didn't get that last mile in, driving around the block a few times or getting a tiny bit lost once. I didn't though, and there you have it. Four thousand sounds like a lot more than 3,999 does; I feel sort of embarrassed for myself.

My window is broken, the crank fell off in Tallahassee on the way down. In order to roll it up or down I have to put the crank back on and turn it slowly and carefully, using one hand to push up the glass. So, mostly I leave it down. I baked like a biscuit yesterday, my left arm is so brown it looks like a branch. Today I'm wearing a long- sleeved white shirt to protect myself. I compromised on wearing long sleeves by going naked underneath it. It's actually cooler this way, compared to yesterday when I drove in my swimming suit top with my hair stuck up like a fountain on top of my head. Plus, I'm having a nervous breakdown. I've got that wild-eyed look.

377

A little four-lane blacktop running through the Alabama countryside, that's what I'm on. It's pretty, too, better than Florida,
which was billboards and condos built on old dump sites. This
is like driving between rolling emerald carpets. You can't see
the two lanes going in the opposite direction because there's a
screen of trees. I'm starting to get in a good mood again. The best
was Georgia, coming down. Willow trees and red dirt and snakes
stretched out alongside the road. I kept thinking, That looks like a
rope, and then it would be a huge snake. A few miles later I would
think, That looks like a *snake*, and it would be some snarl of something dropped off a truck.

Little convenience store, stuck out in the middle of nothing,
a stain on the carpet. I'm gassing it up, getting some coffee. My
white shirt is gaping open and I have nothing on underneath it,
but who cares, I'll never see these people again. What do I care
what Alabama thinks about me. This is a new and unusual attitude for me. I'm practicing being snotty, in anticipation of being
dumped by my husband when I get back to Iowa.

I swagger from the gas pump to the store, I don't even care
if my boobs are roaming around inside my shirt, if my hair is
a freaky snarl, if I look defiant and uppity. There's nothing to
be embarrassed of. I bring my coffee cup along and fill it at the
counter. Various men, oldish and grungy, sit at tables eating eggs
with wadded-up toast. They stare at me carefully while they chew.
I ignore them and pay the woman at the counter. She's smoking
a cigarette so I envy her.

'Great day, huh?' I ask her. She counts out my change.

'It is, honey,' she says. She reaches for her cigarette and takes a
puff, blows it up above my head. 'Wish I wudn't in *here*.'

'Well, it's getting hotter by the minute,' I tell her. I've adopted
an accent in just four weeks, an intermittent drawl that makes me
think I'm not who everyone thinks I am.

'Y'all think this's hot?' she says idly. '*This* ain't hot.'

When I leave, the men are still staring at me in a sullen way. I get in, rearrange all my junk so I have everything handy that I need, choose a Neil Young tape and pop it in the deck, fasten the belt, and then move back out on the highway. Back to the emerald carpet and the road home. Iowa is creeping toward me like a panther.

All I do is sing when I drive. Sing and drink: coffee, Coke, water, juice, coffee. And think. I sing and drink and think. On the way down I would sing, drink, think, and weep uncontrollably, but I'm past that now. Now I suffer bouts of free-floating hostility, which is much better. I plan to use it when I get home.

A car swings up alongside me so I pause in my singing until it goes past. People who sing in their cars always cheer me up, but I'd rather not be caught doing it. On the road, we're all singing, picking our noses, embarrassing ourselves wildly; it gets tiresome. I pause and hum, but the car sticks alongside me so I glance over. It's a guy. He grins and makes a lewd gesture with his mouth. I don't even want to say what it is, it's that disgusting. Tongue darting in and out, quickly. A python testing its food.

I hate this kind of thing. Who do they think they are, these men? I've had my fill of it. I give him the finger, slowly and deliberately. He picked the wrong day to mess with me, I think to myself. I take a sip of coffee.

He's still there.

I glance over briefly and he's making the gesture with his tongue again. I can't believe this. He's from the convenience store, I realize. He has on a fishing hat with lures stuck in it. I saw him back there, but I can't remember if he was sitting with the other men or by himself. He's big, overweight, and dirty, wearing a thin unbuttoned shirt and the terrible fishing hat. His passenger-side window is down. He begins screaming at me.

He followed me from that convenience store. The road is endless, in front there is nothing, no cars, no anything, behind is the same. Just road and grass and trees. The other two lanes are still invisible behind their screen of trees. I'm all alone out here. With him. He's screaming and screaming at me, reaching out his right arm like he's throttling me. I speed up. He speeds up, too, next to me. We're only a few feet apart, my window won't roll up.

He's got slobber on his face and there's no one in either direction. I slam on my brakes and for an instant he's ahead of me, I can breathe, then he slams on his brakes and we're next to each other again. I can't even repeat what he's screaming at me. He's telling me, amid the hot wind and poor Neil Young, what he wants to do to me. He wants to kill me. He's screaming and screaming, I can't look over.

I stare straight ahead through the windshield, hands at ten and two. The front end of his car is moving into my lane. He's saying he'll cut me with a knife, how he'll do it, all that. I can't listen. The front end of his Impala is about four inches from my white Mazda, my little car. This is really my husband's car, my beloved's. My Volkswagen died a lingering death a few months ago. There is no husband, there is no Volkswagen, there is nothing. There isn't even a Jo Ann right now. Whatever I am is sitting here clenched, hands on the wheel, I've stopped being her, now I'm something else. I'm absolutely terrified. He won't stop screaming it, over and over, what he's going to do.

I refuse to give him an inch. I will not move one inch over. If I do he'll have me off the road in an instant. I will not move. I speed up, he speeds up, I slow down, he slows down, I can see him out of the corner of my eye, driving with one hand, reaching like he's grabbing me with the other. 'You whore,' he screams at me. 'I'll *kill* you, I'll *kill* you, I'll *kill* you . . .'

He'll kill me.

If I give him an inch, he'll shove me off the road and get his hands on me, then the end will begin in some unimaginable, unspeakable style that will be all his. I'll be an actor in his drama.

We're going too fast, I've got the pedal pressed up to 80 and it's wobbling, his old Impala can probably go 140 on a straightaway like this. There will be blood, he won't want me to die quickly.

I will not lose control, I will ride it out, I cannot let him push me over onto the gravel. His car noses less than two inches from mine; I'm getting rattled. My God, he can almost reach me through his window, he's moved over in his seat, driving just with the left hand, the right is grabbing the hot air. I move over to the edge of my seat, toward the center of the car, carefully, without swerving.

In the rearview mirror a speck appears. Don't look, watch your front end. I glance up again; it's a truck. He can't get me. It's a trucker. Without looking at him I jerk my thumb backward to show him. He screams and screams and screams. He's not leaving. Suddenly a road appears on the right, a dirty and rutted thing leading off into the trees. He hits the brakes, drops behind, and takes it. In my rearview mirror I see that the license plate on the front of his car is buried in dried mud. That road is where he was hoping to push me. He wanted to push my car off the highway and get me on that road. He was hoping to kill me. He was hoping to do what maniacs, furious men, do to women alongside roads, in woods. I can't stop pressing too hard on the gas pedal. I'm at 85 now, and my leg is shaking uncontrollably, coffee is spilled all over the passenger seat, the atlas is wet, Neil Young is still howling on the tape deck. By force of will, I slow down to 65, eject the tape, and wait for the truck to overtake me. When it does, when it comes up alongside me, I don't look over at all, I keep my eyes straight ahead. As it moves in front of me I speed up enough to stay two car lengths behind it. It says *England* on the back, ornate red letters outlined in black. England.

That guy chased me on purpose, he *hated* me, with more passion than anyone has ever felt for me. Ever. Out there are all those decomposing bodies, all those disappeared daughters, discovered by joggers and hunters, their bodies long abandoned, the memory of final desperate moments lingering on the leaves, the trees, the mindless stumps and mushrooms. Images taped to tollbooth windows, faces pressed into the dirt alongside a path somewhere.

I want out of Alabama, I want to be in England. The air is still a blast furnace. I want to roll my window up, but I'd have to stop and get the crank out and lift it by hand. I'm too scared. He's out there still, waiting behind the screen of trees. I have to follow England until I'm out of Alabama. Green car, old Impala, unreadable license plate, lots of rust. Seat covers made out of that spongy stuff, something standing on the dashboard, a coffee cup or a sad Jesus. The fishing hat with a sweat ring around it right above the brim. Lures with feathers and barbs. I've never been so close to so much hatred in my whole life. *He wanted to kill me.* Think of England, with its white cows and broken-toothed farmers and dark green pastures. Think of the Beatles. I'm hugging the truck so closely now I'm almost under it. Me, of all people, he wanted to kill. Me.

Everywhere I go I'm finding out new things about myself. Each way I turn, there it is. It's Jo Ann he wanted to kill.

By noon I want to kill him. I took a right somewhere and got onto the interstate, had the nerve to pee in a rest area, adrenaline running like an engine inside me, my keys threaded through my fingers in case anyone tried anything. I didn't do anything to earn it, I realize. His anger. I didn't do anything. Unless you count giving him the finger, which I don't. *He* earned that.

As it turned out, my husband couldn't bring himself to leave me when I got back to Iowa, so I waited awhile, and watched, then disentangled myself. History: We each got ten photo albums and six trays of slides. We took a lot of pictures in thirteen years. In the early years he looks stoned and contented, distant; in the later years he looks straight and slightly worried. In that last year he only appears by chance, near the edges, a blur of suffering, almost out of frame.

Just before we split, when we were driving somewhere, I told him about the guy in the green car. 'Wow,' he said. Then he turned up the radio, checked his image in the rearview mirror, and smiled sincerely at the passing landscape.

The Boys of My Youth

WE ADORE DAVE ANDERSON. He plays basketball in his driveway for hours each day, dribble, fake-out, shoot, dribble some more. He has smooth brown hair cut straight across his forehead, like the Dave Clark Five Dave. We watch him until we're so bored we're falling asleep, then we call him up. It's like a commercial during a TV show. His mom hollers at him, he sets the ball down, steadies it with his foot, opens the screen door, and gives it a kick back against the house so it shuts with a flat slam. The last thing we see is tennis-shoe rubber. We always hang up after he says hello, and then a minute later he's back out, drinking a bottle of Pepsi that he holds by the neck, walking around the court, dribbling in slow motion. He has no idea it's us.

We're not even boy-crazy, just bored, watching him from Elizabeth's bedroom window. She has antiqued French Provincial furniture and a princess telephone. The room is a converted front porch, with floor-to-ceiling windows and a barricaded door we use as an escape hatch on summer nights.

We're reclining on the canopied bed, Elizabeth holding back the curtains with her toes so we can watch him without sitting

384

up. We're getting ready to dial him again, although we just did this less than an hour ago.

'She won't call him in,' I predict. Dave's mother has a good sense of humor but it's wearing thin.

'This time I'm telling her who it is,' Elizabeth says, dialing with a pencil. There's a chance she'll panic and hand the phone to me so I roll off the bed and stand up for a while, out of range. I have my hair in two pigtails, thin ones, and I try to fluff them up a little bit.

'You just wrecked them,' Elizabeth informs me, and then suddenly looks alert. 'Hello? Is Dave there?' A moment of silence while she listens. 'Could you just tell him it's Brenda?' Brenda is the name of the most popular ninth-grader. We're seventh- graders. Brenda wouldn't be caught dead doing what we're doing.

'She's getting him!' Elizabeth freaks out, tries to force the phone on me. I won't take it and the receiver lies on the bed while we gesture to each other silently. Finally I hold it and we both listen, breathing steadily while he says his Hello? Hello? Just when we think he's getting ready to hang up he says, in a controlled ninth-grader voice, '*I know who this is.*'

I jam the receiver back on its cradle and we go nuts, leaping off the bed and running into each other. We pull the curtains shut and overlap them, Elizabeth gets a bobby pin from her dresser and pins them shut. We sit on the floor panting and staring at each other, wild-eyed and no longer bored.

My best friend Elizabeth is tall, with lanky blond hair that looks like straw, a long thin face, and black-rimmed glasses in front of green eyes. These are her pre-beautiful days. I'm short and skinny with a pale face and limp brown hair. People are always asking me if I feel well.

We met in French class, taught by Mrs. McLaughlin, the wife of Mr. McLaughlin, who teaches civics. She's the cheer-leading coach, if that gives you any idea, snake-thin with a lantern jaw and hair teased into a brown bubble. She's a monster, although her husband is likable enough.

We all had to take French names, chosen from a list that got passed around the first day. We sat in alphabetical order and my last name starts with a *B* so I got a good one: Colette. Elizabeth, unfortunately, ended up with Georgette, because she comes at the end of the alphabet. In retrospect, I kind of like the name Georgette, but at the time it was the kiss of death. It sounds like the parents were hoping for a boy.

First week of junior high, everyone is terrified of their lockers and the hall monitors. It's the year of the tent dress and loud prints, so all the girls look like small hot-air balloons. Fishnet stockings are not allowed, and dresses can be no shorter than two inches above the knee. People are getting busted left and right for that one, sent to the main office where they have to kneel next to a yardstick. If your dress is too short you get sent home, no discussion.

'What if you just happen to *grow*?' Betsy Thomason asks hotly as she's sent from the room by Mrs. McLaughlin.

'I'd suggest you not,' Mrs. McLaughlin replies lightly. She rolls her eyes at us in a conspiratorial way, says something in French, and we all titter uncertainly. She's wearing a pale green mohair suit, cinnamon hose, and dark green lizard skin high heels. She weighs about ninety-eight pounds, smells like cigarette smoke, her lipstick goes up above her top lip an eighth of an inch. The cheerleaders sit on her desk before class starts and trade jokes with her; they call her Mrs. Mick. Everyone else is utterly terrified of her. Suddenly she stops horsing around and looks directly at me, Colette.

'*Où est la bibliothèque?*' she asks. I stare at her blankly, with a roaring in my ears. I'm so thin my nylons collect in pools at the knees and ankles, I'm wearing a pink plaid dress made out of spongy material, my hair is shoulder-length and supposedly curled into a flip. It's so fine that my ears stick out on either side of my head. Everyone is turned toward me.

I tilt my head to the side and pretend I can almost think of it. The roaring is louder, like seashells are clamped to my head, my heart is clattering. *Où est la bibliothèque* . . . I've heard that somewhere before. Chances are it was last night, listening to my French dialogue record.

'Colette?' she says. '*Où est la bibliothèque, s'il vous plaît?*'

Now, *s'il vous plaît* I've heard of. It means either please or thank you. I somehow manage to disengage myself, and join the other students and Mrs. McLaughlin as they stare at poor Colette, who is thinking with her head tipped to the side, her hair resting on her shoulders in horizontal sausages.

Mrs. McLaughlin finally makes a French-sounding noise of disgust and moves on. As her eyes scan the crowd, I enter my body again, and tug on my dress. She fixes her pewter gaze on the girl sitting in the last seat in the last row. This girl has straw-colored hair falling forward and bangs that come straight down and then swerve to the right. She is looking at the wall next to her intently.

'Georgette?' Mrs. McLaughlin says. '*Où est la bibliothèque?*' Georgette continues to watch the wall, but her left cheek, the visible one, slowly turns red beneath its curtain of hair. Seconds tick past and then she whispers something.

'*Pardon*, Georgette?' Mrs. McLaughlin moves down the aisle to get a better view.

'*Près d'ici,*' Georgette says softly. Then a little louder, '*Près d'ici.*'

'If you were in France, no one would be able to understand you,' Mrs. McLaughlin says shortly. 'Take your hand away from your mouth and roll your r.' She waits.

'Okay,' Georgette says desperately; she holds her hands away from her mouth but they hover in the air about six inches above her desk. 'Okay, *pway dee-cee*.'

Mrs. McLaughlin lets out a genuine laugh, for an instant you can see how Mr. McLaughlin might have ended up marrying her. Then her eyes crinkle at the corners and she exclaims meanly, 'You sound like Porky the Pig!' She laughs again, and then says, '*Pway d'ici*,' in a sputtering fat-cheeked way.

Georgette allows her hands to come back up to her face. She pushes her glasses up and stares once again intently at the wall. The minute hand crawls around the face of the clock, others are called on, dialogue is read out of the book, words are written on the board. At some point I look over at Georgette just as she looks at me. I shake my head, almost imperceptibly, in disbelief; she widens her eyes for an instant, mimicking a look of abject terror.

'That was ninth grade, not seventh,' Elizabeth says. 'We were already friends when that happened.' She's at her office in downtown Chicago, talking to me on the WATS line. 'You wouldn't believe what my desk looks like right now.'

I would because I've witnessed it. She's an editor, and there are manuscripts stacked everywhere and yellow notes with *Urgent* scrawled across them stuck to the carpet. Her office is a wall that's a window surrounded by three orange head-high partitions. The view is of Lake Michigan, and at least in the summer it's spectacular, white triangles of boat sails and a stretching blue horizon. Thumbtacked to the partition next to her desk is a photograph of her and me at age twelve, wearing matching lime green shorts (stretchy) and dark green men's T-shirts (baggy). We both have our hair in braids, mine as slim as snakes, hers thick and bushy. We've got variegated green yarn tied in bows at the ends. We're draped across her canopy bed, listening to records and enjoying our outfits.

'They're actually making me work,' she says disconsolately. I can hear her rifling through papers. I'm at work, too, and I'm an editor, too. My office is in a small town in Iowa, and it's neat and tidy in a very annoying way, according to my co-workers. There's a picture on my bulletin board of the two of us when we were in love with Dave Anderson. We are lying backward against the sloping front terrace of her yard, we have on light blue shorts (stretchy) and dark blue men's T-shirts (baggy); we're using our bodies to form the letter D. I pass this tidbit along to Elizabeth.

'He must've thought we were nuts,' she replies. 'What did we have on?'

I tell her. 'Did we shoplift those shorts?' she asks.

We never shoplifted anything; we were too scared. 'I think I did, didn't I?' she says uncertainly. 'Like underpants or something, and you were chicken?' That rings a bell with me, but I can't quite place it. So, if we didn't meet in French class, then how did we meet?

She thinks for a minute. 'I have no idea,' she says. 'We just *met*, that's how we met.' More paper rifling. 'I'll try to remember and then call you after lunch. I have to proofread this thing this afternoon.' She can proof a manuscript and talk on the phone at the same time; so can I. In school, we had a policy of never studying unless it was absolutely necessary, and still got high-to-mediocre grades. This convinced us that we were smarter than the average citizen, and actually, we're still thinking that way. It might be one of the reasons our husbands divorced us.

We're in our late thirties, childless, and were flung at the same time out of our marriages and back into teenagehood. We spend an hour on the telephone each week talking about boys and clothes. We alternate between hating our exes in a robust, vociferous style, and lying paralyzed on our living room floors sobbing.

'Of *course* you're lying on the floor,' I tell her consolingly. It's a Tuesday morning and I'm ready to leave for work. She just called me from her house in Chicago; she's in her underwear, stretched out full length alongside her coffee table. She's just realized that the husband who recently left her really *did* recently leave her. 'I didn't believe it was actually happening,' she says into the receiver. She's completely stuffed up and having an asthma attack at the same time. I can hear her spraying her inhaler every few minutes. Talking about her divorce is making me think of my own, and I feel like I suddenly need my inhaler, too. I set the phone down quietly while she's weeping and run into the bathroom to retrieve it.

'I'm having an asthma attack,' I tell her.

'Welcome to the *club*,' she replies. 'The *divorce* club.' She's coming out of it a little.

'Can you get up yet?' I ask her. She thinks maybe she can, so I direct her into her bedroom where she starts going through the clothes in her closet. She's on the cordless phone and we have to talk around a big annoying hiss in the background. She picks out something to wear and gets dressed, putting the phone down once to pull a shirt over her head. I keep taking short, recreational hits from my inhaler as I talk her through it. Faint voices distinguish themselves inside the phone hiss, the content is blurred but emotion comes through. The voices rise and fall.

'Who *are* those people?' she asks once, cheerfully. The crisis has passed.

Fall of our eighth-grade year, her sister-in-law has come to stay with them for a while. She's from Thailand, her name is Jinn, and she has a flat, beautiful face and black hair that reaches to her waist in long oily ropes. She is nine months pregnant and perpetually drowsy, alternating her time between sleeping on the living room couch, watching television, and cooking outlandish food that no one else will touch. She eats sitting at the kitchen table with her eyes closed, wielding chopsticks expertly and humming a song called 'Kowloon Hong Kong' that she plays over and over on the hi-fi. The woman on the record jacket looks like Jinn, with a large paper flower behind one ear and black hair wound up and held in place with pointy sticks. Her voice is high and lilting, and basically off-key. We know all the words, even though they aren't in our language. I'm not sure what Jinn is doing here, I've never asked. Elizabeth's stepbrother is in the service, and stares out at everyone from a lacy metal frame on top of the television. He's round-faced and wears a white hat and a navy blue coat with ribbons on the lapel. His cheeks are pink and airbrushed and the whites of his eyes have been enhanced. If the baby turns out to be a boy it will be named Hugh, after him; if it's a girl it will be named Angelique, after a character on *Dark Shadows*, which we all watch religiously each afternoon at three. It comes on right before *The Addams Family*, a show that Jinn dismisses with a grunt and a wave of the hand before turning over on the couch and returning to an unconscious state. She speaks English just fine, but it hardly ever occurs to us to talk to her. We treat her like one of the cats, minus the torture. We ignore her unless she can do us a favor.

Sunday afternoon, family cookout at Blackhawk State Park, Elizabeth and I spend our time looking for boys and trying to act like we're not with her parents. Jinn sits at the picnic table reading a magazine from Thailand full of hieroglyphics and cigarette advertisements. Elizabeth's stepfather turns pieces of chicken on the grill. He has a friendly disposition, warm brown eyes, and a slight limp left over from a stroke. Elizabeth's mother is a little less personable, as are all our friends' mothers. Everyone I know has a mother who operates on the fringes of what's appropriate. Elizabeth's mother, Doris, was especially excitable, and relied on us to calm her down.

'Shut up, Mother,' Elizabeth would tell her. Most of the time Doris would shut up, but occasionally it struck her the wrong way and all manner of hell would break loose. One time she chased Elizabeth into the bathtub and then threw a pop bottle at her.

It broke and glass went everywhere except on Elizabeth, who nevertheless screamed bloody murder and threatened to call the police. I snuck home during that one, and Jinn put a pillow over her head. Afterward Doris took to her bed with a bad back and had to be waited on for a week. Elizabeth was supposedly grounded, which, in practice, meant she wasn't.

So, the picnic. Elizabeth and I entertain ourselves by putting Styrofoam cups on the ends of sticks and holding them like marshmallows over the burning coals. They melt and run fantastically, forming odd arty-looking shapes that impress us. We give each one a name and make plans to spray-paint them when we get home. A rowboat full of boys goes by out in the water and we find a reason to wander down there, where we look upriver and downriver but see no other likely suspects. Suddenly we are being summoned, and quickly, from the picnic area. We head back up at an obedient trot and discover that Jinn has gone into labor sometime after the meal. She didn't say anything, but stopped reading her magazine and began holding her stomach. Pretty soon she was groaning, a big splash occurred, and then everyone was in a hurry.

They made us put our art-cups in the trunk along with all the other crammed-in picnic stuff. Jinn sat in the front seat between Elizabeth's parents, and Elizabeth and I had the back seat to ourselves. Her father actually laid rubber leaving the parking lot but then settled down and drove responsibly through the streets of our city. Most of the way Jinn was silent but every once in a while she would gasp out a long word in Thai that sounded like swearing because it started with an *f*.

None of us were trying to comfort her. Elizabeth and I were slightly out of control, hanging our heads out the car windows and silently screaming *We're having a baby!* to each other. Her dad said, in a cheerful voice, 'Make way, we're coming through,' every time a stoplight appeared up ahead, while her mom kept murmuring, 'How are we doing,' and casting sidelong glances at Jinn, who had her eyes closed and was saying the Thai swear word quietly over and over. Suddenly she made an *oof* noise, like someone had punched her, and then produced a muffled scream. Doris glanced at us in the back seat, where we had quieted down and were coming to the mutual, silent conclusion that we'd never have children.

Jinn screamed again, a short burst, and Elizabeth said, '*Mom*,' two syllables, in an accusing voice.

'*Were doing the best we can do*,' Doris said in a defensive voice. You could tell she thought this was all her fault, and that Elizabeth agreed. I stared out my car window and watched houses going by at a steady clip, refusing to let the sound coming from Jinn get from my ears to my brain. Soon enough we were at the door of the emergency room, and the two females in the front seat got out and went in, Jinn with one hand on her back and one clamped to her mouth, Doris looking frazzled and unprepared.

I got dropped off at my house and Elizabeth and her stepdad went home to theirs.

'Well, I just saw somebody having a *baby*,' I reported to my mother. 'Right at the *picnic*.' She finds this news highly interesting but I don't have much more to say. My older sister follows me upstairs and I tell her everything. 'The entire back of her dress was *soaked*,' I say. I shudder. 'She was in agony, *screaming*, but don't tell Mom.' Our mother isn't keen on extremes of any sort, or on foreigners. For that matter, she doesn't care much for Elizabeth's family, because she thinks they're different from us. The only difference I can see is that the dad isn't an alcoholic, but I don't mention that to her. She's known for getting in bad moods and grounding people for no reason. In the particular case of my older sister who has a mouth on her, my mother is prone to face slaps at odd moments. My sister takes it standing up, sometimes saying '*That* didn't hurt' before stomping upstairs and throwing my clothes all over the place.

Later in the evening Elizabeth telephones. 'I can't talk,' she says, 'because we might get a call from the hospital.' Nevertheless, we spend forty minutes on a review of the afternoon, the boys in the rowboat getting as much airtime as the pregnant lady in the car.

The next morning Elizabeth shows up at the usual time to walk to school with me. I see her coming up the back walk with her head down, yellow hair covering her face. She looks mad.

I ask her if the baby got born. She pushes past me and goes into the living room, sits on the couch and presses her face into the back of it. She starts crying loudly and can't stop.

'It *died*,' she says furiously, 'and it was a *girl*.' At this she begins afresh, with her hands over her cheeks and her mouth a grimace.

My mother is in the kitchen eating oatmeal before work, my dad is shaving using the mirror hanging on the kitchen door. He stops whistling and takes himself upstairs, my mother comes in the living room and looks at Elizabeth.

'Oh Liz, that's awful,' she says. She feels truly bad, I can tell, but she also figures it was to be expected, I can tell that too. I feel somber and useless, I've never seen Elizabeth cry like that, even after the pop-bottle-in-the-tub business. This is something only the moms can handle; mine calls hers, Elizabeth gets sent back home, and I go off to school alone, in a stupid dress that doesn't look right.

Later we talk about it between ourselves, but we don't say a word to Jinn. She goes on, shell-shocked, her beautiful face flat as a photograph and expressionless. She continues to watch *Dark Shadows* and listen to 'Kowloon Hong Kong,' she continues to doze at the kitchen table and on the couch, she glides through the rooms of the apartment in her flowered housecoat as she always did, as visible and invisible as one of the cats.

*

Eighth grade, spring, between classes. The hallway is damp and swampy, loud with clanging lockers and the clamor of overstimulation; popular kids are being hailed, unpopular ones hooted at. A drinking fountain, a line in front of it, me in an impossibly short skirt and white knee socks. The dress code has been lifted for three months now, the boys wear pants as tight as long-line girdles and the girls wear hip-hugger skirts that are less than a foot long. Getting a drink at the fountain involves a cross between kneeling and squatting. The boy in front of me suddenly steps to the side, turns on the fountain, and with a sweep of his left hand says, 'After you, my dear.' I die, recover, squat/kneel, drink, put my head down, and scuttle away, wiping my chin.

I have just discovered love. The *real* thing, none of this Dave Anderson crap.

In the stairwell, I notice for the first time that outside the window the ground is soaked and emerald-colored, jonquils lie supine in the rain, tulips are lolling their fat heads. I take the stairs three at a time, turning my miniskirt into a wide belt, race down the hall to Elizabeth's home-ec class and grab her as she's going in.

'Get sick,' I tell her.

'We're making Rice Krispies treats,' she says. 'Wait 'til math.'

'I *can't* wait, I'm dying,' I say pleadingly, and then, because I know it's true: '*You'll* die too.'

Fifteen minutes later we are reclining side by side on two narrow cots in the nurse's office. Elizabeth has a tremendous headache that requires a washcloth draped across her forehead, I have a tremendous stomachache that requires a metal bowl balanced on my chest.

I'm in love, it's serious, he's beyond what we've encountered before. He is like a *Beatle*, he's that cute. No kidding, honest to God, et cetera.

'He said "my dear"?' she asks in a hoarse whisper. 'He sounds like a queeb.'

He's not a queeb, you had to be there. He made it sound *funny*. Not queebie at *all*, in fact, just the opposite. He's the opposite.

The nurse pokes her head in and we both groan. 'No talking,' she says.

'We weren't,' we say in unison.

Elizabeth is willing to fall in love with him, too, but she needs to see him first, as a formality. We agree to meet after class at the fountain, in case he comes back for another drink. We go out and tell the nurse we're better. She sends Elizabeth back to home-ec but makes me go lie down again.

'You're still pale,' she says shortly.

He doesn't show up at the drinking fountain again, but after school we go to my house to pore over last year's yearbook. I have a feeling he's older than us, and it's true. We find him among last year's eighth-graders.

'Jeff Bach,' I announce, and hand the yearbook over. We're in my living room eating Fritos and drinking pop. My sister hasn't gotten home from high school yet so we're safe, nobody's bugging us.

'He's got blond hair,' she remarks, staring at the picture closely. She takes another handful of Fritos. 'I thought you said he looked like a Beatle.' She puts them in her mouth.

'I said he's as cute *as* a Beatle,' I reply. 'Not that he *was* a Beatle.'

She stares at his face intently as she chews, and then comes to a conclusion. 'Let's face it,' she proclaims, 'he's *cuter* than a Beatle.'

We're both in love with Jeff Bach, ninth-grader extraordinaire.

The back door slams and my sister appears in the doorway to the living room. She is wearing a granny dress, her thick brown hair tucked into a crocheted snood at the nape of her neck. She arches her brows. 'How's kindergarten?' she asks. She takes the bag of Fritos from Elizabeth's lap and heads upstairs with it. 'Clean this house up,' she says as she rounds the curve at the landing.

We leave and walk over to Elizabeth's house, where we tell Jinn about our new boyfriend. We get Elizabeth's yearbook and make her look at the picture. 'Blond,' she says politely, and turns her eyes back to the television. Pretty soon Elizabeth's stepdad comes home from work. We show him the picture. 'How would you like it if I married *this* guy?' Elizabeth asks him rhetorically. He says he'd like it just fine and asks why the newspaper hasn't come yet.

'Who knows, that's why,' Elizabeth replies. I get killed if I'm not there when my mother gets home from work, so I leave and call up Elizabeth ten minutes later from two blocks over.

'What're you doing?' I ask.

There are four girls in our group, plus two best friends who hang around with another group approximately half the time. Besides Elizabeth and me there are Madelyn and Renee, and the two best friends, Carol and Janet. Renee is the oldest of six kids and we stay overnight at her house a lot because both her parents work nights at the post office and leave Renee in charge. They live in a big old house with three floors, and it never seems like there is any food except long loaves of sandwich bread, giant boxes of generic cereal, and powdered milk. If you're looking for mustard, or a bottle of pop, forget it. Renee is the only kid in the family with a room of her own and she keeps potato chips and Pop-tarts in her closet, which locks with a skeleton key. Each bedroom has a fire escape ladder in a metal box underneath the window.

Madelyn is destined to move away unexpectedly when we're in ninth grade, and all I can remember about her is that she was funny and mean, and that she threw a half pound of frozen hamburger at her mother once when she was told she couldn't go to a movie.

'Plus her dad slept in a coffin,' Elizabeth reminds me. She has called me from her bathtub, the water is still running and she's talking loudly to compensate. 'I saw him taking a nap in it once; it was a black box without a lid, and the headboard said *R.I.P.*'

'What a sicko,' I say.

'No kidding,' she agrees. The sound of water running stops abruptly, a splash is heard. 'Wasn't there something suspicious about him?'

'That was Renee's dad.' Renee's dad made everyone uncomfortable, he was very young, just like her mom, and he talked to us like we were adults. He flirted with us, except we didn't identify it as that, because he was a dad. We took on nervous smiles and sidled backward whenever he was around.

'There was more to *that* story than met the eye,' she said, then, 'hang on,' and the sound of a giant lapping wave comes through the phone. 'Jo Ann?' she says loudly. '*Jo Ann?* I dunked my head; now I've got water in my ears.'

I feel cranky suddenly, and want to get off the phone. 'Don't *call* me when you're in the bathtub,' I say. 'I don't want to listen to your personal hygiene. And I'm late for something.'

'Buh-ruther,' she says sarcastically. 'What did I do? I dunked my head, big deal; how'm I supposed to wash my hair?'

'How about on your own time, that ever occur to you?'

'*How about if I smack your head off?*' and she slams her phone down with a huge noise.

We are thirty-eight years old. I wait fifteen minutes and call her back.

'Hi,' she says. 'Guess what I got in the mail?'

Divorce papers, with a smiley face on a Post-it note from her husband. 'That was bugging me, you in the bathtub,' I tell her. 'Jim's the one who should get his head smacked off. Or Tina.' Tina is Jim's receptionist, and the woman he left Elizabeth for.

'I'm not smacking anybody's head off,' she replies dream-ily. 'Because I don't even care.' When Jim first left her for Tina, Elizabeth made the mistake of asking why, and he told her. In the course of the conversation he mentioned a specific sex act that men tend to like a lot.

'You're kidding,' I said.

'Not only am I not kidding,' she replied. 'But the thing is, it's true. I mean, you hate to simplify these things, but he's the one who said it.' She sighed hugely. 'That's what they sit around doing.'

Her voice had the same dreamy quality it has now, but a week later, when it had sunk in, she'd been ready to take out after him with a baseball bat. She'd tried to call him at work to tell him he was a dead man, but Tina wouldn't put her through. 'Uh, I don't *think* so, Liz,' she had said smugly, right before disconnecting her.

So, any idea why Madelyn's dad slept in a coffin?

'He thought it was funny, of course,' she said. 'Men.'

Jeff Bach, blond, the fifth Beatle, a student at our school. Lived below the hill and hung around with guys who were Mexican, which made him seem even more blond. Danny Garcia, one of his friends, yanks on my hair in science.

'Hey,' he whispers. 'You and Liz like Jeff.'

I turn around and roll my eyes, trying for sarcasm. 'I'm *sure*,' I whisper back.

Forty minutes later, Elizabeth and I are side by side in the nurse's office. The next cot is occupied by someone who appears to be truly sick, not faking it. The nurse is excited by this and keeps poking her head in and staring at him.

News has been leaked, if Danny Garcia knows then every-one knows. If everyone knows, then Jeff must know. We think we could actually puke; we groan and stare at the paint on the ceiling. The nurse hears us and thinks she might have an epidemic on her hands.

'You should've said *Jeff who*,' Elizabeth hisses.

I never thought of that. I start pretending like I'm beating myself up. We do our silent screaming routine. The guy on the other cot opens one eye. 'I'm not really sick,' he says.

'Us neither,' we whisper back.

Pretty soon they both go back to class and I get kept for another hour and released at lunch.

'Eat some meat if you can,' the nurse advises.

My own husband didn't have a receptionist, but he had a best friend, and the best friend had a wife. On a bitterly cold Sunday morning he went out to get doughnuts and didn't return for two hours. I took a bath, using my toes to turn the hot water on and off. Pretty soon my knees were brilliant pink, my forehead was sweating, and it came to me that I'd been in there a while. I wondered how come my doughnuts weren't back yet and then suddenly the answer hit me, the way a math problem can solve itself when you're not paying attention. *Oh*, I thought, *he's having an affair*. I stood up immediately, like the tub had ejected me, and began drying off.

When he came home I was dressed, standing in the middle of the living room with an ashtray in my hand, smoking a stale French cigarette I'd found in my desk. I hadn't smoked for four years but was quickly getting the hang of it again; only halfway through my first cigarette, and I already wanted another one. He was clattering around in the kitchen, putting breakfast on a blue plate, pouring a cup of coffee. I prepared a smoke ring and launched it in his direction as he walked into the living room.

He stopped. 'What?' he said. His face turned into clay; on the blue plate were giant melting doughnuts, some with multicolored dots on top, some with white cream oozing from their back ends. 'What?' he said again.

I told him and he didn't disagree. The only thing that happened was his face twitched, like a horse's hide, when I said the word. *Affair.* You are. And I am very. Upset. Actually I also wailed, like a baby in its crib. That scared him and he set down the doughnuts and coffee, took a step toward me, a step back, then sat down on the edge of the couch. Unbelievably, he began to cry, which shut me up instantly.

Do I want to know who?

This from my husband Eric, who had held my hand when they lowered my mother into the ground, who put me in a bathtub once and poured cold water on me to break a fever, who whispered the names of the constellations again and again because I could never remember them. I guess I need to know who.

He tells me the name and the howling baby comes out again before I collect myself. *Kim?* She's a passive-aggressive *rat*, everyone knows that, *nobody* likes her. You like *her*?

Not really, he acknowledges. In some ways she's pathetic, the way she lets Bruce talk to her. He's no longer crying, he suddenly looks pious and overburdened. In as flat a voice as I can manage I suggest he go sit around somebody else's house for a while.

When the door closes behind him I stand in the center of the room and light another prehistoric cigarette. Off in the distance the phone rings. It's Bruce, wondering if Eric's around. I set the receiver back in the cradle without saying a word, and as I do so, the house settles over my shoulders like a stucco cape.

A spring night, one a.m., we have just escaped through the barricaded door of Elizabeth's bedroom into the inky darkness. We let our eyes adjust, breathing in the dusty smell of geraniums. A bridal wreath bush stands laden with tiny white bouquets, the sky is velvety beyond the branches of a sycamore, the stars are tiny pinpricks of light. We have six half-rolls of toilet paper borrowed from various gas stations and public toilets. We are on a mission.

'Let's go,' I whisper and we move out silently, going from house to house, staying in the black shadows of the flowering bushes. Four blocks from her house we find ourselves trapped up against a garage while a man and a woman have an argument in the driveway. They've just pulled in and gotten out of the car, a station wagon with wood on the sides. The concrete driveway is ghostly blue in the moonlight, their faces are doughy.

'Why her?' the woman says over and over again. 'Why her?'

The man tries to pet her head like she's a dog. 'Honey, don't,' he says each time she asks why her. *Honey, don't, honey, don't, honey, don't.* And then they kiss, staggering sideways. We seem to be standing in some unflowering rose bushes, absolutely still in the darkness, like a black and white photograph of two girls who have done this before. Something hits my arm and buzzes, I look down and see a June bug flapping around. Another one hits my cheek. I take Elizabeth's elbow and try to pull her away. She resists and glares at me, points one finger toward the people standing in a blue pool of moonlight twenty feet away. I grab her arm and yank her onto the driveway and run through the next yard and the next, her panting fast and loud behind me. We're laughing silently and hysterically. A ravine appears on the right and we run for it, diving down the hill, where we lay, gasping.

'You *queeb*,' Elizabeth whispers. She punches me in the arm. 'Why did you *do* that?'

I pause. 'There were June bugs smacking into me,' I tell her gently.

She immediately stops laughing and squeezes her eyes shut. A moan escapes from her lips. 'I can't,' she says without opening her eyes. 'I can't keep going if there are June bugs.'

'There aren't,' I say. 'It's not even June – those two are the only ones.'

She still has her eyes closed. 'No sir,' she says in a small voice.

I try to think for a minute. Finally I say, 'Don't wreck everything because of two June bugs.'

She opens one eye and looks at me with it. 'What about if there were *worms*, you wouldn't even walk in case one might *touch* you.' I consider this a low blow and remain silent. 'And you know it,' she finishes.

A minute goes by, both of us staring through the ravine trees at the black sky. 'You *know* it,' she says once more. We get up slowly, like old people, readjust the toilet paper rolls that are tied around our waists on pieces of rope, and set out, subdued, to complete our mission.

A woman friend stops over to visit me one afternoon. She is lonely, melancholy, and at loose ends. Do you ever feel like this? she asks me. That's how the entire world feels, I say. Sit down, have some chips, have some dip. She's not one of my favorite people, but I'd rather talk to her than write, which is what I was doing when she dropped by. She's having husband troubles apparently, and winds up telling me she's thinking of having an affair.

'Have you ever done that?' she asks. Her head is tilted to the side quizzically, a trace of sour cream is adhered to her lower lip. I feel immensely warm and slightly guilty all of a sudden, and the walls of the room step in an inch or so, crowding me.

'Oh, Kim, it's not good to do that,' I tell her. And I mention some lovely traits her husband Bruce has, not the least of which is that he's my own husband's best friend. She takes that for what it's worth and drifts back through the front door, gets in her little yellow car, and peels out.

*

403

Danny Garcia's house is on a cul-de-sac it takes us forever to find. By this time we are walking in the no-June-bug zone in the middle of the street, and talking in normal voices. As it turns out, his house has no trees, so we're momentarily at a loss. There are small bikes and wrecked toys in the front yard, and a sign that says *Koolade 4 Sale*. We caucus for a minute, crouched next to a blue sedan parked at the curb.

'Now what are we supposed to do?' I say. Elizabeth stares up at the split-level ranch house and thinks. She outlines a plan that involves only what we have available – if there are no trees, there are no trees. Simple, really.

Twenty minutes later we have draped giant strands of toilet paper over the roof of the house, seven of them, from one end to the other. We had to hurl them, unraveling whitely against the night sky, one of us in the backyard and one in the front. Our contingency plan was if a light came on or if anyone came out, we would run in two separate directions and meet at Renee's house, five blocks away. The strands are anchored on either side of the house with trikes and dump trucks. We meet in the shadow of the blue car to survey the situation.

'It needs more,' I whisper.

'I'm too tired,' she whispers back.

'We walked all the way over here and it only looks like about two *strands*,' I insist. 'Let's just get rid of the rolls.' So we patiently unwind them, leaving pools of white against the pavement. We travel back up into the yard and, carefully holding the ends, throw the rolls over the roof, one after the other. The last two don't make it, our arms are too tired, and they land with a thud and roll back down the roof and into the bushes in front of the porch. In an instant a light goes on, the door bursts open, and Danny and Stuart Garcia are running barefoot, sixty-five miles an hour. Elizabeth and I are half a block away by this time, and we veer off suddenly, one to the left, one to the right, like a dividing amoeba.

The yards are hard to navigate, there are things lying around everywhere, lawn mowers, rakes, bicycles, and, in one case, a tied-up dog who runs out to the end of his chain and stands up on his back legs, wagging his tail and pedaling his front paws. I can't tell which Garcia followed me, but I can hear him crashing around, one yard over. I stop and crouch under the awning of the dog's plywood house. The dog climbs in beside me happily and we both sit in the straw, me listening for the sounds of a Garcia, him biting a flea. There is a pale light burning in the kitchen of the house, illuminating an ornate clock and the corner of a fridge, harvest gold. Pots of African violets, a mound of spilled potting soil and a pair of gloves are sitting on a table by the back door. The dog, a beagle mix with long silky ears, leans up against me and yawns. I put one arm around him and we're buddies together, in the shade of his little abode. You can tell he doesn't get many visitors in here, but he's a good host. A gnawed-on bone is tucked in the corner. I hold it out and he tilts his head quizzically, then takes it only when he's sure I don't want it, and begins absent-mindedly chewing.

From inside the plywood shelter we watch the night tick along. After fifteen minutes or so I hear voices, and I pull my legs farther inside and scrunch up into the black corner. Through the yard amble Danny and Stuart, wincing on their bare feet, talking in whispers and making little aggressive gestures toward imaginary enemies. The dog fades out into the night and stands on his hind legs again at the end of his chain. Stuart stops for a second and lets the dog rest his front paws against him. All I can see are their legs and hands, they can't see anything of me. Stuart lifts the dog's ear and touches the soft part inside. The dog stops wagging and holds himself very still, in paralyzed pleasure. They walk on, whispering, and the dog gets a drink of water from a dishpan and then wanders back into his shelter. I'm sorry, but I have to go. He's pretty philosophical about it,

405

following me to the end of his chain and then stretching out on the damp ground, back legs stuck out terrier-style, tail moving slowly back and forth.

I walk through backyards until I get to Renee's block and then I walk in the street. One time Elizabeth, Madelyn, and I walked around this block with our shirts off and tied around our waists. It was about three in the morning and the houses were dead and silent, the streetlights shone yellow spots on the pavement. We walked and walked, with our arms over our heads, letting the night air get on our skin. I'm not in the mood for any of that nonsense tonight. There she is, sitting on Renee's front porch.

'I thought they got you,' Elizabeth whispers hoarsely. Her hair is going eight different ways and her cheeks are pink, her voice is croaky.

'I went in a doghouse with a dog,' I say. 'And they came right past me, and are they pissed.' I tell her some of the words Danny and Stuart were whispering.

'Eek,' she says.

Since there are no parents on the premises, we decide to wake Renee up and tell her what happened. Through the front window we can see the two littlest kids asleep on the floor in front of the snowy TV screen. Stacy has on a diaper and socks and has her head resting on a bed pillow without a case. Amy has on a T-shirt and no pants whatsoever, and has her head resting on a skanky stuffed dinosaur. Renee is asleep on the couch under an afghan, a book open across her chest. We tap on the window. Stacy stirs and puts a thumb in her mouth. Amy rolls over so her face is against the dinosaur's face.

'Seems like a shame to wake them up,' I say, and then tap louder. Renee startles awake and the book falls off her chest.

'Don't wake the babies,' she whispers as she lets us in. She has drool on her from sleeping on the couch, and we don't want to point it out but we do anyway. 'Oh,' she says, wiping it off. We follow her out to the kitchen where she sits at the table, yawning. I sit on the counter and Elizabeth looks in the refrigerator.

'We would have been dead if they'd caught us,' I tell Elizabeth. She concurs. We tell Renee what happened. She confirms what we already suspected: Stuart Garcia is dangerous. And she's in a position to know – she went steady with him in grade school.

'He wanted to drop me and go with Maria Valdez,' she says sleepily. 'So he threw a steak knife at me and it hit a tree. He got about forty swats with the wooden paddle from the principal.' I repeat for her in great detail the words I heard him saying while I was jammed into the doghouse. It was an altogether stunning display of swearing, and we can't help but be impressed. Stuart and Danny have suddenly put themselves on the map.

'Those guys will say *any*thing,' Elizabeth remarks. She's having a bowl of cereal, using milk that is thin and watery with a faint blue cast.

'How's that breast milk taste?' I ask her. She stares into the bowl for a second and then shrugs, takes another spoonful.

'What would you've done if they caught you?' Renee asks. In some ways Renee is the perfect friend, she's genuinely nice and asks you just exactly the questions you are prepared to answer. She is also pretty, with thin shiny hair and round brown eyes and a mouth that smiles even when she's just reading or listening to a teacher. The boys love her, too, and cluster around her, which works out well for her friends, who are neither nice nor friendly.

'I would've just started screaming,' Elizabeth answers. And it's true, we all know it.

I make a slow-motion kicking gesture with my foot. 'Right in the old codpiece,' I say. Elizabeth makes a snorting noise and then has a nose attack right in Renee's kitchen. It's when she can't breathe through her mouth – she's still eating cereal – and her nostrils slam shut. She has to reach up and pry them open manually so she can get air.

I try to help her and we wake the babies up accidentally.

'Shit-fuck,' Renee says wearily. The babies wander out to the kitchen, blinking their eyes in the brightness and whimpering. They both try to climb on Renee, who stares patiently at the ceiling for a second and then helps them up on her lap. They look at Elizabeth and me with blank, defensive eyes, Amy with her thumb jammed in her mouth, Stacy with her hand down her diaper.

'Do you have to go on the big-girl potty?' Renee asks her. She shakes her head no and closes her eyes. Suddenly we're all tired, even Elizabeth and me. We take the kids and Renee leads the way upstairs. She pokes her head in all the bedrooms: B.J. is asleep on Renee's bed, Alex is asleep on the rug beside his bed, Cindy is sleeping in B.J.'s bed. I have Amy, who's as heavy as a sandbag and smells like sour milk and baby shampoo. We finally put them on the king-size bed in the parents' room. There's no sheet so we cover them with the funky, crumpled-up bedspread and tiptoe out. B.J. is seven and weighs a ton so I take his feet and Elizabeth takes his arms and we carry him like a hammock between us and dump him into Cindy's bed so Renee can sleep alone. She whispers good night and we're gone, back into the cold spring air.

It takes about two blocks of freezing cold before we decide we have to ride instead of walk. We find a boy's bicycle with a long banana seat in somebody's backyard and take it; Elizabeth pedals standing up and I ride on back, with my legs stuck straight out on either side. When she gets winded I take over, but I sit while I pedal, which scrunches her. I can't help it; I'm tired.

When we get to the big hill we leave the bike leaning against a tree and trudge ourselves straight up for one block and then it's two blocks of flat ground, and then we're at her house, sneaking back in.

I go first in case somebody's up; at least we know they won't throw a pop bottle at me. The coast is clear. Elizabeth steps into her bedroom and suddenly we're wide awake again. We debate about calling up the Garcias, and then, in an unusual display of restraint, don't. Instead, we go out to the kitchen and prepare a cake mix we find in the cupboard. We take it back into the bedroom and lie on the bed in the dark, eating cherry chip cake batter with big wooden spoons. We're wound up now, it's impossible to think about sleeping.

We discuss the Jeff Bach situation for a while. We come to the conclusion that it's hard to like someone so blond. 'I like dark-haired guys, I think,' Elizabeth says. I can see the shadow of her profile in the bed, she's gesturing with her wooden spoon.

'Me too,' I say.

There is a long silence. It's late, four a.m. or something. We're finally getting tired again. She puts the batter on the floor next to the bed; I hand her my spoon and she drops it into the bowl. A few minutes pass.

'I might like Danny Garcia,' she says tentatively. Another minute goes by.

'I might like Stuart,' I say. She thinks this over. I turn on my side and she cuddles up right behind me; we sleep like two spoons whenever we're in the same bed.

'Stuart's dangerous,' she whispers.

'I know it,' I say softly, into the darkness, and then we're both asleep.

It's nineteen seventy-something, summer, nighttime, black country road running through rural Illinois, the sky is immense. Three miles ahead are train tracks that can be sailed over if you approach them right, all four tires will leave the ground at once. We're heading for our house, a two-story farm job with a big garden out back, a bunch of pigs that are not our responsibility, a summer kitchen with spiders and mice, and two dogs who wait patiently all day for us to get home so their lives can begin. I've thrown my lot in with the guy in the driver's seat, and he with me. We're both certain we'll never amount to anything, which only bothers us when we think about it. Right now we're high on dope and each other, and the night air smells like rain. The road is white where the headlights hit it, and everything else is pure black. The car is old and bumperless, with a plywood fender that has a dent where an agitated friend of ours karate-chopped it. The tape deck is not for the faint-hearted; the sound inside the car is huge and all-consuming. Right now it sounds like someone is playing a guitar using a razor blade for a pick, and the question being asked is Are you experienced? The answer is No, we aren't, but we're working on it.

Coming up on the long stretch before the giant Dip in Pavement and the subsequent railroad tracks, Eric glances over at me for an instant, assessing my mood, then pushes the lights off and we streak through the blackness down the center of the highway, dark moving inside of dark, our faces faint in the dashboard light. It sounds for a moment like the guitar player is saying Areyouanidiot? and then I decide to be into it.

I put one arm out my window, to feel the night air and create some drag. He presses harder on the gas. The sky is distinguishable from the ground only because it is blue-black, and the land is black-black. There are stars. This is what they mean by barreling down the road. Not only could this be certain death, but we may take somebody else out, too, which is troubling. He isn't thinking of any of that; in fact, he's got his eyes closed, or else just the one I can see – he's trying to freak me out. That settles it. I put my foot on top of his and press it to the floor. I close my own eyes and imagine myself leaning into it, certain death. Darkness and his girlfriend, Darkness, are out for a ride through the countryside in the summer night. We hit the dip and are airborne for a breathless millisecond, then there's that long, terrible dope-inspired instant that stretches out forever, where you don't know if there'll be a train on the tracks or not, whether you'll get to continue living.

This time we do.

'They clean your room and cook your meals so you can write about Stuart *Garcia*?' Elizabeth asks incredulously. She's at her job in Chicago.

'Apparently,' I reply. I'm in the wilds of upstate New York, at an artist's colony, sitting in a phone booth drawing pictures and talking to her while she formats something on her computer, which keeps beeping.

'You should say he was dangerous,' she suggests.

I hate it here; why did I come here? All there is to do is write.

'You always go through this,' she reminds me. There is the sound of a tiny bomb exploding, a ding, and she exhales loudly. 'I just crashed my whole computer,' she explains.

'I just crashed my whole life,' I tell her mournfully. I'm afraid she's going to try to hang up. 'Who even cares about the boys of my youth? There weren't any, it was all imaginary. I'm making it up as I go along.' I draw a picture of a pit bull on the phone book in the phone booth. It has pointy ears, bowed legs, and giant teeth. 'Now I'm drawing a giant-toothed dog,' I tell her.

'That's good,' she says. 'Remember that time you went to Florida to write and became troubled?'

'In the category of freak-out, *that* was the real thing.' I draw a palm tree with coconuts hanging off it next to the pit bull.

'I made you eat a banana that time,' she reminds me. We muse on that for a moment, until her computer comes back on line and says hello to her in a voice from outer space. We hang up.

*

411

As a matter of fact, there happens to be a banana in my lunch. Every day they give me a lunchbox with a sandwich, a piece of fruit, and a cookie in it. I eat the cookie, think about the sandwich, and put the fruit on my writing table, then I go back to staring out the window of my studio. This is how professional writers work.

I went to Florida once to work on a writing project. I borrowed a house on Key- something, with a million-mile view of the Atlantic, sliding glass doors, expensive furniture, and cockroaches the size of a man's big toe. My friend's sister, who was lending me the house, showed me how you had to spray Raid directly on the bug in order to make it die. At first it seemed unfazed, and then it wandered about a foot away and fell over. 'They aren't cockroaches,' she explained firmly.

'I'm not afraid of bugs,' I told her. 'I *like* bugs, actually.' In fact, I'm married to one, is what I thought to myself. This was during a down phase in my marriage. I was there in Florida because he wouldn't stop seeing the wife of his best friend. 'We're not *doing* anything,' he would explain. 'What are you – nuts?' The wife herself was miffed at me. 'Why can't we still be friends?' she asked. I would speak to her only when cornered, and then only to call her names. She kept trying though, calling my house at odd hours to ask me how I was doing in a concerned, schoolmarm-ish voice.

'Quit calling my house and quit screwing my husband,' I'd reply evenly. She'd sigh; I'd hang up. Once I took the phone off the wall and threw it out the front door into a snowbank. Eric retrieved it wordlessly, dried it off, hung it back on the wall. 'You suck,' I told him. He stared at me for a long moment and then went back to whatever he was doing.

I was trying to make him miss me by going to Florida, but it wasn't working. On the way down, while driving in my car, I would have long imaginary arguments with him, where I hit every point square on the head and he was left speechless and remorseful. I

412

had him apologizing to me left and right, every hundred miles or so. Between that and singing to the radio, it was a pretty productive trip down.

So, my friend's sister left and I wandered around her house, upstairs, downstairs, finally setting up my typewriter in front of a large glass door that opened onto a balcony with a view of the water and some boats. I organized all my writing paraphernalia, sharpened some pencils using a paring knife from the kitchen, and then sat down and began having a nervous breakdown.

Eventually the sun dropped into the water, leaving a fakey sunset, gaudy pink and yellow stripes along the horizon. The boats disappeared, one by one, and a group of long-legged stork-like birds flew past the large glass door, out over the water, and then were gone. They weren't the kind of storks that carry babies, thank God; not bothering to have a baby being one of the things I deeply regretted the minute my marriage started unraveling. As soon as it got completely dark, the glass door turned into a giant black mirror, showing a ghostly image of me sitting in a wicker chair in the dimness. My hands were folded calmly in my lap. I looked like a dark painting of barely controlled hysteria, surrounded by wicker and the long fronds of tropical plants. I felt like I was on an elevator that had burst through the top of the building and was still climbing. At some point I stood up creakily on my stiff legs and went looking for something to put me to sleep.

Three warm beers later I stretched out on the king-size bed and stared at the ceiling. I felt like myself as a six-year-old, lying in bed for hours, making up frightening stories in my head, waiting for my sister to wake up and torture me. Me as a kid: skinny and pale and jumpy, terrified of a particular cartoon character who was thin and wiry with a narrow, whiplike mustache. He wore a black outfit with a string tie and he tied girls to railroad tracks or to conveyor belts with buzz saws at the end. On the way to the bathroom, I heard the sound of a Frito crunching. It was a cockroach, stuck to my foot.

I began freaking out in earnest.

Heart pounding, I scraped the bug off, peed, and stared at myself in the dark mirror. I was spooked and looked it. I walked on my tiptoes back into the bedroom and jumped onto the bed. I pulled the sheet around me and curled into my usual sleeping position (fetal). I imagined everyone in my life abandoning me, all the while assuring me they weren't. I replayed a scene from several years ago: my mother in a hospital bed with Eric at her side, extracting a promise from him, he listening solemnly, speaking to her in a whisper, nodding, holding her hand; me in the hallway, exasperated and worn out, rolling my eyes, one last opportunity for defiance, sassing back even then.

I started a low-grade whimpering to keep myself company. It was dark and dark and dark and then it began to be light and light and then dawn showed up. I used a remote control to turn on the television and page through the channels. There was a religious program on, a Bullwinkle cartoon which was the last thing I needed, a worm's-eye view of a woman doing an aerobic workout, and CNN. I watched CNN intently, with the sound off and my eyes squinted almost shut.

I kept remembering some footage I'd seen of a plane crash that happened a few years back, where a seat with a passenger strapped to it was thrown hundreds of feet from the wreckage. The seat landed in an upright position, and the passenger, slightly charred, was sitting quietly with an arm on each armrest, deader than dead. I replayed the footage over and over, trying to make the passenger wake up, but to no avail.

At some point I went into the bathroom and threw up, then stared at myself again in the mirror, surveying the damage. My eyes looked like two red holes in a pink blanket. My stomach hurt.

I found the telephone, a cordless job, and carried it out onto the balcony with me. The Florida sun was climbing, the air felt like hot, wet lint. The same old boats were making their way back into view, chugging along silently, leaving trails of foam that leveled back out into flat blue. I sat with the phone in my hand until there was nothing left to do but dial it. I called my own number at home and a man answered. He said hello about five times and then hung up. It was my husband.

Everything was overwhelmingly bright, my eyes couldn't stand it. I went back in to the king-size bed. Suddenly the phone, still stuck to my hand, started ringing. I stared at it until it stopped. When the digital clock said 10, I called Chicago.

'Where *are* you?' Elizabeth says cheerfully. 'I called you and Eric said you ran away from *home* or something.'

'I'm in Florida, at Taylor's sister's house,' I say. 'I'm supposed to be writing.'

'You sound weird,' she says. 'Jo Ann? You sound weird.'

I am weird.

'Why are we not talking?' she asks gently. 'Are we okay?'

No, unfortunately we're not. I swallow hard and stare at my clenched and hysterical feet. My stomach still hurts. I'm sitting in the center of a giant bed in a giant house on Key Nightmare.

'I'm freaking out,' I tell her. 'I'm ready to jump off a balcony into the sand or something.'

She considers this for a long moment and then says, quietly, 'Uh-oh, this is a marriage problem, right?' As far as she's concerned, her own marriage is as solid as a house, but the truth is, it's just about this time that her husband is beginning to notice what beautiful eyes his receptionist has, how the sound of her typing is like water rushing over a falls.

For about five minutes I can't talk, but instead nod or shake my head when she asks me questions. Her voice has taken on a soothing, reassuring tone I've never heard her use before. It makes me feel like crying. The bedroom is starting to really bother me so I close my eyes and grope my way out, still holding the phone to my ear.

'I'm walking,' is what I finally say to her.

'*Good*,' she responds quickly. 'If you're walking, then you're okay.'

This is encouraging, so I walk some more. I walk out onto the balcony and stare at the phony boats on the horizon. I try to tell her what is happening to me – that my heart is beating so hard my T-shirt is moving, that I threw up because of some plane crash footage I saw two years ago, that I keep remembering being stalked by a cartoon guy with a whiplike mustache and a string tie.

'Well, I hate to break it to you,' she says firmly, 'but that sounds like *Eric*.' Eric is pretty thin and so is his mustache.

'Well, *Eric's* certainly not stalking me,' I tell her. I start to cry suddenly, which is a relief. 'He's doing whatever the opposite of stalking me is.' Now that I'm crying I can't stop. I'm leaning over the balcony railing and tears are dropping into the sand below me. I tell Elizabeth this.

'Why don't you just *please* get off that balcony, and go back in the house?'

'I'm not going to *jump*,' I say. 'It's only about ten feet from the *ground*, for Chris'sakes.'

'Oh,' she says.

The problem is, whenever it occurs to me that he's leaving me, I start to feel like throwing up again. Also, I haven't slept for a couple of days. Or eaten. And it feels like there's an alien in my chest.

'You can't not eat,' she says. 'That's what we'll fix first.' She sounds so confident that I feel myself relax a little. I'm still trapped in the elevator but I've lost that terrible zooming-upward vertigo feeling. I look at my feet. Under her direction, I walk downstairs with the telephone and stand in the kitchen. 'Tell me everything there is to eat,' she says.

One cupboard has rice cakes, spices, and vegetable oil, another has cans of things, boxes of cereal, and an envelope of mushroom soup, another has pots and pans, the refrigerator has mayonnaise and a jar of green olives. The sight of the pimientos makes me sick for a minute, I have to lean over and think of something else. When I say green olives to Elizabeth she immediately says, 'Don't look at the pimientos.' There is a basket in the middle of the kitchen table that holds two bananas, a paper clip, a packet of sugar substitute, a blue marble, and a ballpoint pen. 'Perfect,' she says.

She wants me to eat a banana.

'*Any*one can eat a banana,' she says smoothly. 'People give them to *babies*, they're so easy to eat.'

'I'll throw up if I look at it,' I tell her. My heart is pounding again.

'Oh no you won't,' she tells me. 'A *rice* cake would make you throw up; bananas don't make people sick, else they wouldn't give them to babies.' I can't argue with her logic, but I can't look at the bananas either. 'I'm going to call you back in exactly half an hour. You take one bite every five minutes.' I give her the phone number, set the telephone down on the kitchen table, and peel a banana without looking at it. Thirty minutes later the phone rings.

'I ate it,' I tell her. Actually I ate half of it.

She has me take the phone in the bathroom and inventory the medicine cabinet. I do so obediently, the banana sitting in my stomach like a wad of clay. 'Midol; emery board; Ramada Inn soap; Nyquil; unidentifiable pills way too big to take; sunscreen; sunscreen; eyeliner; generic aspirin; Bic razor, crusty.' I sit down on the edge of the tub. The medicine cabinet has made me panicky again.

'Perfect,' she says. 'This is what you do now: put your swimming suit on and walk on the beach for one and a half hours, okay? Then come back and drink two doses of Nyquil and lie down on the couch. You don't have to sleep or anything, just lie down.' She reiterates this. 'In fact, it's actually better if you *don't* sleep.' She's using reverse psychology on me.

The beach is empty, except for some old cans and a broken fishing pole. A bloated fish lies half buried in the sand, one tarnished eye staring placidly up at the sun. I step over it and make my way down the beach at the water's edge. Water is soothing, Elizabeth told me, water is soothing, water is soothing. I feel calm all of a sudden, looking at the water and the sky and the fins of sharks circling about two hundred yards out. 'Those are dolphins,' I say out loud. Each time I come across a bloated fish or a squashed something, I say, 'That's not dead.' When I feel like my legs are going to drop off I turn around and head back. By this time the sun is hanging about a quarter-inch above the part in my hair. My shoulders feel scorched and I'm sort of hungry. Back at the house I eat a rice cake with a glass of water. It tastes like Styrofoam, which is somehow better than having it taste like food. I drink as much of the Nyquil as I can stand, stretch out on the couch, and count sheep with my eyes open.

Five hours later the phone rings off in the distance and I come to. I feel swampy and disoriented, stand up quickly, and then sit back down on the couch. It's hard to tell where the phone is located. Staggering through the house, I follow the noise into the bathroom.

'Guess who,' she says cheerfully. I report to her on what I've accomplished – the walk, the rice cake, the Nyquil nap. 'Whew,' she says. 'For a minute there I thought I was gonna have to come *rescue* you; I even called the airline.'

I feel deeply touched by this, and begin weeping. I'm not completely out of the woods.

'Oh honey,' she says quietly.

'He's dumping me,' I wail. 'For some pliant, rat-faced little nurse *practitioner* who doesn't have an unusual bone in her body.'

'What's her husband think about all this?' she asks.

'Who knows. He's probably *relieved*, wouldn't you say?'

We ponder this for a while. 'I called him a couple of days ago and asked him if he missed me,' I say.

'Uh-oh,' Elizabeth says.

'He had one of his honesty attacks.'

'Why, that little fuck,' she starts. 'I'd like to get my hands around his skinny *neck*.'

'He's already left me,' I say, 'he's just too chicken to take his body with him.'

'I know you don't want to hear this,' she says carefully. 'But it seems to me that you wouldn't be this upset about him wanting to leave you. I think you're this upset because *you* want to leave *him*.' This makes my stomach lurch in a very sickening, grain-of-truth-to-it way.

'But I love him,' I tell her. 'He's the only man I've ever loved.' Even I know how trite that sounds. I feel like a character in a Gothic novel.

'Keep in mind who you're talking to here,' she says dryly.

'I can't believe I said "He's the only man I've ever loved." I'm supposed to be a *writer*, for God's sake.' I might be starting to snap out of it.

'It's time for the other banana,' she suggests. 'And I'm gonna talk to you while you eat it.'

Seventeenth summer, a farmhouse full of boys on the edge of town, a car full of girls heading toward it. It's Elizabeth's red convertible, prone to running out of gas and getting stuck in places that cars don't belong. As soon as we leave the city streets and hit the back roads, everyone except Elizabeth gets up and sits on the edge of the car instead of on the seats. When we go around curves there is a long moment where it feels like we might fall out and be run over by the back tires. We like this feeling. Because we're too young to die, we assume we won't. Also, alcohol is involved.

It's the year of Look Ma, No Bra, and extremely long blue jeans that drag on the ground and get caked with mud. Shoes are unheard of; hair is everything. We comb ours frantically as soon as the car stops. My own is long and lank, reaching just above my waist; it's useless to even try and restore order.

'Here.' Renee takes my comb and starts working out the tangles gently, starting at the bottom. She raps me on the head with her knuckles when I tip my head back to finish my beer. 'Stay still,' she commands, in the voice she uses on the babies.

'Ouch,' I say mildly.

Elizabeth assesses herself in the sideview mirror. She's trying to see if her rear end is sticking out. 'Why do I have an egg-butt?' she asks. This is rhetorical.

Renee finishes my hair and asks if she should braid it. A vote is taken: two for the braid, two for leaving it down. I throw my vote in with leaving it, we do some last-minute adjustments, and then, making Janet go first because she has confidence, we step through the front door and into the farmhouse.

The living room walls are painted black and the furniture consists of a sprung couch with no cushions, an old dentist's chair, a black-light pole lamp, and a giant stereo system. Right now a guy named Dave is changing the album. Like a priest performing the sacrament, he kneels before the altar and removes the record from its sleeve. Holding the edges and blowing softly on it, he sets it on the turntable, moves the needle into place, and gently drops it. Deafening sound ensues.

Except for one guy named Bob, all the guys who live here are named either Steve or Dave, all have ponytails of varying lengths, and all worship Ted Nugent. They refer to him as Ted and speculate on his whereabouts constantly. They're a year or so older than us, high school graduates who are busy amounting to nothing. We all have crushes on one or another of them. Mine is in the kitchen right now, mixing up a concoction of lemonade and Everclear. He's a sweet-faced Steve with a charming personality and a massive drinking problem. He hardly ever notices me, but when he does I think I'm going to die. 'Here,' he says, handing me a plastic cup of potion. I take a sip and try not to shudder. It tastes like sugar-flavored eau de cologne. 'Hey, that's good,' I respond brightly. I'm working on having a better personality.

'Ted here yet?' he asks me.

'Uh, no,' I reply. He wanders into the living room and I wait a second, then follow him.

Elizabeth and Janet are sitting on the funky couch reading album covers. Renee is on the floor, cross-legged, smoking a cigarette with her eyes closed. No sign of Carol. I look around. One of the Steves is missing as well. I drink some more of my medicine.

The music is so loud that the sound is distorted. I want to turn it down slightly, but I don't dare. It is an unspoken rule that girls don't touch stereo equipment. When the record ends there is a sudden leaden silence that rings almost as loudly as the music.

Everyone looks startled and uncomfortable. A Dave gets up and pads over in his sock feet to put something else on. A different Dave loads a bong and passes it to his right. Someone switches off the regular light and switches on the black light. This is a relief for those of us who are worried about how we look; now everyone is equal, with velvety faces, lavender teeth and eyes.

The weed is laced with PCP; after two hits I feel like I'm in a hammock on the top deck of a gently rolling ocean liner. I stretch out on my back, using a stack of magazines for a pillow, and crawl inside the music. My head is an empty room, painted white, with high vaulted ceilings. There is a long beat of silence and then the sound of alarm clocks going off. I sit in a straight-backed chair in the middle of my head. Suddenly there is the pinging of a cash register and the sound of coins falling. I open my eyes briefly and see the rapt faces of the other revelers, the purple-toothed smile of a nodding Dave. I retreat back to the dark side of the moon. Money changes hands, guitars echo off the white walls.

When I come to it's some time later, there are more people around, blue-jeaned legs step over me from time to time. I like the party from this angle. Eventually my favorite Steve comes in and sits on the floor next to my head. He has another cup of poison for me. 'You missed Ted,' he hollers into my ear. In honor of trying to have a better personality, I make a disappointed face.

Although there are girls present, none of them seem to be my friends. 'Where's Elizabeth?' I mouth to him. He leans in and puts his lips, then his tongue, to my ear. I pull my head away. 'She's occupied,' he yells, and gestures toward a closed door.

When I ask where everybody else is he shrugs. I truly hate it when this happens.

As it turns out, Renee is in the kitchen, very stoned, doing the dishes. Three guys are sitting at the kitchen table, one cleaning pot, the other two watching Renee like she's a TV show. When she runs out of dishes, one of them obediently picks up another stack off the floor and sets them in the water for her. This place is a pig sty. I pour myself another cup of whatever that crap is.

Renee looks at me foggily, trying to assess my mood. 'Want to dry some dishes?' she asks.

'Not hardly, pal,' I say. The guys at the table give me a long look and I give them one back. A Dave holds out his hand to me.

'C'mere,' he says kindly, pulling me onto his lap. The Beatles are on the stereo. 'The Long and Winding Road,' a song that'll break your heart in about one minute, begins to play. I sit quietly on the Dave's lap and hum a few bars. He pets my hair awkwardly

422

for a while and then puts his hand up the back of my shirt. The other two guys exchange a smirk.

I take Dave's ear by the lobe and whisper into it. His eyes open wide. He puts his hand across his chest protectively as I get up. 'She's *fierce*,' he says to the other two. Renee drops some crusty silverware into the brown dishwater. She struggles for a second to bring me into focus.

'Jo Ann doesn't like that kind of stuff,' she explains to them.

'Well, man oh man,' Dave says. 'What did *I* do.' The other two laugh.

Looks like my old personality is back.

In the phone booth in New York, I draw a picture of a girl with her fists on her hips, eyebrows converging, mouth set. She's wearing my clothes. I have one question to ask Elizabeth, but first she wants to tell me about her weekend.

'I went out with a guy who looks like the Artful Dodger,' she says. 'He's in a band *and* he wears a top hat. He couldn't wear it on the date, though, because we went to a movie.'

'That's good,' I say. I tell her I'm working on a party scene.

'Which party?' she asks suspiciously. 'What am I doing at it?'

'It's sort of a composite of all parties, you know?' There's silence at the other end. 'It's just a *party* party, is all, with those guys who all had the same names.'

'The Ted Nugent guys?' she asks.

Well, yes.

'I never liked any of those guys, did I?' she says hopefully. Uh, I think Dave Nelson would be hurt.

She probes her brain, comes up with a memory. 'Oh.' She thinks for a second. 'Well, he was a nice guy,' she says firmly. 'Wasn't he?'

We ponder for a minute and finally both admit we can't

remember. I say they all look alike to me, and then instantly regret it, because I'm going to hear a lecture. Here it comes.

'Your attitude towards men s-u-x,' she begins. 'Look at me. I got divorced, too, and I'm not bitter.'

Well, I'm willing to be bitter on both our behalfs. In the meantime, the one question I have to ask is Why were you always with guys and I never was?

'Because you were mean, that's why,' she says gently. 'Remember how mean you used to get?' This makes me feel awful. I was a mean person.

'You weren't a mean *person*,' she says. 'We were just weird back then. We were insecure.'

But you weren't mean.

'Well, I had the exact opposite problem,' she replies.

I light a cigarette illegally in the phone booth and try to blow the smoke into my coat pocket. The conversation goes on and on, more about the Artful Dodger.

Meanwhile, back at the party, Renee shows me her pruny fingers.

'Exhibit A,' she says. 'This is exactly why you shouldn't take speed and go to a party.' I pour her a cup of liquid nitrogen and she downs it quickly, the way she's doing everything else. 'I keep thinking I want to clean the bathroom,' she says.

'I'd steer clear if I were you,' I advise her. 'Five guys live here.' She can see the wisdom in that.

Pretty soon Carol comes into the kitchen, blinking her eyes against the light. Her hair is a mess, her shirt is buttoned wrong, and she's been crying. He has hurt her feelings, which isn't hard to do. He forgot her name or something. 'Let's go,' she whispers. We rustle up Elizabeth and the three of us fade through the living room and out the door. The Steve I have a crush on is sitting on the front porch steps, smoking a joint, waiting for Ted. He reaches out and places his hand gently around my ankle. I stand there patiently until he lets go, and then continue down the steps. 'See you,' he says.

At the car, there is a moment of silence. Elizabeth tries to hand the keys off to me but I'm not in the mood. I climb in the back and hold on to my hair as we pull from the drive to the road. Carol stops crying and claims she's never going to another party.

Elizabeth and I exchange a look in the rearview mirror. 'In my whole entire *life*,' she says emphatically, 'so don't even try asking me to.' The sky is full of diamonds, the moon is a narrow sliver, the road winds and curves, the drugs are wearing off. We left Renee and Janet at the party without a ride.

The voice of Motown comes on the radio and we sing quietly to ourselves. All the houses have their eyes closed as we sweep silently past them. Carol fixes her shirt, lights one cigarette off another, and I wave good-bye to them from the alley behind my house. Through the bushes, up the back walk, still humming. In the kitchen, two cookies and a long drink of water, up the stairs and into the bedroom. Across the hall my parents sleep peacefully behind their closed door, innocent as children.

On the way back from Florida I drive a hundred miles out of my way in order to visit my mother's grave. Small Illinois town where she grew up; the gas station, body shop, and ice cream parlor are owned by my uncles, on the edge of town a small barren cemetery is full of my dead relatives. My mother's tombstone is dark granite, on either side of it are pink geraniums, planted by my father. In front, beneath her name, is a coffee can full of wildflowers withering in the sun. Someone has been here before me, an aunt probably, driving past on her way into town from one of the nearby farms. The withering flowers prompt a maudlin scene in which I am both the actor and the audience. A red-tailed hawk circles overhead, a tractor chugs by on the highway, holding up a line of cars. A daughter weeps in the afternoon sunlight, a mother remains silent beneath a load of dirt.

Hours later my street appears in front of me, a tall catalpa tree, a child's scooter, and then the driveway where the husband stands, just off his bike, home from work. 'Hi,' he says cordially, putting an arm across my shoulders. And then, 'I have a meeting tonight.' His hand looks as white as paste next to my Florida arm. Inside, he goes into the study and closes the door. I hear the long beep of the answering machine as he listens to the messages and then erases them.

In bed that night I remain stationary as he toils in the darkness. Afterward, there is silence and the sound of breathing. Next to the bed, my big collie whines in her sleep. Finally, he says quietly, with something in his voice I don't recognize, 'It's good you're back.'

Tick, tock. Breathe in, breathe out. There is no mercy at this hour of the night, and my own voice sounds strange in the darkness. *I'm not*, is what I tell him. He rolls over and puts his face in the pillow. Everywhere you turn these days there's someone crying.

Billboards, fence posts, and cows go by at seventy miles an hour, a van honks as we pass it and someone gives us the finger in a friendly manner. We're caravaning our way to the rock quarries for a swimming party. Three cars and two vans are full of people and beer; I'm riding on back of a motorcycle, driven by my unofficial date, a charming madman named Wally. Wally is already in the party mood and so am I, because it's my nineteenth birthday. I have on a microscopic swimming suit, a Rolling Stones T-shirt, and Wally's helmet. He has on cut-off blue jeans, sunglasses, and a baseball cap. Every once in a while he'll holler, 'Hold on!' and then execute an amazing maneuver that involves other vehicles on the road. I'm absolutely terrified, and keep imagining what skin

THE BOYS OF MY YOUTH

on pavement would feel like. Nevertheless, I can't quit egging him on.

The water is like cold silk when you first get in. Elizabeth and I float ourselves around on air mattresses until we see a water snake swimming directly toward us with its head stuck up like a periscope. We take off for the beach and sun ourselves on an outcropping of rock. Somewhere in the vicinity, Wally is tapping the keg while others are running speaker wire. Eventually music comes forth and beer makes its way over to where we are. Guys start catapulting themselves into the water.

I get special treatment because it's my birthday. People keep calling me over to their cars and vans. 'Here,' they say generously. 'Do some of this.' In an effort to stay awake for my birthday, I decline almost everything. I'm a famous lightweight; even beer in the afternoon makes me sleepy. I stretch out on my rock and let the sun bake me while the others swim and get wasted. Elizabeth keeps up a running monologue next to me which I can tune in and tune out at will. Wally comes over to shake water on us from time to time; we bat him away like an insect.

Sometime during the early evening he produces three pills, one for each of us. 'What are these?' I ask him. He looks at one of the pills closely, turning it over in his hand.

'"Lilly,"' he reads. 'They're lilies, that's what. Red ones.' Down the hatch.

Within an hour I'm singing a medley of Beatles tunes to anyone who will listen. My legs are not working correctly. 'Hey, Jude,' I say to the guy sitting next to me. His name is Tom. 'Did you have any of those red lilies?' He doesn't know what I'm talking about. Elizabeth is nowhere in sight but I can see Wally off in the distance, slapping his leg and laughing silently and hysterically. He squints over in my direction and motions me to come hither. I point to my legs and shake my head. We give each other the peace sign.

There's a fire going, and some people are roasting things over it. I hear my name being called. 'Liz is looking for you,' Tom tells me. He stands, stretches, and heads for the beer. She comes tripping up, still in her swimming suit, with a man's workshirt over it. 'Let's take a walk,' she says. She's listing slightly to the right, but other than that, doing okay.

'I can't stand up,' I tell her. I indicate the grass next to me. 'You sit down.'

We watch the other campers for a while, roasting their things, drinking their stuff, laughing and punching each other. 'I can't stay here if you're going to sing,' Elizabeth tells me. I stop singing.

Off in the distance the lizardy sound of Mick Jagger starts up, more cars arrive, people shout for no reason. The red lily has made me feel both weightless and heavy at the same time. The night air is cool against my sunburned arms. I can't remember what I did with my shoes. The only thing that would make me happier at this moment is if I could sing *Bang, bang, Maxwell's silver hammer*, but Liz won't let me. I try humming it softly but she starts to stand up so I have to cut it out. I wonder where Waldo is.

Renee and her boyfriend Pete emerge out of the darkness. She has my T-shirt and shoes. Even though my arms are balloon strings, I manage to get the shirt on and slip my swimming suit top off; the shoes I cannot even begin to contend with. Pete is short and very cool, with bedroom eyes, dark curly hair, and an uncivilized manner.

Renee is working on taming him. He likes it that I took my swimming suit top off even though he didn't get a glimpse of anything. 'Nice tits,' he says generously. We send him to get beers but right before he leaves he bestows a big, fat birthday kiss on me. I dry my face on my T-shirt.

Here comes Janet, so tan her blond hair looks fake. She's got a concerned look on her face. Well, there's bad news. Wally's fiancée, Leeann, has just arrived unexpectedly. It was a surprise;

she blew in from the north like bad weather, and now my birthday is wrecked. Everyone groans, including Tom and Pete, who like it when I'm in a good mood. *Bang, bang, Maxwell's silver hammer came down upon her head*. I shrug and put a decent face on it. I can't think of anything to sing.

At some point during the evening Wally catches my eye. Leeann is standing with her back to me, looking wifely and cruel. He holds his hands palms-up in the age-old gesture of *Hey, this is not my fault*. I look away with no expression on my face. Tom brings me a roasted marshmallow that burns the roof of my mouth. I lean my head on his knee and he pats my sunburned shoulder. It's my nineteenth birthday and here I am, Eleanor Rigby.

'She married him right out from under me,' I say. We're back to the phone booth.

All I have to do is close my eyes and I can see his long, pipe-cleaner legs, his hazel madman's eyes. He still remains the legendary good kisser.

She wants to know what made it legendary. I don't know; it was almost twenty years ago. Probably the fiancée in the background. 'He was nuts,' she says. Yeah, that didn't hurt either.

All the sweet, absent boys. Smoking jays like they were cigarettes. Playing their air guitars. Doling out their legendary kisses. We have a moment of long-distance silence for ourselves, perpetually the back-up singers.

'Hey, man,' Elizabeth says, 'speak for yourself.'

It's 1976 or thereabouts. Feminism strikes suddenly, leaving destruction in its path. I've always had a tendency to be mean to men; now there's a reason for it. I'm learning to keep my hands in my pockets, so they won't see my fists.

Someone's living room, floor pillows, chamomile tea, soft-voiced women in painter's pants and big hoop earrings. Consciousness-raising. We learned why Susan B. Anthony should get her face on a coin. We learned that the speculum can be our friend. Some of us learned that the word *orgasm* actually described a real phenomenon.

'Hey,' we said in unison.

I'm here to tell you that sisterhood is a powerful thing. We worked on constructing egos for ourselves; we tried to convince each other that our lives were worth inhabiting. We stopped shaving our armpits and gave ourselves wash-and-wear hairdos called shags. Occasionally, one of us would lob a beer can at the head of a deserving male. Feminism. The only down side I can remember is that the shags were hard to grow out.

The separate-but-equal principle held sway for a brief time. The guys who used to remove our clothes with their sliding glances dressed us right back up again when they saw our armpits. Women stalked out of the room when men accidentally called them honey. Eventually, though, we all calmed down a little and attempted to harmonize. Some lean-torsoed men tried to even the odds by putting on glittery eyeshadow and climbing up on platform heels to play their guitars. With the advent of cocaine, parties suddenly got livelier and longer.

Across the room, a guy navigates his way through the smoky throng to play with the equalizer. From there he goes to the front porch, where he adjusts a slide projector.

This is his party, apparently. He's projecting slides of a David Bowie/Iggy Pop concert on the house across the street. There's a rivet punched through his ear lobe, a silver star, a small tribute to androgyny. He's simultaneously mellow and wired but he speaks thoughtfully and listens carefully. At some point, while one of us is talking, he presses his hand against the small of my back and doesn't move it. It stays there for more than a decade.

Some highlights. Early days: long evenings in the country house, I make drawings and smoke cigarettes, drink cups of tea. He stokes up the blue glass bong, plugs in an electric guitar, and plays 'Secret Agent Man' over and over. We populate our house with dogs and have long, monotonous discussions about how to make them behave better. We go in the bedroom sometimes and close the door to get away from them, then feel sorry and open it again and let them boil up onto the bed and stick their noses in our faces. We do a wavery but heartfelt rendition of 'Good Night, Irene' as we're driving, late, back from friends' houses. On a beach in South Carolina we lie on our backs and stare at the night sky and congratulate ourselves on getting along so well.

Months later we discover grains of sand in the cuffs of his trousers, remember, and give each other secret, sappy looks.

We're pretty nice people for the most part, although neither of us ever sands off the edges we started out with. I am prone to my usual fits of melancholy and self-doubt; he has a tendency toward a manic energy that is enervating for anyone who beholds it. I have long ago lost all interest in drugs and alcohol but each evening he disappears inside a plume of smoke and emerges mellowed and distant. Rock and roll, of course, never dies. Sometimes very late at night we sit in the dark living room listening to the voices of various dead guys – Tommy Bolin, Jimi Hendrix, Bob Marley – while studiously ignoring each other. I observe that he isn't fully present past eight o'clock each night, and surprise myself by feeling grateful. I am left free to traipse around in my own psychic landscape. When we have fights he has a tendency to reply in baby-talk, which causes me to go berserk. I rant, then I rave, berating him in such florid terms that no one can keep a straight face. We get sheepish, we make up. The years tick by.

My lifelong addiction to books wanes, leaving me feeling bored and bereft. Some time later I discover that I've left off reading them because I've decided to write them instead. He thinks this is a fine idea and supports it unconditionally, but finds that he is unable to read what I write because drowsiness overtakes him. I watch him several nights running as he nods and dozes, tries with an enormous effort to focus, and finally gives up. We agree without much discussion that it isn't necessary for him to read my writing. His own work is too consuming, he doesn't need one more task piled on top of the others. The match stops flaring, the bong stops bubbling, the old familiar chords of 'Secret Agent Man' no longer bounce like tennis balls around the room. The dogs skulk into their corners.

His own work. Political organizing that begins on a power-to-the-people grassroots level and gradually works its way up to power-to-the-person. He educates the sheep and then becomes the shepherd. It's a rush to have them all listening, paying attention, laying down their votes. Another case where reefer has led to the hard stuff.

We're on the slippery slope now, it's only a matter of time. It's women galore. He begins to look at me with an appraising eye. Familiarity, that good friend of contempt, makes me seem plain as dishwater. Once when we fight over something and apologize later, he admits that he might have been a bit stern with me. For hours the word hangs in the air above my head like a grand piano. *Stern.* He might have been stern with me. I realize that one of the reasons he doesn't want children is that he thinks he already has one. I start listening to how he talks to others compared to how he talks to me. In a crowded room one night I catch myself getting ready to take him by the necktie and heave him up against the wall. I feel like a rabid dog, but I smile placidly and make idle chat with the wife of his best friend, the future chiseler. In the car on the way home I say to him in the most dangerous tone I can come up with, '*You have got to treat me like an equal.*' The wiper blades clock back and forth, car lights bear down and then pass. He says,

432

THE BOYS OF MY YOUTH

looking straight ahead through the glistening windshield, simply and sadly, 'I can't.'

An update on the Artful Dodger. Turns out he's our age and has a day job, besides playing the drums.

'Well, you've gotta love a guy in a band,' I say encouragingly.

'I agree,' she says. 'I just wish he played the *guitar*.'

A woman walks by the phone booth in a nightgown, carrying a coffee cup and a cigarette. It's early afternoon. I knock on the glass and wave hello. There are any number of eccentrics around here. She's a painter.

Here's a good one: After the divorce I was on my way somewhere early one morning and saw Eric's brand-new girlfriend walking from his house to her own, wearing nothing but a pale lavender nightgown and a pair of Birkenstock sandals. Her hair was stuffed into a rubber band and hung down her back like a horse's tail, she was holding a sheaf of papers and a long leash, at the end of which was her dog, a big black biter.

The nightgown was one of those Indian-style jobs, with embroidery along the bodice. It's the sort of thing you could convince yourself didn't look *totally* like a nightgown if you only had three blocks to walk and it was too early for anyone to be out driving around.

Except I was. Out driving around. I spent the rest of the morning draped over someone's couch, sobbing and eating cinnamon toast.

I tell Elizabeth about this. Yeah, yeah, she remembers. Well, never again, I vow. Thank God *that's* in my past. Who *needs* it. Blah blah blah. The boys of my youth give me the malaise.

'Oh brother,' she says.

Don't oh brother me. And I gotta go, I'm late for my nap.

The truth is, I'm weary of all that men stuff. It's either so boring that I'd rather hang around with my girlfriends or it's like gunfire to the chest. I actually *like* it inside the bell jar – I don't have to breathe anyone's air but my own and I still get a view of the landscape. There's a woman here at the colony, Stasia, a film-maker who went to a workshop to learn how to walk over a bed of hot coals. She tells me about it postnap, as we're waiting for the dinner bell, having drinks on the terrace. The thing is, why would anyone want to walk over a bed of hot coals?

'I saw a flyer for it on a lamppost,' she explains.

They spent an afternoon in the presence of a short charismatic man, talking about their feelings and consulting various higher powers. At about four-thirty they took their shoes off and per-formed the miracle. So, what did it feel like?

'It felt like hot coals,' she says.

I knew it would.

The door to the terrace swings open and out walks our friend Frank. Right behind him is a new guy. Frank immediately starts filling us in on how much work he got done during the day. I feel vaguely guilty about the magnitude of my afternoon nap. Somehow the quality of the light has changed on the terrace, there's a dangerous peach glow coming over the horizon. The new guy is introducing himself to a group of people. There are handshakes around. Today Frank finished a painting and started two new ones.

Stasia says that you don't burn your feet because the coals are too light. The new guy looks over in this direction. It's like when you put your hand in a hot oven; the coals are almost light as air, they're hot but have very little density so they don't burn you. I can feel the frayed edge of his denim jacket and he's standing all the way over there. I look at my hand. Frank asks me how the boys of my youth are doing.

'They're boring,' I say absently. Here he comes.

*

Pertinent details. Blond poet. A slightly jaded and weary air about him. Something recognizable in the sideways glance, the set of the shoulders. He's sober now, but from what I can tell the former bad boy is buried in a shallow grave. The color of his eyes escapes me but not the quality of the gaze. He appears to be fully and alarmingly present at all times. I have to get out of here.

He leaves me a note on the mail table, full of charming misspellings. We meet and walk, describe our lives. He puts his hand on my arm as we cross a street and continues listening, offering kindness and advice. I have a sudden overwhelming desire to touch his face. I put my hands in the pockets of my jeans. It feels crowded inside my bell jar; condensation forms and I begin weeping. He watches calmly, one foot on the bumper of a car. At some point he reaches out, lightly touches my face.

I take to wearing a Walkman and earphones everywhere I go, piping music directly into my head. The phone booth is the only place it doesn't work.

'I can only talk for a minute,' I tell her. My days are numbered here; I feel a longing for my empty living room, for the grizzled face of Sheba the dog. The blue enamel breakfast table, the rug with a picture of New Zealand on it, the bird's nest we found outside the country place years ago, made from hair shed by my old dead heroic-hearted collie. I'm tired of being here. I miss my stuff.

'I'm sick of *my stuff*,' she says. 'I want all new everything.'

I want I want I want. I want to go home.

'What's going on?' she asks. After a short pause a lightbulb goes on over her head. 'Uh-oh,' she says.

Yeah.

435

'Heck,' she says cheerfully. 'That's *good*. Is he nice?'

I don't think I know what nice means these days. 'Well, he hasn't pulled a gun on me,' I tell her. She sighs.

I've spent my whole life in this phone booth. I want my circus footstool, my pink coffee table, my Albert Payson Terhune books. I want my Bruce Springsteen records. The Walkman lies dormant in my lap. I push the On button and the tiny voice of Van Morrison emanates from the earphones. 'The thing is,' I tell her, 'he already has a brown-eyed girl. Back home.' Thank God.

'Oh.' She's thinking this over. 'Hmmmm.'

A pall settles over the conversation. I stare at my reflection, distorted in the chrome of the telephone. 'This is still my youth,' I finally tell her.

'Uh, whatever you say.' She sounds skeptical.

I peer closer at the chrome mirror. My vertical wrinkle is still visible and it's afternoon. It's usually faded back into my face by mid-morning. Also, I might be getting jowls.

'I'm looking at my vertical wrinkle in the telephone,' I say.

'Isn't it supposed to be gone by now?' she asks. 'It's one o'clock.'

'I hate to break it to you, but it's two o'clock here,' I inform her. 'I need oil-of-old-ladies.' I can't even bring myself to mention the jowls, for which there's no cure anyway. All the women in my family begin to look like bulldogs right around the age of thirty-eight; it's a legacy.

The Artful Dodger has taken a turn for the worse. 'He's religious,' Elizabeth says. 'And not only that, but he thinks I'm going to church with him this Sunday.' Oh boy. To my way of thinking, the problem isn't necessarily that he's religious; it's more that he doesn't have anything to counter it with, like a drinking problem or weird sexual tastes. 'Well, actually he is a little weird in that category,' she admits. This livens up the conversation for a few minutes.

Before leaving the phone booth I plug the music back into my head. More hollering from Van. I notice as I set out on my walk that the New York landscape has taken on the blurred and sepia tones of a distant memory. I'm already back in Iowa, waiting for my body to join me.

Once home, I discover that I'm bored. Outside, long blank fields of corn and the blue midwestern sky. Inside, the same dustballs in the same corners. The cat carries tiny corpses up to the back step and arranges them in rows. The kid next door plays basketball with earphones on in his driveway, mouthing lyrics that would turn your hair white if you could hear them. Squint your eyes and he looks a little bit like Dave Anderson. Close your eyes altogether and the blond poet appears.

I perfect the art of brooding, gazing for hours at the paint on my living room ceiling, smoking and smoking. Elizabeth comes to visit me one weekend and we try on each other's clothes and paint our toenails maroon.

'I'll say one thing,' she remarks. 'I do happen to have decent *feet*.' And she turns them this way and that, admiring.

My own feet look like they belong to a stranger with too much time on her hands. I stretch out on the couch and feed myself a potato chip. There is a long hair-sized crack running down the center of the ceiling.

'Don't brood in *front* of me,' she says.

Mister Spider has built a web right above my giant, dying, phallic-looking cactus. It's a little trampoline and he's bouncing around in the center of it right now. Even the spiders are bored.

'It could be worse,' she mentions. 'We could be having to entertain those two mopes.' She means our ex-husbands, the Jim and Eric show.

If they were here, this is what they'd be doing: nothing, that's what. They'd be placidly sitting around, waiting for us to make something happen.

437

'So we'd still be bored,' she concludes, '*and* we wouldn't even be able to paint our toenails, for fear of ridicule.' It's true. Not only would it be boring but I'd have that old feeling back of constantly imagining myself as a widow wearing a great outfit. The phone rings.

'Who could be calling me here?' Elizabeth says.

We let it ring and ring until the answering machine kicks in and then we tiptoe over to listen. 'This is what I do when you call,' I tell her.

My answering machine voice lies about my whereabouts and then the beep comes on. Suddenly I'm standing on my circus footstool like a mouse has been let loose in the room. It's the guy.

'Hi, Jo Ann, this is X,' he says and then leaves a long, rambling, totally coherent message and hangs up. Oh man. He's shimmering in my living room like a genie released from a bottle.

I don't know whether to faint or kill myself. Elizabeth laughs unbecomingly. I put both hands around my own neck. We do our silent screaming routine.

We are no longer bored.

Acknowledgments

I WOULD LIKE TO EXPRESS MY GRATITUDE to the Corporation of Yaddo and the MacDowell Colony, for their generous gift of time, and the Constance Saltonstall Foundation in Ithaca, for much-needed financial support at a crucial point in my career. My sincere appreciation as well to the Whiting Foundation, the Guggenheim Foundation, and the Amercian Academy of Arts and Letters.